Statistics:

A Model for Uncertainty

Frank P. Soler and Chris W. Avery

De Anza College

Cupertino, California

KENDALL/HUNT PUBLISHING COMPANY
4050 Westmark Drive   Dubuque, Iowa 52002

Table of Contents

Preface

Chapter 1   Uncertainty, Randomness and Data

Chapter 2   Displaying, Organizing, and Describing Single Variable Data

Chapter 3   Probability

Chapter 4   Discrete Probability Distributions

Chapter 5   Continuous Probability Distributions

Chapter 6   The Normal Distribution

Chapter 7   Sampling Distributions, the Central Limit Theorem, and The Law of Large Numbers

Chapter 8   Estimation and Confidence for Means and Proportions

Chapter 9   Testing Statistical Hypotheses and Inference as Decision

Chapter 10 The Student's–t Distribution

Chapter 11 Testing Means and Proportions about Two Populations

Chapter 12 The Chi-Square Distribution and its Applications

Chapter 13 The F Distribution and its Applications

Chapter 14 Bivariate Data: Correlation and Regression

Answers and Solutions to Selected Problems

Appendix

Index

Preface

Statistics: A Model for Uncertainty is a general, yet comprehensive, introduction to statistics for students at two-year and four-year colleges and universities and for advanced high school students preparing for the AP Examination in Statistics. In this preface we will briefly describe the book in order to give teachers and students an overview of its content and direction.

The driving principle behind the book is to bring out statistical concepts and ideas while keeping computational and algorithmic driven activities to a minimum. We assume that the students have passed a second course in Algebra. Both, student and teacher, are given ample opportunity to engage in the business of learning and teaching. Many of the examples and problems in the book are intended to stimulate discussion of basic statistical issues. We are fully aware that many of these issues are open in nature, that is, there are no unique solutions or approaches. However, there are underlying concepts and ideas that should be part of any approach. Throughout, we emphasize the latter.

Many statistical procedures are influenced by probabilistic thought. As such, there is no escaping the study of probability. We acknowledge that the issue of how to present probability in a course of this nature will be the subject of discussion for years to come. Research in learning probability documents the fragility of probabilistic concepts. To this end, we have included very little formal probability. The chapter on probability (Chapter 3) deals with elementary ideas about a sample space, simple events, and compound events. The examples and problems we have given follow the motto: "if it can't be done with a Venn diagram, tree diagram, or a table, then it is not done..." Mutually exclusive, independence, and conditioning are presented in order to facilitate their later role in the treatment of inference.

We focus on the idea of a random variable and develop it early. We do this without any formal probability. We view the random variable as a tool that facilitates the study of random phenomena. Chapters 1 and 2 get the student thinking in terms of uncertain (rather than deterministic) outcomes. The emphasis is in gathering data to study these phenomena and in organizing and displaying the data in order to obtain useful information about them.

Chapter 4 covers discrete random variables. It starts by introducing expectation and variance and continues with Bernoulli trials and coverage of the major discrete distributions (Binomial, Geometric, Pascal, Poisson, and Hypergeometric). We do this without using computational formulas, with the exception of tables for the Binomial and very simple computations for the Geometric. We are mostly interested in having the student recognize different ways of thinking about discrete phenomena. All but the Binomial distribution may be skipped without loss of continuity.

The transition from discrete to continuous random variables occurs in Chapter 5. The key distribution here is the Uniform. We emphasize the idea of probability as an area. We cover two additional distributions: Exponential and Triangular. We recognize that most of this chapter can be easily skipped without any loss of continuity.

The Normal distribution is the subject of Chapter 6. We feel that a good understanding of this distribution goes a long way toward paving the study of other continuous distributions (i.e., t, F, Chi-square).

Chapter 7 introduces the fundamental idea of the sampling distribution of a statistic. This leads to the Central Limit Theorem. We work with both versions, averages and sums. We thought it would be appropriate to introduce the Law of Large Numbers as a way of interpreting the population mean in terms of a long run relative frequency.

Chapter 8 marks the beginning of inference. It gives an overview of estimation and proceeds to develop the methodology for constructing confidence intervals.

Chapter 9 gives a formal introduction to hypotheses testing. We develop the p-value, tying it to previously developed material, and then we talk about decision making, including the Type I and Type II error probabilities, and issues of significance (fixed and practical).

Chapters 10–13 explore additional hypotheses testing situations using the Student's-t distribution, Chi-square and F. We devote some material to examining assumptions about these distributions and pointing out pitfalls and checkpoints.

Chapter 14 introduces bivariate data, starting with the scatterplot and continuing with correlation, outliers, influential points, and least-squares regression.

Many examples and problems throughout the book are real. We cite references where appropriate. In many instances, the applications come from the authors' experience and expertise. In such cases, no references are given.

We struggled with the usual format of including a problem set after each section. We decided against this. Our thinking was that most chapters are fairly brief, with plenty of examples for the student to work through. The one advantage to having a single problem set at the end of each chapter is the ability to immediately incorporate concepts from the entire chapter throughout most of the problem set.

We encourage the use of calculators. In fact, it would be impossible to read through these materials without a handy calculator. Any calculator that is capable of accumulating sums will be sufficient. The best way to check this is to make sure that keys such as $\bar{x}$, s, σ, appear on the calculator.

Algebra Review

As part of the Appendix, we have included a brief Algebra Review. This is done in terms of problems to be solved. Complete solutions are included.

Software Supplement

There are many places in the book where we mention the use of a computer or "appropriate software". While the exposition and problems are free of computer software, we recognize that having access to pedagogically sound statistical software is advantageous. We recommend *Statistics,* by The Math Lab. It is available for the IBM or compatibles and the Macintosh in 3.5 inch disk format. For students who wish additional practice, this package, complete with a User's Manual, contains an extensive tutorial, covering all of the major topics in this book, complete with random generation of problems, hints, and a self-scoring system. Additionally, it allows for extensive simulations using fourteen distributions, producing empirical and theoretical graphs, and allowing for the computation of probabilities and critical values. Extensive demonstrations of difficult statistical issues are also included. For instance, in Analysis of Variance, the user can easily simulate the trade-off between sample size and magnitude of the unknown population variance. Also, it is enlightening to demonstrate the statement of the Central Limit Theorem by sampling from any number of distributions and comparing the shape and statistics of the corresponding sampling distribution of averages or sums to that of the underlying population. The software is priced in the $12–$18 range.

Acknowledgements

We wish to acknowledge a former student of ours, Teck Ky, for his assistance in providing solutions to many of the problems in the problem sets. Lenore DeSilets, a mathematics instructor at De Anza College, reviewed parts of the original manuscript and provided us with useful comments. James Lum, of San Jose State University and adjunct faculty at De Anza College, pointed out areas of difficulty and ambiguous wording while teaching from our first draft. A special thanks to Professor Lum for sharing with us his keen understanding of statistical issues.

Most of all, we are indebted to the many students who, since 1986, have learned statistics from our previous textbook. Their triumphs have inspired us. Their struggles drove us to produce this book. We are equally grateful to all those instructors, especially at De Anza College, who have taught from our materials and used our software over the last nine years. We have learned much from them. Many of their comments and constructive criticisms are very much a part of this work.

Chris W. Avery and Frank P. Soler
August 1996

Chapter 1

Uncertainty, Randomness and Data

1.1 The need to model uncertainty

Some phenomena have predictable outcomes: drop an object from a known height and the time it takes to fall can be precisely predicted (banning small measurement errors) from known physical equations. However, there are other types of phenomena that are not so predictable. For instance, take a fair coin and flip it. We cannot predict whether it will come up heads or tails. That is, the outcome is *uncertain*. Yet, note that coin flipping is not haphazard or chaotic. Intuition indicates that if we flip a fair coin a large number of times, the proportion of heads (or tails) will be very close to one-half. This long term regularity is not a theoretical construct, it is an observed fact.

Quantifying uncertainty involves the related topics of *data* and *chance*.[1] Uncertain situations appear everywhere in the world around us. Each of the following is an example of an uncertain situation. For each one, think of how data and chance are a part of the phenomena.

- The closing price of Apple stock at the end of the next business day

- The number of people who will buy the new exercise machine built by NordicTrack

- The winner of the Baseball World Series for the current season

- The number of dart throws before the thrower hits the bulls' eye

- The improvement shown by patients for a given dosage of a new medication

- The numbers that will come up in the next lottery drawing

1.2 Random Variables

Phenomena with predictable outcomes are said to be *deterministic*. We typically use mathematical functions to describe and quantify deterministic phenomena. Here are some examples of deterministic situations and their associated functions.

- The area of a rectangular plot of land 30 ft. by 50 ft.
  Area function = length•width = 30•50 = 1500 square ft.

---

[1] **Statistics** deals with the study of data while **Probability** deals with the study of chance

- The total distance traveled after 4 hours at a constant rate of 15 miles per hour.
  Distance function = rate•time = 15•4 = 60 miles.

- The profit made if revenues are $1 million and costs are $0.75 million.
  Profit function = revenue − cost = 1 million − 0.75 million = $0.25 million.

Phenomena with unpredictable outcomes are classified as *random*. A **random variable** is a function with an uncertain outcome.[2] Outcomes may be numerical in nature or exhibit an inherent non-numerical characteristic. The following are examples of random phenomena and some of their possible outcomes.

(1) X = number of cars passing a toll booth during a fixed time period
Possible values of X: X = 50; X = 300.

(2) Y = type of computer a company will use in 5 years
Possible values of Y: Y = Apple; Y = IBM; Y = Compaq.

(3) X = the length, in minutes, of the next phone call to your most significant other
Possible values of X: X = 1; X = 25; X = 1.2.

(4) W = the height, in inches, of the students in your Statistics class
Possible values of W: W = 62; W = 76.9.

(5) An urn contains 3 red marbles and 7 yellow marbles. One marble at a time is selected, without replacement, until a red marble appears. X = the number of marbles selected.
Possible values of X: X = 2; X = 5. Note that for convenience, it is customary to denote the case X = 2 by the outcome: **YR**. This means that a yellow marble was chosen first and then a red marble was chosen. The case X = 5 is denoted by the outcome: **YYYYR**.

We will study three different types of random variables: *quantitative discrete*, *quantitative continuous* and *qualitative* (also called *categorical* or *attribute*.) A discrete random variable keeps track of counts. A continuous random variable obtains its values from measuring. Outcomes associated with discrete and continuous random variables are numerical. The set of all possible outcomes for a situation involving uncertainty is called the *range* of a random variable. For each of the five examples directly above, the type of random variable and range are as follows.

---

[2] It is customary to denote random variables using capital letters from the tail end of the alphabet. For example, W, X, Y, Z, etc. This notation will be most prominent later in the book.

(1) Quantitative discrete. Range: non-negative counting numbers

(2) Qualitative or categorical. Range: name of all computer manufacturers

(3) Quantitative continuous. Range: positive real numbers

(4) Quantitative continuous. Range: positive real numbers

(5) Quantitative discrete. Range: 1,2,3,4,5,6,7,8. (Why not 9 or 10?)

1.3   Definition of key terms

Besides random variables, the following terms will be used extensively throughout the remainder of this book.

Experiment: A planned activity that yields meaningful results

Population: The complete collection of objects, items, persons, or things under study

Parameter: A statement or measurable characteristic pertaining to the population

Sample: That part of the population that is readily available

Statistic: A statement or measurable characteristic pertaining to the sample

Data: Values of the random variable produced by the experiment.

We illustrate all of the above terms with the following two examples.

___

Example 1

We wish to estimate the average age of all the homeowners of the city of San Francisco.

Experiment: the process of obtaining the ages of San Francisco homeowners

Population: all San Francisco homeowners

Random Variable: age of homeowners

Parameter: the average age of all San Francisco homeowners

Sample: all homeowners around Golden Gate Park

Statistic: the average age of those homeowners around Golden Gate Park

Data: counting numbers representing age.

Example 2

We are interested in examining the number of heads when 3 fair coins are flipped. Let H = heads comes up and T = tails comes up. Thus, the outcome **HTH** denotes the 1st and 3rd coins came up heads and the 2nd coin came up tails.

Experiment: the act of flipping 3 fair coins

Population: all possible outcomes when 3 fair coins are flipped

Random Variable: number of heads that come up when 3 fair coins are flipped

Parameter: the largest number of heads that can come up on a single flip of the 3 coins (i.e., 3)

Sample: TTH, HHT, TTT

Statistic: 2 (note this is the largest value of the random variable for the outcomes in the sample)

Data: 1,2,0 (note these are the values of the random variable for the outcomes in the sample)

1.4   Data and sampling

Data are gathered in order to study the behavior of random variables. The gathering, analysis, and representation of data are major components of the field of *Statistics*. Securing data that are meaningful and trustworthy takes a great deal of planning. The data that statisticians are most interested in stems from carefully planned experiments. We classify the different types of data in the same manner in which we classified random variables. That is, data may be quantitative (numerical: discrete, continuous) or qualitative (categorical). The following are examples of experimental situations where the random variable of interest produces numerical or categorical outcomes.

Example 3

Experiment: obtain the age, in years, of randomly selected students from the student body

Random variable: age of the students

Possible outcomes: discrete data such as: 20, 35, 18

Example 4

Experiment: add the faces that come up when two fair dice are rolled

Random variable: sum of the faces that come up

Possible outcomes: discrete data such as: 2, 6, 10, 12

Example 5

Experiment: determine which type of bread is eaten more frequently for lunch at a prominent San Francisco sandwich shop

Random variable: different types of bread

Possible outcomes: qualitative data such as: wheat, sourdough

Example 6

Experiment: determine the useful life, in hours, of a set of neon light bulbs

Random variable: number of hours before neon light bulbs burn out

Possible outcomes: quantitative continuous data such as: 1005.7, 950, 2375

Often we wish to extend the conclusions we draw from analyzing sample data to some larger group of individuals (i.e., the population). If the data don't fairly represent the larger group, our conclusions will not apply to the larger group. In order to gather data that are trustworthy, careful attention must be paid to **sampling**. The whole idea of sampling is to study a part of the population.

The following two examples illustrate the danger of believing results of experiments conducted with poorly produced data.

Example 7   In the early 1970's, newspaper columnist Ann Landers once asked her readers, "If you had to do it over again, would you have children?" A few weeks later, her column was headlined "70% OF PARENTS SAY KIDS NOT WORTH IT." In fact, 70% of the nearly 10,000 parents who responded said they would not have children if they could make the choice again.

Social agencies, alarmed by the public uproar caused by the Ann Landers' data, conducted a statistically designed opinion poll on the same question and found that over 90% of parents *would* have children again. How is such a contradiction possible? Ann Landers used a *voluntary response sample*, in which people chose themselves to be in the sample. Voluntary response samples overrepresent people with strong opinions, especially negative opinions.

In most data producing situations, it is preferable to gather data produced by an experiment. In doing an experiment we just don't observe individuals and ask them questions. We knowingly impose some sort of treatment in order to observe the response. The reason for conducting experiments is that nature will not give out answers willingly. We must obtain answers (in the form of reliably produced data) by imposing some condition and then observing the response. The following example will further clarify this point.

Example 8   In 1940, a psychologist conducted an experiment to study the effect of propaganda on attitude toward a foreign government. He made up a test of attitude toward the German government and administered it to a group of American students. After reading German propaganda for several months, the students were tested again to see if their attitudes had changed.

Unfortunately, while the experiment was in progress, Germany attacked and conquered France. There was a profound change of attitude toward the German government between the test and the retest, but it will never be known how much of this change was due to the reading of propaganda and how much to the historical events of that time. That is, it is not possible to extract from the data any information about the effect of reading propaganda.

The problem with the propaganda experiment is one of **confounding.** Two variables are confounded when their effects on a response cannot be distinguished from each other.

Hopefully these two examples make it painfully clear that we must think about how to produce data that is reliable and trustworthy. These ideas are simple, yet, they are among the most important in statistics. This is so because statistical analysis and statistical inference *assume* that the data are reliable, trustworthy, and representative.

Data that systematically favors a certain outcome is said to be **biased**. In the Ann Landers' example, the data were biased by the response of angry parents. In the propaganda example, the data were biased by mixing the reading of propaganda with historical events.

To remedy the problem of producing biased data, statisticians allow chance mechanisms to choose the sample so that there is neither favoritism nor self-selection. Choosing a sample by chance eliminates biases by giving all individuals in the population an equal chance of being included in the sample. The simplest design for using chance in sampling amounts to placing names in a hat (the population) and drawing a handful (say *n*, the sample). This is called **simple random sampling**. Simple random sampling not only gives each individual an equal chance to be chosen, but also gives every possible sample of size *n* an equal chance to be chosen. There are other random sampling schemes that give each individual, but not each sample, an equal chance. One such design, **systematic random sampling,** is described in the problems set for this chapter.

Schemes for sampling from large populations spread out over a wide area or easily classified in different categories (i.e., age, income, etc) are more complex than simple random sampling. The most common of such schemes is called a **proportionally stratified random sample.** Stratus are obtained by dividing the population in groups of similar individuals and then selecting a simple random sample from each strata. The proportional part comes into play when deciding how many individuals are to be selected from each strata.

Example 9   We wish to conduct an experiment to determine the average annual income of the full time faculty at a major university. Assume there are 500 full time faculty. Time and budgetary considerations only allow for a sample of 100 such faculty. Furthermore, a proportionally stratified random sample is preferred.

One way to proceed is to stratify the full time faculty by age. Suppose it is known how many faculty members fall in each age category.

Age category	Frequency	Proportion
25 or younger	50	50/500 = 0.10
26 – 39	150	150/500 = 0.30
40 – 53	180	180/500 = 0.36
54 – 67	100	100/500 = 0.20
over 67	20	20/500 = 0.04

Using the column of proportions, simple random samples of sizes 10 (i.e., 10% of 100), 30, 36, 20, and 4 are taken from the respective age categories. Such a sample of 100 full time faculty should provide unbiased data that is representative of all 500 full time faculty.

Chapter 1 Problems

For problems **1-20**:

Classify each situation as *deterministic* or *random*. If the situation is random, then:

    a. Use a complete sentence to describe the random variable.

    b. Give three descriptive examples of possible outcomes.

    c. Describe the range of the random variable.

    d. State if the random variable is discrete, continuous or qualitative.

1. The closing price of the Dow Jones Industrial Average on the last trading day of August 1995.

2. The closing price of the Dow Jones Industrial Average at the end of the next business day.

3. People are interviewed for a debating team that will contain 6 members. We are interested in the number of people rejected until the team is chosen

4. The area of a circle with radius 5 inches.

5. Color of a car that will pass through a given toll booth.

6. A coin is flipped 20 times. Of interest is the number of heads that will come up.

7. The number of mis-routed phone calls in the Western United States at the time of the next natural catastrophe.

8. One share of Intel stock is purchased. Of interest is the number of days it will take for the value of the share to increase by 20% of the purchase price.

9. An urn contains 5 red marbles and 3 yellow marbles. Five marbles are selected, one at a time and with replacement. Of interest is the number of red marbles selected.

10. An urn contains 3 red marbles and 5 yellow marbles. Five marbles are selected, one at a time and without replacement. Of interest is the number of red marbles selected.

11. An urn contains 3 red marbles and 5 yellow marbles. Marbles are selected without replacement until a red marble appears. Of interest is the number of marbles selected.

12. An urn contains 5 red marbles and 3 yellow marbles. Marbles are selected with replacement until a yellow marble appears. Of interest is the number of marbles selected.

13. Of interest is the brand of calculator a student will purchase for this class.

14. The number of times a coin is flipped until 3 heads appear.

15. The area of a rectangle whose dimensions are random positive real numbers.

16. A dart is thrown until the bulls' eye is missed.

17. The time it takes a commercial airline flight to travel from San Francisco to New York.

18. The magnitude of the next quake to hit the San Francisco Bay Area.

19. A committee of 5 persons is to be chosen from a group consisting of 50 men and 60 women. Of interest is the number of women in the committee.

20. The solution to the equation $2x + 5 = 21$.

21. Refer to Example 9, section 1.4. Suppose instead that in order to obtain an estimate for the average annual income for the full time faculty at the university, all Department Chairpersons were sampled. Give reasons why it is not likely that this particular sampling scheme will produce reliable data.

22. Refer to Example 9, section 1.4. Consider the following sampling scheme instead. The experimenter is presented with an alphabetical list of all full time faculty: (1) Abrams, (2) Anderson, ..., (500) Ziegler. The sample of 100 faculty is obtained by simply going down this list and picking every 5th faculty. That is, pick the persons associated with the numbers 5, 10, 15, 20, ..., 495, 500. This is the so called *systematic random sampling*. Explain why this sampling scheme may produce biased data.

23. An experiment is conducted to determine if a certain food supplement increases the weight of laboratory rats. A litter of 20 rats is divided into two groups of 10 rats each. One group is given the food supplement for a period of 8 weeks and the other group of 10 rats is given a placebo. Except for the food supplement, the rats are fed the same type and amount of food. At the end of the 8 weeks the average weight gain for each group is computed. Explain how it is possible for confounding to have an effect on the outcome of the experiment.

24. A flour company wants to know what percent of San Francisco households bake some or all of their own bread. The company selects a simple random sample of 500 San Francisco addresses, and sends interviewers to these addresses. The interviewers work during regular working hours on weekdays and interview only during those hours. Explain why this sampling method is biased. Is the percent of the sample who bake bread probably higher or lower than the percent of the population who bake bread?

25. A large corporation employs 4000 males and 1000 female engineers. A stratified random sample of 400 males and 100 females gives each engineer one chance in 10 of being chosen. This sample design gives every unit in the population the same chance to be included in the sample. Is this a simple random sample? Explain your answer.

26. Identify the seven key terms appearing in Example 1 and Example 2, section 1.3, for the following situations:

    a. It is desired to ascertain the average market value of homes used as principal residence for all full time faculty at your school.

    b. We wish to establish the minimum useful life of a batch of neon light bulbs.

For problems **27-34**, classify each situation as *statistical* (data), *probabilistic* (chance) or neither.

27. Winning your state lottery.

28. Determining the average annual income of all full time faculty at your school.

29. You are given a coin and asked to figure out if it is fair.

30. Comparing scores in a reading comprehension test of two different sections of English 1A.

31. Finding the cheapest air fare in going from San Francisco to Hawaii.

32. Deciding if Willie Mays was a better home run hitter than Mickey Mantle.

33. Assessing the likelihood that in a game of poker, one of the players has drawn 4 aces.

34. The number of football games to be played in determining next season's Super Bowl winner.

Chapter 2

Displaying, organizing, and describing single variable data

2.0   Introduction

In Chapter 1, a function called a **random variable** was introduced in order to describe and quantify uncertain phenomena. Knowledge of the random variable is typically obtained from data. Information can be obtained from data by:

- sorting
- producing graphical displays
- calculating statistics that describe the data and the underlying random variable.

For large data sets, the above operations are tedious. That is why you will use calculators or computers for most of your work. We firmly believe that the understanding of underlying concepts takes priority over the actual performance of the above operations. Only then can numbers or graphs be interpreted in their appropriate context.

2.1   The graphical display of data

Once data have been gathered, the first step in almost any analysis is to graphically display them. Graphical displays quickly reveal overall trends and other features that could easily go unnoticed.

Stem-Leaf

For small data sets (generally speaking, "small" means the number of data points does not exceed 30), stem-leaf displays are most useful. The display consists of an ordered listing of the data broken into two parts: the stem and the leaf. The stem is the most significant numerical component of the data. The leaf is almost always a single digit. The following is a stem-leaf plot of the number of home runs Babe Ruth hit in each of his 15 seasons with the New York Yankees baseball team.

stem	leaf
2	25
3	45
4	1166679
5	449
6	0

The display 2 | 25 stands for seasons with 22 and 25 home runs respectively. As the data get more complex, it is not as simple to decide between the stem and the leaf. Interpretation of the data in the display is straight forward. The number of home runs Ruth hit per season is clustered in the 40's. He had the one outstanding season when he hit 60 and never hit less than 22 home runs in a season.

Suppose we wish to compare Ruth's home run production with that of Roger Maris. In 1961 Maris broke Ruth's record of 60 home runs in a single season. This is a record that still stands today. Here is a back-to-back stem-leaf comparison of their yearly home runs:

```
          Ruth        Maris
          leaf   stem  leaf
                 0 | 8
                 1 | 346
            52   2 | 368
            54   3 | 39
       9766611   4 |
           944   5 |
             0   6 | 1
```

Note how Maris' 61 home run season differs from the rest of the data. Ruth's 60 home runs came as no major surprise, but Maris' 61 home runs were a total surprise. There is no doubt that Ruth had the greater home run power of the two.

In general, to see the overall pattern of the distribution of single variable data, we learn to look for symmetry or skewness, for single or multiple peaks, for the center, and the spread of the data about the center. More on these ideas as we progress through this chapter.

Histograms

For large data sets, it is preferable to group near values together into class intervals and form a histogram. The data below represents the percent of residents 65 years or older for each of the 50 states (as of 1991).

State	Percent	State	Percent	State	Percent
Alabama	12.0	Alaska	4.2	Arizona	13.2
Arkansas	14.0	California	10.5	Colorado	10.1
Connecticut	13.7	Delaware	12.2	Florida	18.3
Georgia	10.1	Hawaii	11.4	Idaho	12.0
Illinois	12.5	Indiana	12.6	Iowa	15.4

Kansas	13.9	Kentucky	12.7	Louisiana	11.2
Maine	13.4	Maryland	10.9	Massachusetts	13.7
Michigan	12.1	Minnesota	12.5	Mississippi	12.4
Missouri	14.1	Montana	13.4	Nebraska	14.1
Nevada	10.8	New Hampshire	11.6	New Jersey	13.4
New Mexico	10.9	New York	13.1	North Carolina	12.3
North Dakota	14.5	Ohio	13.1	Oklahoma	13.5
Oregon	13.7	Pennsylvania	15.5	Rhode Island	15.1
South Carolina	11.4	South Dakota	14.7	Tennessee	12.7
Texas	10.1	Utah	8.8	Vermont	11.9
Virginia	10.9	Washington	11.8	West Virginia	15.5
Wisconsin	13.3	Wyoming	10.6		

Note that the data spans from 4.2% to 18.3%. We now create class intervals by forming intervals of equal width covering the span of the data. Class intervals must be specified so that each data value falls exactly into one and only one class. The width of the class intervals is arbitrary. You must use your judgment when choosing a class width. Too many class intervals will give the histogram a flat look, while too few gives the histogram a very peaked or skyscraper look. It is customary to form somewhere between 5 and 15 class intervals. After the class intervals are formed, we then tally the number of data points that fall in them. The best way to organize all of this information is in tabular form as shown below.

Class Interval	Freq.	Rel Freq.[1]	Class Interval	Freq.	Rel Freq.
4.1 to 5.0	1	$0.02 = 1/50$	12.1 to 13.0	10	0.20
5.1 to 6.0	0	0	13.1 to 14.0	12	0.24
6.1 to 7.0	0	0	14.1 to 15.0	5	0.10
7.1 to 8.0	0	0	15.1 to 16.0	4	0.08
8.1 to 9.0	1	0.02	16.1 to 17.0	0	0
9.1 to 10.0	0	0	17.1 to 18.0	0	0
10.1 to 11.0	9	0.18	18.1 to 19.0	1	0.02
11.1 to 12.0	7	0.14			

The histogram is now drawn. Label the scale for the variable on the horizontal axis "percent of residents 65 or over". The scale on the horizontal axis runs from 4.0 to 19.0. The vertical axis consists of the frequencies or relative frequencies. Each bar represents a class. The base of the bar covers the class and the bar height is the class frequency or count. Draw the graph with no horizontal space between the bars unless a particular class is empty (i.e., has a zero frequency). The completed histogram is shown below. Note that using frequencies or relative frequencies on the vertical axis does not effect the shape of the histogram.

---

[1]   Rel. Freq. = Relative frequency = $\dfrac{\text{frequency}}{\text{total number of data points}}$

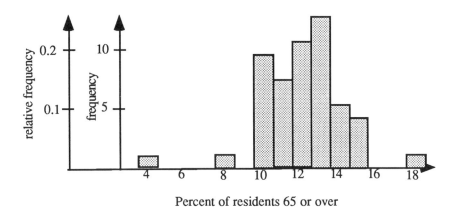

Percent of residents 65 or over

Making graphical displays is not an end in itself. The purpose of any graph is to assist in understanding the data. Look for an overall pattern as well as for striking deviations from that pattern. In the above histogram, two states stand out. Florida and Alaska seem not to fit the general pattern. Utah is not nearly as strikingly deviant from the rest of the states. Once these deviant data are identified, we look for an explanation. Sometimes the wrong data value was entered or copied. If the data came from taking measurements, perhaps there was a malfunction on the measuring device. A possible explanation for Florida and Alaska is that Florida, with its warm weather and year around benevolent climate, attracts lots of senior citizens; while Alaska, the northern frontier, with its cold climate and endless days or nights, attracts very few seniors.

Computers can create histograms of large data sets faster than we can blink our eyes.[2] They allow the user to experiment with different class widths and different number of class intervals. Sometimes the software will choose the class width for you. However, nothing replaces your intuition, judgment, and understanding of the data.

The histogram below shows the distribution of length of words used in Shakespeare's plays. This distribution is skewed to the right. That is, there are many short words (mostly with 3 or 4 letters) and few very long words (10 letters or more). The right tail of the histogram extends out much farther than the left. The vertical scale, even though not shown in the histogram, is not a count or frequency but the percent of all of Shakespeare's words that have each length. A vertical scale of percents rather than counts is convenient when the counts are very large or when we wish to superimpose several distributions on the same axis.

Length of words	1	2	3	4	5	6	7	8	9	10	11
Percent of words	4	17.5	24	25	15	7	3	2	1	1	0.5

[2] Also, note that with a bit of imagination, a stem-leaf display mirrors a histogram (rotate the stem-leaf 90 degrees to the left and put bars around the vertical columns).

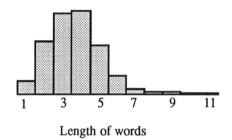

1   3   5   7   9   11

Length of words

2.2   Describing the center of the data

Once data have been obtained, we must think of ways to intelligently examine it. Data sets containing information about a single numerical variable should first be placed in numerical order (typically from lowest to highest). If the data set is fairly large (say, over 30 or so pieces of data) and there are repetitions of the same data value, a table of grouped frequencies will best display it.

The following grouped data consists of the monthly income of 100 randomly chosen college students in Northern California.

X = Monthly income	f = Frequency	rf = relative frequency
100	5	$0.05 = {}^5\!/_{100}$
200	10	0.1
300	10	0.1
400	5	0.05
500	8	0.08
600	10	0.1
700	20	0.2
800	15	0.15
900	12	0.12
1000	5	0.05

Of immediate interest about any data set are ways of describing the **center** of the data. Measures to describe the center of a data set are obtained by performing computations on the data. The wide use of calculators and computers render most hand computations obsolete. In general, we will look at formulas only to provide insight into what is being computed and to intuitively interpret the results of such computations. Unless otherwise stated, we always treat data sets as samples from some larger population. As such, any numbers computed from the data are considered to be **sample statistics.** Of outmost importance is the relationship of these sample statistics to their corresponding **population parameters.** Ultimately, this is a theme of fundamental concern to statisticians and one that will be often revisited in future chapters.

There are four different measures of center: **arithmetic mean** or **average**, **median**, **mode**, and **midrange**. If a data set consists of n pieces of data denoted by $x_1, x_2,..., x_n$, their arithmetic average or mean is

(1)
$$\overline{x} = \frac{x_1 + x_2 + \cdots + x_n}{n}$$

or in more compact notation,

(2)
$$\overline{x} = \frac{\sum_{\text{all } i} x_i}{n}.$$

The symbol $\sum$ in the formula is short for "add up all of the data." Thus, $\sum f_i = n$ and $\sum rf_i = 1$ The subscript i on the observations x_i are just a way of denoting n distinct data values. The symbol $\overline{x}$ is read "xbar" and will always denote the **sample mean.** The symbol μ (pronounced "mu") will be used to denote the **population mean.** Note that the computational formula for both the sample and population means is the same.

If the data are grouped, formula (2) takes the form

(3)
$$\overline{x} = \frac{\sum_{\text{all } i} x_i f_i}{n}$$

where f_i stands for the frequency associated with the corresponding data value x_i.

Since $\dfrac{\sum_{\text{all } i} x_i f_i}{n} = \sum_{\text{all } i} x_i \dfrac{f_i}{n}$, and recognizing that $rf_i = \dfrac{f_i}{n}$, we can express (3) in terms of relative frequencies (this representation will be useful in later chapters),

(4)
$$\overline{x} = \sum_{\text{all } i} x_i \, rf_i$$

Using formula (3) it is straight forward to compute the average monthly income for the sample of 100 Northern California college students given in the above table.[3] That is,

---

[3] You are encouraged to use your calculator (or a computer) to carry out these computations. To reiterate, we do not expect readers to carry out hand computations.

$$\text{average monthly income} = \bar{x} = \frac{100 \cdot 5 + 200 \cdot 10 + 300 \cdot 10 + \cdots + 1000 \cdot 5}{100} = \frac{59300}{100} = \$593.$$

Could we claim that the average monthly income for all Northern California college students is \$593? Probably not. The question calls for knowledge of μ, which we do not have. However, if the sample of 100 students is representative and there is ample evidence that the data are trustworthy and reliable, then the value of μ should be close to \$593.[4]

Another way of describing the center of a data set is to use the "middle value" of the data. That is, find the number with half the data values falling below it and the other half above. This is the **median** of the data set. Although the idea of the median as the midpoint of a data set is quite natural, we need a precise rule for finding it.

Rule to find the median of a data set:

1. Order all the data, from smallest to largest.

2. If the number n of data values is odd, the median is the center observation in the ordered data list. The location of the median is found by counting $(n + 1)/2$ data values starting from the smallest value of the list.

3. If the number n of data values is even, the median is the average of the two center observations in the ordered data list. The location of the median is again $(n + 1)/2$ up from the smallest value of the list.

If the data set is large and it has not been ordered, finding the median could be quite laborious. Most calculators do not find the median of a data set, but computers do. It is a trivial matter for computers to arrange large lists of numbers in ascending or descending order. For the monthly income data, the median is the average between the 50th and 51st data values.[5] It so happens that both of these values correspond to \$700; thus, the median is \$700.

In general, the mean and median of a data set will not coincide. Note that the mean is highly influenced by the presence of extreme numerical values in the data but the median is not.[6] To make things worse,

---

[4] Quantifying "close" will be the theme of subsequent chapters.

[5] Since $n = 100$ is an even number, use part **3.** of the rule to find the median.

[6] Consider: data set A = {1,4,10}, mean = 5, median = 4; data set B = {1,4,100}, mean = 35, median = 4. Note how the extreme value of 100 on data set B pulls the mean up, while the median remains the same for both data sets.

it may very well be that such extreme values are not representative of the data. A close look at the formula for computing the mean will reveal that extreme values will have the effect of pulling the mean towards them. In light of this, it is not surprising that sometimes the median gives a better representation of the center of a data set than the mean. The fact that the mean is the most widely used measure of center bears witness mostly to the simplicity of its computational formula. However, statisticians are always aware of situations where the median might be a more adequate measure of center.

The remaining two measures of center are the **mode** and **midrange**. The **mode** is the most frequent data point in the data set. A data set without a most frequent data point is said to have no mode. A data set with only one most frequent data point is said to be unimodal, with two most frequent data points it is called bimodal, etc. For the monthly income data, the mode is $700 (it appears the most frequent number of times: 20). The **midrange** is the average of the two extreme values in the data set. That is,

$$
(5) \qquad\qquad \text{midrange} = \frac{\text{smallest data value} + \text{largest data value}}{2}.
$$

For the monthly income data, midrange = (100 + 1000)/2 = $550.

2.3 Describing the spread of the data

The mean and median are the two most commonly used measures of center. However, for a data set, a measure of center alone only begins to tell the story. For example, the data set consisting of the weights, in pounds, of NFL defensive linemen has little variation about its center, while a medication with a perfectly safe mean concentration of an active ingredient could be very dangerous if variation in the manufacturing process causes some batches to have a very high concentration and others much too low. In the above situations, we are interested in the **spread** or **variation** of weights and drug concentration as well as their centers. The simplest way to numerically describe a data set is to both calculate measures of center and spread. We will discuss three measures of spread: **range, interquartile range**, and **standard deviation**.

The simplest measure of spread is the **range** of the data set.[7] The range is calculated by obtaining the difference between the largest and smallest data values. That is,

$$
(6) \qquad\qquad \text{range} = \text{largest data value} - \text{smallest data value}.
$$

For the monthly income data of section **2.2**, range = $1000 - $100 = $900. The range shows the full spread of the data. One danger with the range is that either the largest value or smallest value may be an

---

[7] Note that " range" of a data set = {largest - smallest} differs from "range" of random variable = {all possible outcomes}.

extreme value. If this is the case, the range may misrepresent the spread. One way to remedy this is to consider the spread of the middle half of the data. The **quartiles** determine the middle half. The **first quartile** is the number below which 25% of the data values fall. The **third quartile** is the number below which 75% of the data values fall. Note that the **second quartile** is the median, because 50% of the data values fall below the median. The difference between the third and first quartiles is called the **interquartile range**. That is,

(7)   interquartile range = third quartile – first quartile.

As with the median, we need a rule to find the quartiles.

Rule for finding quartiles:

1. Order the data set, from smallest to largest, and locate the median.

2. The first quartile is the median of the data values to the left of the location of the median of the entire data set.

3. The third quartile is the median of the data values to the right of the location of the median of the entire data set.

The following examples will illustrate the rule for finding quartiles.

Example 1   Fifteen male gynecologists in the San Francisco Bay Area were randomly chosen. Of interest is the number of hysterectomies they have performed over the last year. Here is the ordered data set:

15 25 25 27 28 31 33 **34** 36 37 44 50 59 85 86

Since there is an odd number of data values, the median of the data set is 34. The median of the data set consisting of those data values to the left of 34 is 27. That is, **first quartile = 27**. Similarly, the median of those data values to the right of 34 is 50. That is, **third quartile = 50**.

Example 2   Ten female gynecologists in the San Francisco Bay Area were randomly chosen. Of interest is the number of hysterectomies they have performed over the last year. Here is the ordered data set:

$$5 \quad 7 \quad 10 \quad 14 \quad 18 \mid 19 \quad 25 \quad 29 \quad 31 \quad 42$$

Since there is an even number of data values, the median of the data set is the average of the two middle values. That is, median = (18 + 19)/2 = 18.5. The location of 18.5 is marked by the | in the above list. The first quartile is the median of the 5 data values below 18.5. That is, **first quartile = 10.** Similarly, the median of the 5 data values to the right of 18.5 is 29. That is, **third quartile = 29.**

The above rule for finding quartiles is well suited only for relatively small data sets. Most calculators do not give the quartiles. For large data sets, computers are the only reasonable alternative.

Returning to the monthly income data of section **2.2**, and using the first and third quartiles instead of the largest and smallest data values,

$$\text{interquartile range} = \$800 - \$350 = \$450.$$

The question of which measure best represents the actual spread of the data, range or interquartile range, is a matter of judgment on the part of the person analyzing the data. The point to remember is that the presence of extreme values, that is, values that strikingly deviate from the rest of the data, makes the *interquartile range* a more viable measure of spread than the *range*.

The most common measure of spread is the **standard deviation**. The standard deviation measures spread around the mean of the data and should be used only when the mean is chosen as the measure of center. The standard deviation for sample data is computed as follows:

$$(8) \qquad \text{sample standard deviation} = s = \sqrt{\frac{\sum\limits_{\text{all } i} \left(x_i - \bar{x}\right)^2 f_i}{n-1}}.$$

The standard deviation of the entire population is computed via the formula:

$$(9) \qquad \text{population standard deviation} = \sigma = \sqrt{\frac{\sum\limits_{\text{all } i} \left(x_i - \mu\right)^2 f_i}{n}} = \sqrt{\sum\limits_{\text{all } i} \left(x_i - \mu\right)^2 rf_i}$$

The calculations in (8) or (9) are most efficiently done by a calculator or computer once the data have been keyed-in. The square of the standard deviation is called the **variance**. Thus, s^2 stands for the sample variance and σ^2 (pronounced "sigma square") stands for the population variance. The computation of the sample variance for the monthly income data of section **2.2** is as follows:

$$s^2 = \frac{(100 - 593)^2 \cdot 5 + (200 - 593)^2 \cdot 10 + \cdots + (1000 - 593)^2 \cdot 5}{100 - 1} = 67728.28; \text{ thus, the}$$

sample standard deviation $= s = \sqrt{67728.28} = \$260.25$. Here is a possible interpretation of this quantity: if a randomly chosen student from the sample of 100 is chosen, that student's monthly income is likely to deviate from the mean income of \$593 by an average of \$260.25.

A few comments about the standard deviation are in order. The ability to measure and interpret variation is key in statistics. The standard deviation goes a long way towards achieving that goal. The value of s is always non-negative, with s = 0 in the case when the data have no spread. This condition happens only when all the data have the same value. As the data values become more spread about the mean, s increases in magnitude. Also, the standard deviation, just like the mean, is strongly influenced by data values that differ significantly from the rest of the data. In fact, even a single extreme value can make s very large.[8] For most data sets, the percent of the data found within 3 standard deviations from the mean is rarely less than 90%. That is, at least 90% of all the data values in any data set fall in the interval $\bar{x} - 3s$ to $\bar{x} + 3s$. Note that the sample standard deviation, s, varies for different samples from the same population. That is, even though σ is assumed fixed, s will vary randomly from sample to sample.[9] We will study this variation in further detail in later chapters.

2.4   Measures of location

Have you ever wondered what it means to score in the 90th *percentile* of some examination? How about if your score fell in the first *quartile*? Furthermore, what does it mean to have a *standard score* of 1.5? The answers to these questions are based on knowledge of measures of location.

Percentile

The kth percentile is a number such that k percent of the data falls below it. So, the 90th percentile represents a number so that 90% of the data in the set falls below it. Verify that for the monthly income data of section **2.2**, the 90th percentile is \$900. Note the following:

---

[8] For the data set {2,3,4}, s = 1. However, for the data set {2,3,4,200}, s = 99.5.

[9] Think of any sample statistic as varying randomly for different samples, even for samples from the same population. In this sense, sample statistics behave like random variables.

- 25th percentile = 1st quartile

- median = 50th percentile = 2nd quartile

- 75th percentile = 3rd quartile

Standard score

The standard score, also called the *z-score*, tells us how many standard deviations a data value falls away from the mean and in which direction. That is,

(10) $$z = \frac{x - \overline{x}}{s} \text{ or } z = \frac{x - \mu}{\sigma} \ .$$

Using (10), and for the monthly income data of section **2.2**, a student with a monthly income of \$300 is assigned a z-score of: $z = \frac{300 - 593}{260.25} = -1.125$. This means that \$300 is located 1.125 standard deviations below (negative sign) the mean of the data set. Think of the z-score as a new way of scaling the data. Note the following:

- The z-score associated with the mean of any data set is always zero

- It is rare for any number on any data set to have a corresponding z score exceeding 4 or below –4. (Why do you think this is so?)

- z-scores are unitless and allow for the comparison of data from different data sets.[10]

2.5 Data transformations

Often times it is desired to transform (change, re-scale) the original data set. The exact reason for the transformation and the type of transformation applied is up to the experimenter and largely depends on the type of analysis being considered. Let's illustrate. Consider the grouped data set in the table below:

---

[10] Suppose Joan's score on the Math part of the SAT is 620. For the year she took the SAT, the mean Math score was 520 with standard deviation = 80. Joseph scored 27 on the Math part of the ACT. For the year he took the ACT, the mean Math score was 21 with standard deviation = 6. We assume both tests are mathematically equivalent. Note that: Joan's z-score = 1.25; Joseph's z-score = 1. Thus, Joan did better.

Data	Frequency	Relative Frequency	Data	Frequency	Relative Frequency
1	1	$1/36 = 0.02778$	81	3	$3/36 = 0.08333$
4	2	$2/36 = 0.05556$	100	2	$2/36 = 0.05556$
9	3	$3/36 = 0.08333$	121	1	$1/36 = 0.02778$
16	4	$4/36 = 0.11111$			
25	5	$5/36 = 0.13889$			
36	6	$6/36 = 0.16667$			
49	5	$5/36 = 0.13889$			
64	4	$4/36 = 0.11111$			

The following is a histogram of the data, with class intervals width = 1:

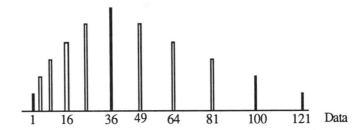

Now, apply a square root transformation to the data and form class intervals, each of width = 1. The histogram follows:

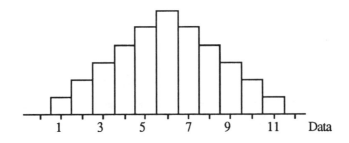

Note that the histogram of the transformed data is symmetrical about its center while the histogram of the original data is skewed to the right. So, in this case, the square root transformation made it possible to transform a skewed shape to a symmetric one.

Of interest is not only what happens to the shape of graphs when data are transformed, but also what happens to the center, spread and location of the original data. We will concentrate on linear transformations (they are easy to work with) and their effects on the above measurements.[11]

Consider the data set {1,2,3,4,5}. Verify, in any way you can, the following statistics about the data set:

- $\bar{x}$ = median = 3
- s = 1.581
- 80th percentile = 4.5 (or any number between 4 and 5)
- 1st quartile = 1.5.

Performing a linear transformation with a = 1 and b = 5 produces a new data set: {6,7,8,9,10}. We note the following (the reader should verify these):

- mean = median = 8 = 3 + 5 = original mean + b
- s = 1.581 (same as the original)
- 80th percentile = 9.5 = 4.5 + 5 = original percentile + b
- 1st quartile = 6.5 = 1.5 + 5 = original quartile + b.

Also, how about the shape of the original histogram and the histogram of the transformed data? (answer: same shape but shifted to the right 5 units).

So, based on the above evidence, we make the following observations. If a data set has mean $\bar{x}$, st. deviation s, median $\tilde{x}$, and kth percentile = p, and the data are linearly transformed with a = 1 and b = any real number, then the corresponding statistics, in terms of the original data set, for the transformed data set are:

- mean of transformed data set = $\bar{x}$ + b
- st. deviation of transformed data set = s
- median of transformed data set = $\tilde{x}$ + b
- kth percentile of transformed data set = p + b

It will be left as an exercise (see the problem set) to explore what happens to an original data set when the linear transformation takes the form:

- a = any real number; b = 0
- a = any real number; b = any real number.

---

[11] A linear transformation is of the form ax + b where x is a data value and a, b are conveniently chosen real numbers.

Chapter 2 Problems

1. Thirteen male pediatric surgeons in the New York metropolitan area were asked for the number of surgeries they performed during the last 12 months. The following data were collected: 28, 38, 44, 16, 10, 50, 90, 80, 85, 42, 30, 20, 34.

     a. Write the ordered data set.
     b. Find the arithmetic average. What is the meaning of this number?
     c. Find the median.
     d. Find the mode.
     e. Find the midrange.
     f. Construct a stem-leaf graph.

2. Ten female pediatric surgeons in the New York metropolitan area were asked for the number of surgeries they performed during the last 12 months. The following data were collected: 40, 46, 18, 12, 16, 8, 6, 24, 25, 15. Answer questions **a–f** as in **1.** above.

3. A mother wants to know the number of annual surgeries performed by a typical female pediatric surgeon in the New York metropolitan area. Based on problem **2.**, what would this number be?

4. Examine the data of problems **1.** and **2.** An observer makes the following statement: "It seems that male pediatric surgeons are more likely to perform surgery than female ones." Can this be readily concluded from these data? Explain.

5. Suppose a discrete random variable produces the sample data displayed in the histogram below. The histogram begins at 1.5 and the class width is 1. The vertical axis gives the frequency.

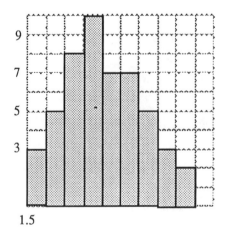

a. Complete the table.

X	2	3	4	5	6	7	8	9	10
f									

b. How many data points are in the sample?

6. From time to time, local newspapers provide summary information on real estate sales in their service area. One such recent summary read as follows:

Area: Los Altos Hills   **No. of sales:** 2

Average price: $750,000   **Median price:** $800,000

Lowest priced sale: $600,000

a. Find the total dollar amount for the two sales.
b. Find the dollar amount for the highest priced sale.
c. Assuming the calculation of the mean price is correct, can the median be $800,000? Explain.
d. What can be said about the average and the median of a data set with exactly two data values?

7. A well known statesman of modern times once made the following statement: "I look forward to the day when every American worker earns wages that exceed the average wage..." Explain the meaning of this statement.

8. You wish to measure the average speed of vehicles on an interstate highway in which you are driving. You adjust your travel speed until the number of vehicles passing you equals the number of vehicles you are passing. Have you found the mean or median speed of vehicles on the interstate highway?

9. Certain federal agencies, when computing the median income of any group of people, omit all members of the group who had zero income. Give an example to show that this type of reporting may cause the median income of a group to go <u>down</u> even when group members become better off economically.

10. You are interested in applying for employment in a small accounting firm. At the local career placement center you find that the mean annual salary paid by this firm is a whopping $75,000. You investigate this firm and find that 10 people work at the firm, including the owner. The owner's annual salary is $300,000.

a. Excluding the owner, what is the mean annual salary for the remaining 9 employees?

b. Would the median annual salary give a more accurate picture of the typical salaries the firm pays? Would you include the owner's salary in the median computation? Explain.

11. Create a list of 10 numbers such that each number is either 1 or 9 and such that the variance is:

a. as large as possible,

b. as small as possible.

12. Data from a random sample describing the height of the first grader population in Santa Clara County yield the following information:

mean height = 39 inches; standard deviation = 3 inches; mode = 37.5 inches;
first quartile = 32 inches; third quartile = 42 inches.

a. Find the most frequent height.

b. The shortest 25% of these first graders have heights below _____.

c. Find the variance of the heights.

d. Find the heights that are 3 standard deviations away from the mean.

e. First graders with heights in the 75th percentile are taller than _____.

f. Find the z-score corresponding to a height of 36 inches.

g. Is 39 inches μ or $\bar{x}$?

h. Is 3 inches s or σ?

i. Find the inter-quartile range.

13. Consider the data set {1,2,2,3,5,8}.

a. Calculate the mean, median, and standard deviation.

b. Perform a linear transformation on the data letting a = 2 and b = 0. List the transformed data set.

c. Calculate the mean, median, and standard deviation for the transformed data set.

d. Compare the results of **a.** and **c.** Generalize this result (hint: similar to the discussion at the end of section **2.5**).

14. The stem-leaf graph below represents a sample of the ages of the adult (over 21) population in the Northeastern United States.

2	2578
3	02234677889
4	2348
5	018
6	027
7	26
8	0
9	1

a. Find the sample size.

b. For this data set, which is larger, the median or the mean? Explain <u>without</u> computing either one.

c. Is the standard deviation of the data larger or smaller than 10? Explain <u>without</u> computing the standard deviation.

15. For the data of problem 14. above, carry out the computations to verify that at least 90% of the ages in the sample are found within 3 standard deviations from the mean.

16. A student took four tests in a Statistics class. The following information were recorded.

Test	Score	Class average	Class st. deviation
1	40	30	20
2	50	53	8
3	60	65	15
4	70	69	10

a. Calculate the z-score for each test.

b. On which test did the student have the worst performance? Explain.

17. For each of the following, X_1 and X_2 represent samples from two different populations. Determine the correct relationship (i.e., <, =, >) for the sample mean and the sample standard deviation.

a. $\overline{X}_1$ < = > $\overline{X}_2$ $\qquad\qquad$ s_1 < = > s_2

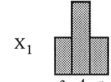
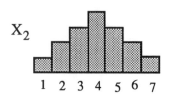

b. $\overline{X}_1$ < = > $\overline{X}_2$ $\qquad\qquad$ s_1 < = > s_2

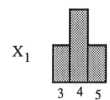
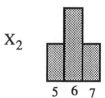

c. $\overline{X}_1$ < = > $\overline{X}_2$ $\qquad\qquad$ s_1 < = > s_2

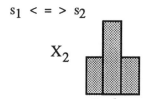

d. $\overline{X}_1$ < = > $\overline{X}_2$ $\qquad\qquad$ s_1 < = > s_2

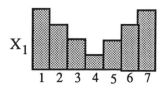
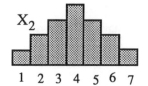

18. The following summary pertains to the survival time, in days, of 80 laboratory rats after they were injected with a cancerous substance in a medical experiment. Survival times, whether of devices or animals or humans, have distributions that are skewed to the right.

mean = 141; median = 102; standard deviation = 110; minimum = 40; maximum = 600;
first quartile = 82; third quartile = 155.

  a. Explain how the relationship between the mean and the median reflects the expected skewness of the data.
  b. Find the 75th percentile of the data.
  c. Find the number of survival days corresponding to a z-score of 2.
  d. Find the range of the data.
  e. Find the inter-quartile range.
  f. Find the midrange of the data.
  g. How many of the 80 rats lived longer than 82 days?
  h. Why is there such a discrepancy between the range and the interquartile range? Which of the two measures best represents the overall spread of the data?

19. The US Army reports that the distribution of head circumference among soldiers has a mean of 23 inches and standard deviation 1 inch. Helmets are mass produced for all soldiers except for the smallest and the largest 5% of head sizes. Soldiers in the smallest or largest 5% get custom made helmets. Find the head sizes that get custom made helmets.

20. A physical device dispenses tablets that are poured into bottles. For this particular bottle, the mean number of tablets is 1000. To check the process, quality control personnel select random bottles and count the number of tablets in each. Over the course of one day, 2000 such bottles are produced and 100 random bottles are selected. A recent sample of 100 bottles gave the following distribution of tablets:

Number of tablets in bottle	250	999	1000	1001
Frequency = number of bottles	1	1	97	1

Could there be something wrong with the device filling the bottles? How could you explain the one bottle with only 250 tablets?

21. Consider the data set {5,7}.

  a. Verify that $\bar{x} = 6$ and $s = \sqrt{2} \approx 1.4142$.
  b. Find real numbers a and b so that applying the linear transformation $ax + b$ to the original data set produces the data set {110, 130}. Hint: find the mean and st. deviation of the transformed data set.

22. Given the data set:

X	frequency
1	8
2	15
3	30
4	25
5	12

a. Find the mean

b. Find the median

c. Construct a histogram

23. The following data set is a sample of 100 randomly selected IQ scores as measured by the Stanford-Binet IQ test.

65	81	88	93	97	100	102	106	112	119
71	83	89	93	98	100	102	107	112	119
71	83	89	95	98	100	102	107	113	120
72	84	89	95	98	100	102	107	113	122
73	85	90	96	98	100	103	108	114	123
74	85	91	96	98	100	103	110	114	126
76	85	92	96	99	100	103	110	115	126
77	86	92	97	99	100	104	111	117	127
80	86	92	97	99	101	105	111	118	130
81	87	92	97	99	101	106	112	118	137

For parts **a–h**, find the indicated quantity.

a. mean

b. median

c. mode

d. midrange

e. standard deviation

f. 1st quartile

g. 90th percentile

h. IQ score corresponding to a z-score of –1.5.

i. Construct a histogram of the data. Choose your own starting point and class width in order to produce a histogram that is symmetric about its center.

j. Find the percent of the IQ scores falling within: (i) 1 st. deviation from the mean; (ii) 2 st. deviations from the mean; (iii) 3 st. deviations from the mean.

2 4. Given the two data sets:

X_1	f		X_2	f
1	1		1	5
2	2		2	2
3	5		3	1
4	2		4	2
5	1		5	5

a. Sketch both histograms

b. Based on the histograms, circle the correct relation for the means and the standard deviations:

$$\overline{x_1} \quad < \; = \; > \quad \overline{x_2} \qquad\qquad s_1 \quad < \; = \; > \quad s_2$$

c. Find $\overline{x}_1$, $\overline{x}_2$, s_1, and s_2. Do they agree with your answer for **b.**?

25. Consider the following table of grouped data:

X	f	rf = relative frequency
1	10	_____
2	15	_____
3	35	_____
4	45	_____
5	_____	_____
6	5	_____
Total	125	_____

a. Complete the blanks

b. Find $\overline{x}$ using the **rf** column.

Chapter 3

Probability

3.0   Introduction

In Chapter 1, a function called a random variable was introduced. In Chapter 2, data was used to obtain an understanding of the random variable. In this chapter, we will lay the theoretical foundation for the study of random variables. The basis for this foundation is the concept of probability. This is an extremely complex topic. Fortunately, we can condense the major ideas in a few easy to grasp examples.

In Chapter 2, we used frequency, relative frequency[1] and histograms to gain an insight into random phenomena. In simple terms,

$$\boxed{\textbf{probabilities are theoretical relative frequencies}}.$$

Example 1   An experiment consists of rolling a die 600 times. We can either physically roll the die or we can run a simulation using a computer or some other similar random device. If the die is fair it is reasonable to expect each number to come up about 100 times. Even though the empirical data gathered from each experiment will differ, the expectation remains the same. Data 1 and Data 2 are the results for two experiments when the die is rolled 600 times. Observe that the data changes but the theoretical expectation remains the same.

	Data 1			Data 2			Theory	
Die	Freq.	Rel. Freq.	Die	Freq.	Rel. Freq.	Die	Frequency	Probability
1	101	$^{101}/_{600}$	1	97	$^{97}/_{600}$	1	100	$^{100}/_{600} = ^1/_6$
2	98	$^{98}/_{600}$	2	104	$^{104}/_{600}$	2	100	$^{100}/_{600} = ^1/_6$
3	99	$^{99}/_{600}$	3	102	$^{102}/_{600}$	3	100	$^{100}/_{600} = ^1/_6$
4	103	$^{103}/_{600}$	4	100	$^{100}/_{600}$	4	100	$^{100}/_{600} = ^1/_6$
5	97	$^{97}/_{600}$	5	96	$^{96}/_{600}$	5	100	$^{100}/_{600} = ^1/_6$
6	102	$^{102}/_{600}$	6	101	$^{101}/_{600}$	6	100	$^{100}/_{600} = ^1/_6$
Totals	600	1	Totals	600	1	Totals	600	1

---

[1] Relative frequency $= \dfrac{\text{number of times outcome occurs}}{\text{total number of times experiment is conducted}}$

3.1   The Probability Space

A probability space consists of the following:

1. A set of all possible outcomes called a **sample space**. The individual elements are called **simple events**.

2. An assignment of theoretical relative frequency or probability, p, to each simple event. The assignment must be such that each p is non-negative and the sum of all the p's totals 1. That is: $\boxed{p \geq 0 \ \text{ and } \ \Sigma p = 1}$.

Example 2   Roll a fair die. Sample space = {1, 2, 3, 4, 5, 6}. The probabilities for each simple event are: P(1) = P(2) = ... = P(6) = 1/6

Example 3   Flip a fair coin. Sample space = {T, H}. The probabilities for each simple event are: P(H) = P(T) = 0.5

Example 4   Roll two fair dice. The sample space consists of the following 36 simple events

Die #1

		1	2	3	4	5	6
D	1	1,1	1,2	1,3	1,4	1,5	1,6
i	2	2,1	2,2	2,3	2,4	2,5	2,6
e	3	3,1	3,2	3,3	3,4	3,5	3,6
	4	4,1	4,2	4,3	4,4	4,5	4,6
#2	5	5,1	5,2	5,3	5,4	5,5	5,6
	6	6,1	6,2	6,3	6,4	6,5	6,6

Since the two dice are fair: P(3,4) = 1/36. In fact, for the above table, P(any simple event) = 1/36.

Note that if a sample space consists of n equally likely simple events, then each event has probability $\frac{1}{n}$.

Quite often, a tree diagram may be used to analyze a sample space. The following example will illustrate.

Example 5   Flip a fair coin three times.

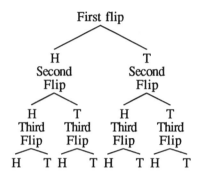

Sample Space = {HHH, HHT, HTH, HTT, THH, THT, TTH, TTT}. P(simple event) = 1/8.

3.2   Events

Any subset of a sample space is called an event. The probability of an event is the sum of the probabilities of the simple events.

Example 6   Roll two fair dice. Consider the event, {sum of the faces is three}.
P(sum of the faces is three) = P[(1,2), (2,1)] = 2/36 = 1/18

Example 7   Flip three fair coins. Consider the event, {at least one head occurs}.
P(at least one head occurs) = P(HHH, HHT, HTH, HTT, THH, THT, TTH) = 7/8.

Example 8   The following example will be used to illustrate many of the concepts to follow.
A company employs 1000 people in three areas, Technical, Clerical and Management. The people work in one of three locations, Plants 1, 2 or 3. The information is summarized in the following two- way chart.

| | Plants | | | |
	1	2	3	Total
Tech.	50	110	340	500
Mgr.	30	30	140	200
Clerical	20	60	220	300
Total	100	200	700	1000

For instance,

P(a person selected at random is a Technician) = 500/1000 = 0.5,

P(a person selected at random is from Plant 3) = 700/1000 = 0.7.

3.3   The Compound Event "and"

If A, B are two events then the event (A *and* B) = A $\cap$ B is composed of those simple events contained in both events A, B. We can use a **Venn diagram** to illustrate this idea. The shaded region represents the event A $\cap$ B.

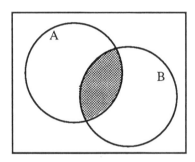

From **Example 8**, there are 30 people who are Managers and work in Plant 1. Thus, $P(\text{Mgr.} \cap \text{Plant 1}) = \dfrac{30}{1000} = 0.03$. The Venn diagrams below illustrate this situation.

Count diagram

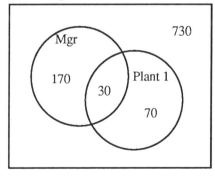

Probability diagram

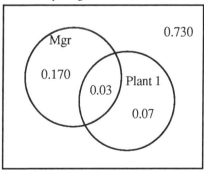

Note that there are 170 Managers who are not in Plant 1 and 70 people in Plant 1 who are not Managers. There are 730 people who are neither Managers nor in Plant 1. The probability diagram is essentially the same as the count diagram.

When events contain nothing in common, they are called **mutually exclusive**. Again, a Venn diagram is used to illustrate this condition. In the following, A and B are mutually exclusive.

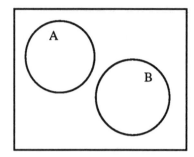

A, B mutually exclusive

There are no people who work at Plant 1 and Plant 2. Therefore, Plant 1 and Plant 2 are mutually exclusive events. The following pairs in example 8 are all mutually exclusive:

{Plant 1, Plant 2}, {Plant 1, Plant 3}, {Plant 2, Plant 3}, {Mgr., Clerical}, {Mgr., Technical}, {Clerical, Technical}

3.4   The Compound Event "or"

If A, B are two events then the event (A *or* B) = A $\cup$ B is composed of those simple events contained in one or the other or both events. The shaded region represents A $\cup$ B.

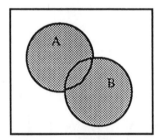

A or B is the combined region

From **Example 8**, there are 270 people who are Managers or work in Plant 1. That is,

$P(\text{Mgr.} \cup \text{Plant 1}) = \dfrac{270}{1000} = 0.27$. This can be readily seen from the Venn diagrams below:

Count diagram

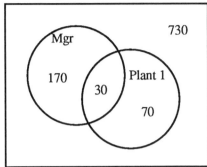

Probability diagram

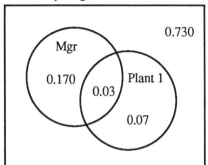

Using counts, notice that:

count{Mgr. or Plant 1) = count{Mgr.} + count{Plant 1} – count{Mgr. and Plant 1} = 200 + 100 – 30 = 270.

In terms of probabilities, note that:

P(Mgr. or Plant 1) = P(Mgr.) + P(Plant 1) – P(Mgr. and Plant 1) = 0.2 + 0.1 – 0.03 = 0.27.

The following rule generalizes this relation between the compound connectives "and" and "or":

for any two events A, B: $\boxed{\textbf{P(A or B) = P(A) + P(B) – P(A and B)}}$.

Observe that if A and B are mutually exclusive, then P(A and B) = 0 and for this case,

P(A or B) = P(A) + P(B).

3.5   The Complement of an event

The complement of and event A, denoted by A′ (pronounced "A prime"), consists of all the events in the sample space which are not in A.   A′ is shaded in the diagram below.

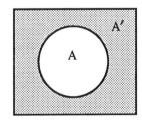

Observe that $A' \cup A = S$ = sample space and $A' \cap A = \emptyset$; therefore, $P(A' \cup A) = P(A') + P(A) = 1$. That is, for any event A,

$$\boxed{P(A') = 1 - P(A)}.$$

From **Example 8**, P(a person selected is not clerical) = 1 – P(person selected is clerical) = 1 – 0.3 = 0.7.

From **Example 4**, P(at least one head appears when a coin is flipped 3 times) = 1 – P(no heads appear when a coin is flipped 3 times) = 1 – 1/8 = 7/8.

3.6   Conditional Probability

An important concept in probability is the effect on an event given that another event has occurred. From Example 8, P(a technical person is selected) = 0.5. But, what happens if we are to select people from Plant 2? That is, what is the probability that a technical person is selected *given* that we select from Plant 2)? This is written as P(Tech. | Plant 2), where the "|" means *given* or *conditioned* on. In other words, we have reduced our sample space to Plant 2. Using the new sample space of Plant 2, we obtain: $P(\text{Tech. | Plant 2}) = \dfrac{110}{200} = 0.55$ Notice that the reduced sample space has changed the probability of selecting a Technical person. Also, notice that the same result is obtained

by considering: $\dfrac{P(\text{Tech.} \cap \text{Plant 2})}{P(\text{Plant 2})} = \dfrac{0.11}{0.200} = 0.55.$

The general result is as follows:
$$\boxed{P(\textbf{A given that B has occurred}) = P(\textbf{A | B}) = \frac{P(\textbf{A} \cap \textbf{B})}{P(\textbf{B})}}.$$

Another way to write the same relation is:
$$\boxed{P(\textbf{A | B}) \; P(\textbf{B}) = P(\textbf{A} \cap \textbf{B})}$$

This conditional relation is not commutative. Again, from **Example 8**:

$$P(\text{Plant 2 | Tech.}) = \frac{110}{500} = 0.22 \neq 0.55;$$

thus, P(Plant 2 | Tech.) ≠ P(Tech. | Plant 2).

3.7   Independent Events

Two events are said to be **independent** if the occurrence of one does not change the likelihood of the occurrence of the second. In **Example 8**, consider the two events, Manager is selected, person selected works at Plant 3. The probability of selecting a Manager given we have selected a person from Plant 3 is,

$$P(\text{Mgr. | Plant 3}) = \frac{140}{700} = 0.2 = P(\text{Mgr.}).$$

Thus, the fact that we select from Plant 3 has no effect on the likelihood of selecting a Manager. We say that the two events, being a Manager and working in Plant 3, are **independent**.

If we reverse the two events the numbers change but the independence condition still holds. That is,

$$P(\text{Plant 3} \mid \text{Mgr.}) = \frac{140}{200} = 0.7 = P(\text{Plant 3}).$$

In general, if A and B are independent then: $\boxed{P(A \mid B) = P(A)}$. That is, independence means that the *conditional* probability is the same as the *unconditional* probability.

Recall that $P(A \mid B) = \dfrac{P(A \text{ and } B)}{P(B)}$. It follows that if A, B are independent, then $P(A \mid B) = P(A) = \dfrac{P(A \text{ and } B)}{P(B)}$. From $P(A) = \dfrac{P(A \text{ and } B)}{P(B)}$ we obtain $P(A \text{ and } B) = P(A) \, P(B)$, from which the following result follows:

$$\boxed{\text{if events } \mathbf{A} \text{ and } \mathbf{B} \text{ are independent then } \mathbf{P(A \text{ and } B) = P(A) \, P(B)}}.$$

From **Example 8**:

Note that: P(Tech.) = 0.5, P(Plant 1) = 0.1; P(Tech. and Plant 1) = 0.05.
Since $0.5 \cdot 0.1 = 0.05$, the events selecting a Tech. person and working in Plant 1 are **independent**.

Also, from **Example 8**:

Note that: P(Mgr.) = 0.2, P(Plant 2) = 0.2; P(Mgr. and Plant 2) = 0.03.
Since $0.2 \cdot 0.2 = 0.04 \neq 0.03$, the events selecting a Manager and working in Plant 2 are **not independent**.

Note that the independence condition is only expressible numerically. That is, it can not be pictured in a Venn diagram. Independence is a condition on the probabilities of the corresponding events.

Chapter 3 Problems

1. A box contains 4 slips with the numbers {1, 2, 3, 4}. Two are chosen one at at time and with replacement.

   a. List the sample space

   b. List the outcomes for the events A = {second slip is a 3}, B = {sum of the slips is 4},
      C = {at least one 2 appears}

   c. Fill in the Venn diagram with the appropriate whole numbers.

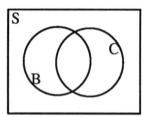

   d. Determine the following probabilities:

$P(A)$	$P(B)$	$P(C)$
$P(A \text{ and } B)$	$P(A \text{ and } C)$	$P(\text{not } B)$
$P(A \text{ given } B)$	$P(A \mid C)$	$P(C \mid B)$
$P(A')$	$P(C')$	

   e. Which of the pairs A, B, C are independent?

   f. Which of the pairs A, B, C are mutually exclusive?

2. A six-sided die is weighted so that 1 is twice as likely to appear as any other face. The other faces are equally likely to appear. Let A = {even number appears when the die is rolled}. Let B = {odd number appears when the die is rolled}. Let C = {number is less than 3}. Let D = {number is greater than 3}

    a. Describe the sample space.   **b.** P(A) =

    c. P(B) =   **d.** P(C) =

    e. P(A and B)   **f.** P(A or B)

    g. P(B and C)   **h.** P(B or C)

    i. P(B | C)   **j.** P(D | A)

    k. Which pairs of A, B, C, D are mutually exclusive?

3. A husband and wife have the following nightly TV viewing habits. The husband watches TV 60% of the time.

    a. If 80% of all their time is spent watching TV and if their viewing habits are independent, find the probability that the wife watches TV.

    b. If 80% of their time is spent watching TV and if their viewing habits are mutually exclusive (they never watch at the same time), find the probability that the wife watches TV.

    c. If the husband and wife watch together 25% of the time, find the probability that the wife watches when the husband is watching.

    d. Suppose that the wife watches 30% of the time when the husband is watching. Find the probability that the husband and wife watch TV together.

4. The table below summarizes the majors for three classes at a certain college. We let M = Math, H = History, L = Liberal Arts, F = Freshmen, S = Sophomore, and J = Junior.

	Math	History	Lib. Arts	Total
Fresh	20	30	150	200
Soph	40	60	200	300
Junior	40	110	350	500
Total	100	200	700	1000

a. Find the following: $P(M)$, $P(H)$, $P(L)$, $P(F)$, $P(S)$, $P(J)$

b. Find the following: $P(M \cap F)$, $P(M \cap H)$, $P(F \cap H)$, $P(S \cap L)$

c. Find the following: $P(H \cup F)$, $P(M \cup L)$, $P(J \cup H)$, $P(S \cup H)$

d. Find the following: $P(H \mid S)$, $P(S \mid H)$, $P(F \mid L)$, $P(L \mid F)$

e. Find P(a freshman is also a math major)

f. Find P(a freshman is also a liberal arts major)

g. Find P(a person is a freshman and a liberal arts major)

h. Find P(a person is a freshman or a liberal arts major)

i. Find all pairs that are mutually exclusive.

j. Find all pairs that are independent.

5. A company uses three plants to produce a new computer chip. Plant A produces 30% of the chips. Plant B produces 45% with the rest produced by Plant C. Each plant has a known defect rate (the % of defective chips is known). Defect rates for A, B and C are respectively 3%, 1%, and 5%.

    a. For the tree diagram below, write the appropriate probability for each branch in the appropriate box.

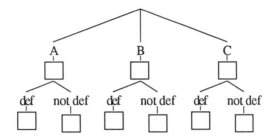

    b. Find the probability that a given chip is defective and from plant C.

    c. Find the probability that a given chip from Plant C is defective.

    d. Find the probability that a given chip is defective.

    e. Find the probability that a given defective chip is from plant C.

6. Assume that $P(A) \neq 0$ and $P(B) \neq 0$.

    a. Explain why if A and B are mutually exclusive events then A and B are dependent events.

    b. Explain why if A and B are independent events then A and B are not mutually exclusive.

7. A doctor is trying to determine if a patient has one of three diseases, d_1, d_2 or d_3. Two tests are to be carried out, each of which results in a positive (+) or negative (–) outcome. There are four test patterns: + +, + –, – +, – –. The data in the table below is available for 10,000 people having one of the three diseases.

Disease	Number having the disease	+ +	+ −	− +	− −
d_1	3,215	2110	301	704	100
d_2	2,125	396	132	1187	410
d_3	4,660	510	3568	73	509
Total = 10,000					

From the above table, it is easy to estimate the prior probabilities for each of the diseases and, given a particular disease, the probability of a particular test outcome. For example, the prior probability of disease d_1 is estimated by the ratio 3215/10000 = 0.3215. Likewise, the probability of test result +−, given disease d_1, is estimated to be 301/3215 = 0.094. This type of probability is called a "posterior" probability.

a. Express the information in the table in a tree diagram by placing the appropriate frequencies along each branch.

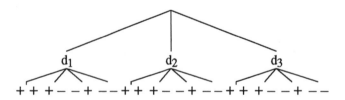

b. Estimate the prior probabilities for diseases d_2 and d_3.

c. Estimate the posterior probabilities of each test result conditioned on each of the diseases.

d. Estimate the posterior probabilities of each disease conditioned on each of the test results.

e. Reverse the probabilities by completing the following tree diagram. Place probabilities along each branch.

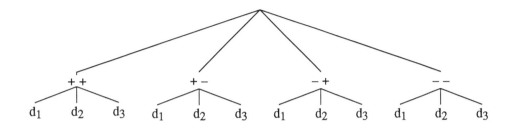

8. Two coins are in a bag. One of the coins is fair while the other coin is biased such that P(heads) = 1. One coin is randomly chosen from the bag and flipped once.

    a. Produce a tree diagram for this situation.

    b. What is the probability that the result of the flip was tails?

    c. If the result of the flip was heads, what is the probability that the biased coin was flipped?

9. In a closet there are two pairs of shoes. One pair is brown and the other pair is black. The shoes are randomly arranged on the floor of the closet. Without looking, you reach in the closet and take out two shoes.

    a. Construct a tree diagram for this situation.

    b. What is the probability that the two chosen shoes are of the same color?

    c. Suppose instead that the two pairs of shoes in the closet are identical. What is the probability that the two chosen shoes can be worn?

Chapter 4

Discrete Probability Distributions

4.1   Probability distribution functions for discrete random variables

In Chapter 3, we covered various ways of computing probabilities by using basic probability rules. However, prior to carrying out any of the probability computations, knowledge of the sample space was almost always necessary. We saw that a sample space could be listed or graphed (tree, Venn diagram). We also realize that there are situations where it is impractical to list or graph the sample space. In this chapter we will see how working with random variables simplifies our access to the sample space and facilitates the computation of the corresponding probabilities.

Recall that numerical random variables could be either discrete or continuous. Discrete random variables arise when the numerical assignment is done using counts. Continuous random variables arise when the numerical assignment is done using measurements. In this chapter we will cover only discrete random variables. The next chapter is dedicated to the topic of continuous random variables.

Consider the experiment of flipping three fair coins once (or its equivalent, flipping a fair coin three times). The following is a listing of the sample space: {HHH, TTT, HHT, HTT, HTH, THT, TTH, THH}. All eight outcomes in the sample space are equally likely. Suppose that we are interested in the number of heads that come up. It will make sense to define a random variable to count the number of heads that come up on a single trial of the experiment. Thus, if we let X = number of heads that come up, then X takes the values 0,1,2,3. That is, the range of the random variable is {0,1,2,3}. We can now assign probabilities to each of the values in the range. We organize the information in table form.

X = number of heads	$P(X = x)$[1]	Corresponding Outcomes
0	1/8	TTT
1	3/8	HTT, TTH, THT
2	3/8	HHT, THH, HTH
3	1/8	HHH

For instance, from the table we see that $P(X = 1) = 3/8$. That is, the probability of obtaining exactly one head in a single flip of 3 fair coins is 3/8. Note that summing the $P(X = x)$ column yields 1.

A listing, such as the one in the above table,[2] of the probabilities associated with the range of a

---

[1] Note that capital X denotes the random variable while small x stands for the values in the range of X. Also, the notation $P(X = x)$ is read "find the probability that X takes the value x".

[2] Only the first two columns are needed. The third column is included here to facilitate understanding.

random variable, where each of the probabilities is a number between 0 and 1, inclusive, and the sum of all the probabilities equals 1, is called a **probability distribution**.

Let's consider the situation of rolling a single biased die once. The die is biased such that the even faces are twice as likely to come up as the odd faces. Let Y = number on face. Thus, the range of Y is $\{1,2,3,4,5,6\}$ (these are the small y's). We build the probability distribution.

Y = number on face	$P(Y = y)$
1	1/9
2	2/9
3	1/9
4	2/9
5	1/9
6	2/9

Note that each of the probabilities is a number between 0 and 1 and that the $P(Y = y)$ column sums to 1. Sometimes we can collapse a probability distribution into a formula. Basically, the formula is equivalent to the information contained in the probability distribution table. The advantage of the formula is that it is easier to manipulate and a lot more compact. By carefully paying attention to the pattern in the above table, we write the following formula:

$$P(Y = y) = \begin{cases} 1/9, & \text{if } y \text{ is odd} \\ 2/9, & \text{if } y \text{ is even} \end{cases}$$

Formulas obtained from probability distributions are called **probability distribution functions** (or **PDF** for short). Think of a probability distribution function as a mathematical model for uncertainty. The formula models the uncertain phenomena using a random variable. On a given trial it is impossible to predict what is going to happen; however, the power of the PDF is that it allows for the modelling of unpredictable phenomena via the generation of probabilities.

Here is a surprising formula for the experiment consisting of rolling two fair dice where W = sum of the faces. The range of W is $\{2,3,4,5,6,7,8,9,10,11,12\}$. The PDF for this situation is given by:

$$P(W = w) = \frac{6 - |w - 7|}{36}.$$

For example, when $W = 7$ (meaning: the sum of the faces is 7), $P(W = 7) = 6/36 = 1/6$. Verify that the formula gives the correct probabilities for all values of W.

It would be great to have a formula for every conceivable probability experiment. Unfortunately, nature is not all that accommodating. However, there are a number of discrete situations where such formulas are well documented and, in some cases, extensive probability tables are available. We will discuss these situations in section **4.3**.

4.2   Expectation and variance of a random variable

Since a random variable consists of a numerical assignment, it makes sense to ask about its mean and variance. In a way, this is no different from the mean and variance of a data set as studied in Chapter 2. However, the formulas in Chapter 2 will take a different look, since we are now using probabilities to model the behavior of a random variable. Also, since a random variable takes into account all possible outcomes of an experiment, we take the set of all outcomes to be the population and not a sample. Therefore, when we talk about the mean and variance of a random variable we refer to μ and σ^2 instead of $\bar{x}$ and s^2.

Expectation

To compute the expected value of a random variable, we start with the formula for the average of a data set. That is, $\mu = \dfrac{\sum\limits_{\text{all } i} x_i f_i}{n}$. Note we can rewrite this formula in the form $\mu = \sum\limits_{\text{all } i} x_i \left(\dfrac{f_i}{n}\right)$ where the n is moved inside the summation sign. But, $\dfrac{f_i}{n}$ is just the probability that the value x_i occurs; thus,

(1) $$\mu = \sum_{\text{all } i} x_i\, P\left(X = x_i\right) .$$

Returning to the example from the previous section where the random variable X = number of heads on three flips of a single fair coin, we ask: if the experiment is performed a large number of times, on average, how many heads are expected to come up? That is, the average number of heads that comes up, known as the **expected value** of X, is nothing more than the average of X over many repetitions of the experiment. From (1) above we obtain

$$\mu = 0\left(\frac{1}{8}\right) + 1\left(\frac{3}{8}\right) + 2\left(\frac{3}{8}\right) + 3\left(\frac{1}{8}\right) = \frac{12}{8} = 1.5 .$$

Thus, on average, 1.5 heads are **expected** to come up when a single fair coin is flipped three times.

In terms of a histogram, the mean or expected value of a random variable is the point where the histogram balances. The histograms below illustrate this idea.

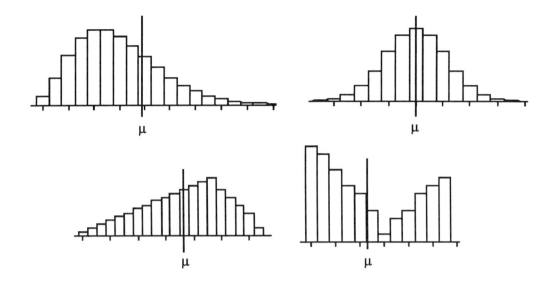

Most of the interesting applications of expectation are found in the world of gaming and insurance. The following examples will illustrate.

Example 1

Insurance companies would not be profitable without the use of probability and expected value. The premiums that are charged for different types of insurance coverage are determined via the use of probability computations that take into account the likelihood of making payoffs to costumers. Suppose the cost of damages, in dollars, incurred in a certain type of accident during a given year are: 100, 1000, 5000, and 10000 with probabilities 0.8, 0.1, 0.08, and 0.02 respectively. The insurance company offers a plan with a $500 deductible (i.e., the insurance company only pays for damages over $500) for each accident. If the company wishes to make an expected profit of $100 for each policy contract written, what premium amount should the company charge?

Let X = cost, in dollars, to the insurance company for each accident. Note that the range of X consists of the values: $0, –$500, –$4500, and – $9500, corresponding to the cost of damages and taking into account the fact that there is a $500 deductible associated with each accident. We use the above information to build the probability distribution table,

X = cost to insurance company	P(X = x)
$0	0.8
–$500	0.1
–$4500	0.08
–$9500	0.02

Using equation (1), the expected cost to the insurance company per accident is given by,

$$\mu = \$0 \cdot (0.8) + (-\$500) \cdot (0.1) + (-\$4500) \cdot (0.08) + (-\$9500) \cdot (0.02) = -\$600.$$

This means that the insurance company stands to lose, on average, $600 per accident. Since the insurance company wishes to make an expected profit of $100 per contract written, the premium charged per policy contract should be $700.

Example 2

You are presented with the following game. Roll a fair die. You get paid a dollar amount equals to the face that comes up. That is, if a 5 comes up, you are paid $5, etc. In order to play, you must pay $3 per roll. Should you play? Here is a way of analyzing the average payoff per game played using expectation. Let X = player's profit on a single roll of the die. The range of X is given by (number on face − $3). That is, the range of X is: {−$2, −$1, $0, $1, $2, $3}. We build the probability distribution table and compute μ.

X = player's profit	P(X = x)	Outcome
−$2	1/6	1 comes up
−$1	1/6	2 comes up
$0	1/6	3 comes up
+$1	1/6	4 comes up
+$2	1/6	5 comes up
+$3	1/6	6 comes up

Thus, $\mu = (-2) \cdot (1/6) + (-1) \cdot (1/6) + 0 \cdot (1/6) + 1 \cdot (1/6) + 2 \cdot (1/6) + 3 \cdot (1/6) = 1/2 = \$0.50$. That is, on average, the player will profit 50 cents per game. If it so happens that someone offers to play this game, by all means play it! (you stand to make a lot of money very quickly).

And, while we are on the subject of games, casino games have a negative expectation. That is, the games are designed so that the player looses a small amount, on average, per game played. Over many such games, and with many people simultaneously playing, it is no wonder that casinos make large profits. In fact, even games with a positive expectation can lead the player to ruin.[3]

---

[3] Take the case where a player wagers the entire existing capital on each flip of a fair coin. If a tail comes up the player profits an amount twice the size of the stake. The player will lose everything when the first head comes up. Each flip has a positive expectation; however, the player will definitely lose, since a head will eventually come up.

Variance

Recall that the formula for the variance of a data set representing the entire population is given by

$\sigma^2 = \dfrac{\sum\limits_{\text{all } i}(x_i - \mu)^2 f_i}{n}$. Bringing the n inside the summation symbol, we write, $\sigma^2 = \sum\limits_{\text{all } i}(x_i - \mu)^2 \dfrac{f_i}{n}$.

If you think of $\dfrac{f_i}{n}$ as the probability that the data value x_i occurs, we then write:

(2)
$$\sigma^2 = \sum\limits_{\text{all } i}(x_i - \mu)^2 \, P(X = x_i).$$

The implementation of (2) is straight forward. For the die game in the above example, the variance of X is calculated as follows:

$$\sigma^2 = (-2 - 0.50)^2 \cdot (1/6) + (-1 - 0.50)^2 \cdot (1/6) + \ldots + (3 - 0.50)^2 \cdot (1/6) = 17.5/6 \approx 2.917.$$

This means that the standard deviation of X is $\sigma = \sqrt{2.917} \approx 1.708$. That is, the amount of money a player is expected to win or lose on each game deviates from 50 cents by approximately \$1.71.

4.3 Bernoulli trials

Any random variable with only two possible outcomes on a single trial,[4] such that:

- the two outcomes are mutually exclusive,

- if P(success) = p then P(failure) = 1 – p,

- successive trials are independent of one another,

is said to be a **Bernoulli random variable**. There are many physical phenomena that can be modelled by a Bernoulli random variable. Here are a few: a single flip of a coin; the outcome of a horse race; a recent stock purchase has been profitable or not; your status at the end of this class (pass/fail).

Of interest to us will be to study random variables composed of a sequence of Bernoulli trials.

---

[4] The two outcomes are typically characterized as *success* and *failure*. Depending on the situation, this characterization may take other forms: yes/no, right/wrong, on/off, correct/incorrect, defective/non-defective, etc. Note that the two outcomes are the opposite of each other.

Phenomena such as the number of heads that come up when a coin is flipped 30 times or the number of flips it will take before the first tail appears or the number of people who will have to be interviewed before a committee of 10 people are formed, are all variations of sequences of Bernoulli trials. Note that each of these situations involves a count, each trial is composed of only two possible outcomes, and each trial is independent of any previous trial. Discrete random variables where each trial is Bernoulli differ only by what the experimenter is counting. There are four major discrete distributions where each trial is Bernoulli: *Binomial, Poisson, Geometric,* and *Pascal.* A fifth one, the *Hypergeometric* distribution, is not a pure Bernoulli; however, under certain circumstances, each trial may be reasonably approximated by the Bernoulli definition.

Binomial

The Binomial distribution is the most common of the discrete distributions. It arises when we are interested in counting the number of successes in a fixed number of trials. The key feature to remember is "in a fixed number of trials". The two parameters that completely define the Binomial distribution are the number of trials, n, and the probability of success in a single trial, p. Note that since the trials are independent, p remains constant from trial to trial. When we determine that a random variable X is binomially distributed, we write $X \sim B(n,p)$. The wiggle (i.e., ~) is read: is distributed. Computing binomial probabilities is not all that easy. However, extensive tables are available. In most cases, computers can carry out the calculations, and can also produce histograms of the probability distribution for different values of n and p.

Example 3

Flip a fair coin ten times. What is the probability distribution for the number of heads that can come up?

Let X = number of heads. The range of X is: 0,1,2, ... ,10. Note that $X \sim B(10,0.5)$ since n = 10 and p = probability of heads on a single flip of the coin = 0.5. Find the Binomial Table in the back of the book and look for n = 10 and p = 0.5. Note the following probabilities for the range of X:

X	P(X = x)
0	0.0010
1	0.0098
2	0.0439
3	0.1172
4	0.2051
...	...
10	0.0010

Note that summing the P(X = x) column yields 1. If we wish to know the probability that exactly 4 heads come up when the coin is flipped 10 consecutive times, we look at X = 4, and write P(X = 4) = 0.2051.

If we wish to find the probability that at least 4 heads came up, we write P(X ≥ 4), and we sum the probabilities corresponding to X = 4,5,6,7,8,9,10. That is, P(X ≥ 4) = 0.8281. Sometimes it is easier to work with the complement. That is, P(X ≥ 4) = 1 − P(X ≤ 3) = 1 − (0.0010 + 0.0098 + 0.0439 + 0.1172) = 0.8281.

Suppose we are interested in the 90th percentile of the distribution of heads.[5] That is, how many heads must come up so that in 90% of the times the experiment is conducted, the number of heads will not exceed this number? We write this in the form P(X ≤ x) = 0.9. Note that x stands for the 90th percentile. From the table, we accumulate the probabilities, starting at X = 0, until we reach or surpass 90%. That is, 0.001 + 0.0098 + 0.0439 + 0.1172 + 0.2051 + 0.2461 + 0.2051 + 0.1172 > 0.90. Note that 90% was reached and surpassed when X = 7.

Example 4

A manufacturer of light switches produces defective switches with probability 10%. Suppose you buy a package of 15 of these switches.

    a. What is the probability that exactly 2 of the switches in the batch are defective?

    b. What is the probability that 10 or more switches in the batch will work?

    c. How many defective switches are expected to be found in the batch of 15?

    d. The package of 15 switches comes with the following guarantee: if 2 or more switches are defective, you may return it. What is the probability that the package you purchased violates the guarantee?

    e. How can the manufacturer decrease the number of packages returned due to the terms of the guarantee?

Let X = number of defective switches in the batch. The range of X is {0,1,2, ... , 15} and X ~ B(15,0.10). Use the Binomial Table with n = 15 and p = 0.10.

    a. P(X = 2) = 0.2669

_____

[5] Percentiles of probability distributions are sometimes referred to as "critical values". Later on, these two terms will be used interchangeably.

b. 10 or more working means that 5 or less will not work. That is, we want $P(X \leq 5)$ which is equal to 0.9978. Another way of answering this question is to consider the random variable Y = number of non-defective switches in the batch. Then, $Y \sim B(15,0.90)$. From the Binomial Table we obtain: $P(Y \geq 10) = 0.0105 + 0.0428 + 0.1285 + 0.2669 + 0.3432 + 0.2059 = 0.9978$.

c. We wish to find the expected number of defectives. You may use equation (1), or realize that if 10% of the switches are defective and there are 15 switches in the batch, the expected number of defective switches is given by $15 \cdot 0.10 = 1.5$. That is, the expected value of a binomial random variable is given by the product of n and p.[6] We write this as $\mu = np$.

d. The guarantee is violated if 2 or more switches are defective. That is, we want $P(X \geq 2)$. It is easier to compute the complement. That is, $P(X \geq 2) = 1 - P(X < 2) = 1 - P(X = 0) - P(X = 1) = 1 - 0.2059 - 0.3432 = 0.4509$. This means that the return rate is about 45%. Clearly, this is not good for the manufacturer.

e. In order to improve the guarantee, the manufacturer has different options. First, the process of making switches may be revamped so that fewer than 10% of the switches will be defective. If revamping the process is not possible or too costly, the guarantee may be rewritten in terms of requiring 3 or more, or perhaps even 4 or more, switches to be defective. If the guarantee is restated so as to require 3 or more switches to be defective, the return rate drops to 18.4% (verify). If 4 or more defective switches are required, then the return rate drops to only 5.55% (verify).

Most Binomial Tables only go up to $n = 15$ or 20. How are probabilities obtained for cases when tables are not available? Computers (and some calculators) are capable of obtaining these probabilities for most values of n and p. Besides, the Poisson distribution (see below) can also help. Also, the so called Normal Distribution (Chapter 6) will also be of assistance. There are plenty of ways of computing Binomial probabilities if they are needed.

Poisson

This distribution is named after the French mathematician Simeon Poisson (1781-1840). The original use of this distribution was to alleviate computational problems encountered with the Binomial distribution. At present, this distribution is closely connected with processes that are countable but rare.

---

[6] Similarly, the variance of a binomially distributed random variable is conveniently given by $\sigma^2 = np(1 - p)$.

For instance: emission of radioactive particles, waiting for teams to score a goal in a soccer match, the distribution of runs scored in the game of baseball, waiting times at a supermarket checkout counter. Perhaps the most popular application of this distribution is waiting for the green light when entering a busy freeway during rush hour.

Poisson discovered a mathematical connection between the Binomial PDF[7] and a totally separate formula, the Poisson PDF, which gives suitable approximations to the binomial probabilities when n is "large" and p is "small".[8] The histograms below illustrate how close the two distributions actually are for the cases $X \sim B(100, 0.1)$ and $X \sim B(500, 0.02)$. Note that in both instances, $\mu = 10$. The Poisson has the advantage that it is only driven by the parameter μ. It doesn't need to know n or p explicitly.[9] We write $Y \sim P(\mu)$ to indicate a random variable Y, distributed Poisson, with mean $= \mu$.

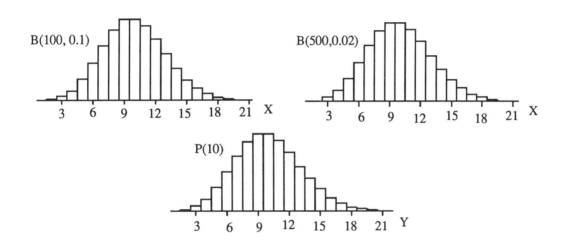

Example 5

At a traffic intersection, the probability that an individual car is involved in an accident is p. Assume that n cars pass through the intersection in a given week. Also, assume that the average number of accidents per week is 1.

a. Let X = number of accidents that occur per week. Note that $X \sim B(n,p)$. Since we

---

[7] PDF's for the discrete distributions in this chapter appear in the Appendix.

[8] As a rule of thumb, $p \leq 0.10$ and $n \geq 50$.

[9] In some practical situations it is impossible to realistically define n and p. For instance, if a soccer team scores 100 goals in 50 matches, $\mu = 2$ goals/match. However, we can't say anything about the probability of the team scoring at any particular moment during a given match or the number of such moments.

want $\mu = 1 = np$, let's arbitrarily pick $n = 100$ and $p = 0.01$. Thus, $X \sim B(100,0.01)$. Also, since accidents at this intersection are rare, X may also be modelled with the Poisson distribution. Thus, we may also write $X \sim P(1)$. We use a computer to produce the histograms below. Note how the Binomial and Poisson distributions are quite close.

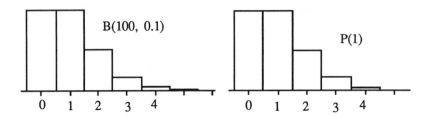

b. Identical to a. above but we now choose $n = 1000$ and $p = 0.001$. Thus, $X \sim B(1000,0.001)$ or $X \sim P(1)$. The histograms appear below. Note that the distributions are identical.

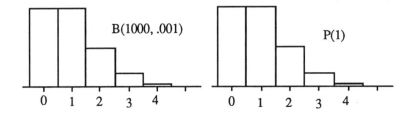

Geometric

The Geometric distribution is associated with a random variable that counts the number of trials until the first success appears. For instance, if we let X = number of times a fair die is rolled until the first 5 appears, then we say that X is distributed geometrically with parameter $p = 1/6$. This is written as $X \sim G(p)$. For the fair die, $X \sim G(1/6)$. Note that the range of X is infinite. That is, X takes the values $\{1,2,3, ...\}$. There is no universal rule that says that a 5 must ever be rolled! In practicality, we expect a 5 to be rolled once every sixth roll, but this is only an expectation. There are no tables to compute geometric probabilities. The PDF[10] is quite simple (compared to other PDF's) and hand computations are not all that messy. The expectation of a geometrically distributed random variable is $\mu = 1/p$.

---

[10] The eager reader may verify that the PDF for this distribution is $P(X = x) = p \cdot (1 - p)^{x - 1}$

Example 6

Joe makes free throws with 60% accuracy.

    a. What is the probability that Joe will make the first free throw on the fifth free throw taken?

    b. How many free throws is Joe expected to shoot until he makes the first one?

    c. What is the 90th percentile for the number of free throws taken until the first one is made?

    d. Provide a histogram for this distribution.

Note that if we let X = number of free throws taken until the first free throw is made, then $X \sim G(0.60)$. The range of X is 1,2,3, ...

    a. Using the formula in footnote 10, $P(X = 5) = (0.60)(1 - 0.60)^{5-1} = 0.0154$. It may help to visualize this outcome as: **Missed Missed Missed Missed Made**. That is, the first four free throws were missed, each with probability 0.40, and the fifth one was made, with probability 0.60.

    b. $\mu = 1/p = 1/0.60 = 1.6667$. This means that, on average, Joe would make the first free throw either on the first or second free throw taken.

    c. One way to attack this problem is to build the probability distribution table using the PDF given in footnote 10. The third column in the table accumulates probabilities. We want to look for a 90% in that column (i.e., the 90th percentile).

X = number of free throws taken	$P(X = x)$	Cumulative Probabilities
1	0.60	0.60 = 60%
2	$0.40 \cdot 0.60 = 0.24$	0.60 + 0.24 = 0.84 = 84%
3	$(0.40)^2 \cdot 0.60 = 0.096$	0.84 + 0.096 = 93.6%

We can see that the 90th percentile is about 3 shots. That is, if Joe repeats this experiment many times, 90% of the time he would have made the first three throw by the third shot taken.

d. Continue to build the P(X = x) column in **c.** above until X = 8. Build the histogram starting at 0.50 and a class width of 1. Put the probabilities in the vertical axis.

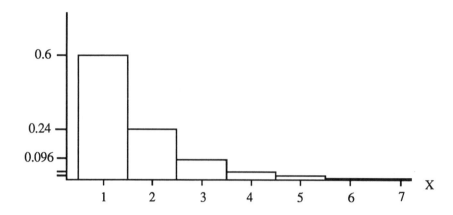

Pascal

The Pascal distribution is named after another French mathematician, Blaise Pascal (1623-1662). This distribution models the number of failures until the rth success occurs, where $r > 1$.[11] In a sense, it is related to the Geometric distribution. In fact, when $r = 1$, it is precisely the Geometric distribution. The PDF is not nearly as simple to manipulate as the PDF for the Geometric. The distribution is driven by two parameters: r and p. Note that p = probability of success in a single trial, regardless of the fact that the random variable is counting failures. We write $X \sim Pa(r,p)$. Answers to probability or percentile questions are supplied by computer or an appropriate calculator.

Example 7

Suppose we are interested in tossing a coin until the third head occurs. That is, we are interested in modelling the occurrence of outcomes such as: HHH; THHH; HTHH; THTHTTTH; etc.[12] It is clear that if we let the random variable X = number of failures (tails) until the third success (heads) occurs, the range of X is {0,1,2,3,...}. That is, there might be no failures (i.e., HHH), or the number of failures could be

---

[11] Sometimes the PDF is written in order to model the total number of trials. This will not be the case here.

[12] Recall that the outcome THHH means: tails came up on the first flip and heads came up on the second, third, and fourth flips.

very large until the third success finally appears. The length of the number of failures is pretty much predicated by the magnitude of p = probability of success in a single trial. If the coin is fair, we don't expect to fail too many times before the third head appears; however, if the coin is biased against heads, that is, p is small, then we expect a high number of failures before the third head appears. If the above coin is fair, we write X ~ Pa(3,0.50). The expected number of failures until the rth success is obtained is given by the formula $\mu = \dfrac{r(1-p)}{p}$. Using a computer, the first few entries of the probability distribution for X ~ Pa(3,0.50) are given below:

X = number of failures until 3 heads appear	P(X = x)
0	0.125
1	0.1875
2	0.1875
3	0.15625
4	0.11719
5	0.08203
6	0.05469
7	0.03516
8	0.02197
9	0.01343

From the table, it is easy to answer probability questions such as:

a. What is the probability of obtaining the third head on the seventh flip of the coin?

We want P(X = 4). That is, to flip seven times, there must be four failures, since failures + successes = total number of flips. From the table, the required probability is 0.11719.

b. What is the 90th percentile of the distribution of failures?

To work this out, we need a column of cumulative probabilities. Using the above table, we can construct such a column.

X	P(X = x)	Cumulative
0	0.125	0.125
1	0.1875	0.125 + 0.1875 = 0.3125
2	0.1875	0.5
3	0.15625	0.65625
4	0.11719	0.77344
5	0.08203	0.85547
6	0.05469	0.91016
...	...	...

Thus, in about 90% of the cases, the third head would appear by the sixth failure. That is, it would take about 9 total flips to be 90% certain that the third head would have appeared.

c. How many trials are expected until the third head appears?

The expected number of failures until the third head appears is $\mu = \dfrac{r(1-p)}{p} = \dfrac{3(1-0.5)}{0.5} = 3$. Therefore, we expect a total of 6 trials until the third head appears.

d. Here is the histogram for this situation.

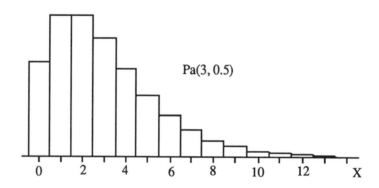

Pa(3, 0.5)

Example 8

The histograms below are for the following Pascal distributions:

a. $X \sim Pa(5,0.1)$ b. $X \sim Pa(5,0.9)$
c. $X \sim Pa(30,0.5)$ d. $X \sim Pa(50, 0.2)$

Note how the magnitude of p controls the skewness. When p is small, the histogram is skewed to the right. This causes a long right tail. That means that a high number of failures are to be expected before the rth success occurs. When p is large, the right tail is very short. This means that there won't be too many failures until the rth success appears.

When r is large, note that the histogram tends to be symmetrical. This is especially true if p hovers around 0.50. Whenever p takes extreme values (close to 0 or close to 1), a very large r is needed to maintain any resemblance of symmetry.

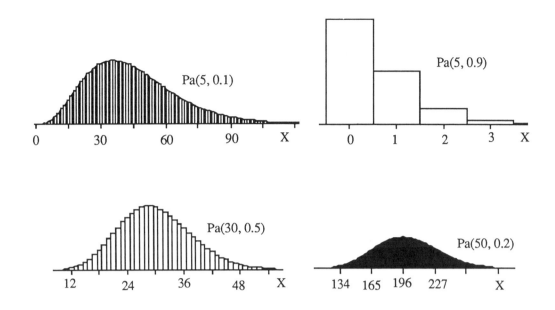

Hypergeometric

The Hypergeometric distribution arises when considering a population divided into two groups in such a way that one of the groups is of interest to the experimenter and sampling is done without replacement. The random variable counts the number of successes (i.e., how many things are drawn from the group of interest) in a fixed number of trials. By far, the most popular application of this distribution is to model lottery drawings. When the sampling is done without replacement, the probability of success from trial to trial changes; thus, the independence requirement for a Bernoulli trial is lost. However, in cases where the population being sampled is infinite or very large, it is reasonable to assume that the success probability remains about the same from trial to trial regardless of whether or not there is replacement. It is this assumption that allows for the Hypergeometric to be approximated by the Binomial distribution. The PDF for this distribution is sufficiently cumbersome to relegate all the computations to a computer or calculator. The set up for this distribution is as follows:

X = number of successes from a group of size n_1 (this is the group of interest),

n_2 = size of group of no interest,

n = sample size (i.e., number of things drawn from the entire population of size $n_1 + n_2$). Note that $n \leq n_1 + n_2$.

The range of X is $\{0,1,2,3, ..., n_1\}$ if $n_1 \le n$; otherwise, the range is $\{0,1,2,3, ... , n\}$. The notation used to denote this distribution is $X \sim H(n_1,n_2,n)$. The size of the group of interest must always be listed first. The order in which the three parameters is written is important, especially when inputting the information into a computer.[13] The expected value of X is $\mu = n\left(\dfrac{n_1}{n_1 + n_2}\right)$.

Example 9

An urn contains 5 red balls and 10 black balls. A random sample of 6 balls is taken (i.e., this is the same as drawing 6 balls, one at a time, and without replacement). We are interested in the probability distribution for the number of red balls drawn.

Letting X = number of red balls drawn, write $X \sim H(5,10,6)$. The range of X is $\{0,1,2,3,4,5\}$. The probability distribution is given below (courtesy of a computer).

X = number of red balls drawn	P(X = x)
0	0.04196
1	0.25175
2	0.41958
3	0.23976
4	0.04496
5	0.00199

a. What is the probability that 3 or fewer red balls will be drawn?

We need to find $P(X \le 3)$. Use the above table to get $0.04196 + 0.25175 + 0.41958 + 0.23976 = 0.95305$.

b. What is the expected number of red balls drawn?

Expected number of red balls drawn $= \mu = n\left(\dfrac{n_1}{n_1 + n_2}\right) = 6\left(\dfrac{5}{5 + 10}\right) = 2.$

---

[13] The point being that $H(n_2,n_1,n)$ defines a totally different distribution.

Example 10

The California state lottery consists of drawing 6 numbers, one at a time and without replacement, from an urn containing the positive integers from 1 to 51. For short, this is called a 6|51 lottery. The cost of a ticket is $1 and it consists of a player choosing 6 numbers. We are interested in the distribution of the number of matches between the numbers the player chooses in one ticket and the 6 numbers picked by the state. Since the sampling is done without replacement and there are two distinct groups of numbers (the 6 the player chooses for the one ticket and the remaining 45 numbers), the distribution of X = number of matches is Hypergeometric. We write, $X \sim H(6,45,6)$. The range of X is $\{0,1,2,3,4,5,6\}$. Using a computer, the probability distribution is as follows.

X = number of matches	P(X = x)
0	0.4523
1	0.4071
2	0.1241
3	0.0158
4	0.0008
5	0.00001
6	0.0000001

note: $\sum P(X = x) \neq 1$ due to round-off.

The probability of hitting the jackpot (i.e., matching all 6 numbers) if a single ticket is purchased is a miniscule 0.0000000555. This is near a mathematical impossibility.[14] Note that the probability of matching 2 or fewer numbers is quite large (i.e., $P(X \leq 2) = 0.9835$). Of course, matching 2 or fewer numbers represents a zero payoff. A player may improve the probability of winning by buying more than one ticket, but note that even when buying 10,000 tickets for a single drawing (this represents a $10,000 gamble), the probability of matching all 6 numbers is still a small number (i.e., 0.000555 or about 1 in 2,000). With the aid of a computer we are going to simulate buying 10,000 tickets. The computer will sample 6 numbers from 1 to 51 and will compare them to the 10,000 tickets. It will then count the number of matches. Here are the results.

---

[14] There are 18,009,460 different combinations of 6 numbers that can be formed from 51 numbers. Note that 1/18,009,460 = 0.0000000555, accurate to 10 decimal places.

X = number of matches	Frequency = number of tickets
0	4,710
1	4,060
2	1,090
3	130
4	9
5	1

Disappointing, yes, but not surprising. None of the tickets matched all 6 numbers, but one ticket matched 5 of the numbers.[15] Was this a good investment? Typical payoffs for matching 3,4, or 5 numbers are $5, $100, and $2,000, respectively. For the simulation, the total return was $5•(130) + $100•(9) + $2,000•(1) = $3,550. Sadly, the $10,000 investment turns into a $6,450 loss. This is great for the state but bad news for the player's bank account.

Is playing the lottery ever a good investment? On an expected value basis, if the expected return is positive, then we may be tempted to take a chance. A positive expectation occurs when the jackpot reaches a high amount (after accumulation due to several drawings of nobody matching all 6 numbers). We can actually solve for the amount of the jackpot, call it J, that will produce a positive expectation. The computation of J is set up using equation (1) and the probability distribution from above:

$$(-\$1)\bullet(0.983) + (\$4)\bullet(0.015) + (\$99)\bullet(0.0008) + (\$1,999)\bullet(0.00001) + (J-\$1)\bullet(0.0000000555) > 0.$$

Verify that the solution is J > $14.76 million. That is, if the jackpot exceeds $14.76 million, the lottery might be worth a try. Of course, this assumes that there is only one ticket matching all 6 numbers. In other words, if more than one jackpot winner is projected, the $14.76 million jackpot will have a negative expectation.[16]

Example 11

Consider an urn with 100 red balls and 400 black balls. A sample of 5 balls is taken, one at a time and without replacement. Let X = number of red balls drawn. The range of X is {0,1,2,3,4,5}. Clearly, X ~ H(100,400,5). Note that the probability of drawing a red ball on the first draw is 100/500 = 1/5. If a red ball is drawn on the first draw, the probability of drawing a red ball on the second draw is 99/499. If instead, a black ball is drawn on the first draw, the probability of red on second is 100/499. For

---

[15] The authors run this simulation quite often (just for fun...) and this is the first time that more than 4 matches have ever occurred!

[16] Large jackpots cause a "buying frenzy". As more tickets are bought, the chances of more than one ticket matching all 6 numbers increases dramatically.

Chapter 4   66

all practical purposes, $1/5 \approx 99/499 \approx 100/499$. That is, we might assume independence of draws, even though we are sampling without replacement, and each draw may now be classified as a Bernoulli trial. If we make this assumption, then the distribution of X is approximated by the Binomial with $n = 5$ and $p = \dfrac{n_1}{n_1 + n_2} = \dfrac{100}{500}$. That is, $X \sim B(5, 1/5)$. The probability distributions are shown below (from our friendly computer). Note that the corresponding probabilities are almost identical. Thus, the Hypergeometric distribution may be approximated by the Binomial when the combined group sizes is large relative to the sample size.[17]

X = number of red balls drawn	P(X = x) for X ~ H(100,400,5)	P(X = x) for X ~ B(5,1/5)
0	0.3260	0.3277
1	0.4117	0.4096
2	0.2053	0.2048
3	0.0506	0.0512
4	0.0061	0.0064
5	0.0003	0.0003

4.4   Summary

Random variables may be effectively used to assist with probability computations if a PDF can be found. Once a PDF is found, there is a formula for modelling uncertainty. This formula is driven by the random variable of interest and its corresponding range. Probabilities are readily computed from this formula.

From the PDF we may create a table of probabilities. This table is useful in calculating expected value and variance for the random variable.

For certain discrete distributions, the PDF's are well known. In some cases, they are also tabulated. The major discrete distributions are: Binomial, Poisson, Geometric, Pascal, and Hypergeometric. Their differences hinge only on how the random variable is defined. That is, they differ mostly on the nature of what is being counted. In the summary that follows, p = probability of success in a single trial.

---

[17] For our purposes, we will consider the Binomial to reasonably approximate the Hypergeometric if the ratio $n/(n_1 + n_2) \leq 0.05$.

Binomial

X = number of successes in a fixed (n) number of trials.

Range of X = {0,1,2,3, ..., n}

Notation: X ~ B(n,p)

μ = expected number of successes in n trials = np and σ^2 = np(1 – p)

Use Binomial Table to compute most probabilities. Could be approximated by Poisson and later on (Chapter 6), by the Normal distribution.

Poisson

X = number of successes in a fixed (n) number of trials, even though n may not be known.

Range of X = {0,1,2,3, ..., n}

Notation: X ~ P(μ) where μ = expected number of successes = np

Use a computer or calculator to compute probabilities

Geometric

X = number of trials until the first success

Range of X = {1,2,3, ...}

Notation: X ~ G(p)

μ = expected number of trials until the first success = 1/p

Probabilities may be easily computed from the PDF (see footnote 10)

Pascal

X = number of failures until the rth success

Range of X = {0,1,2,3, ... } with total number of trials = x + r

Notation: X ~ Pa(r,p)

μ = expected number of failures until the rth success = $\dfrac{r(1-p)}{p}$

Use a computer or calculator to compute probabilities

Hypergeometric

X = number of items sampled from the group of interest. The size of the group of interest is denoted by n_1 (note: sampling is done without replacement)

$$\text{Range of } X = \begin{cases} 0,1,2,3, \ldots, n_1 & \text{if } n_1 \le n, \text{where } n \text{ is the sample size} \\ 0,1,2,3, \ldots, n & \text{if } n_1 > n \end{cases}$$

Notation: $X \sim H(n_1, n_2, n)$, where n_2 = size of group 2

μ = expected number of items drawn from group 1 = $n \left(\dfrac{n_1}{n_1 + n_2} \right)$

Use a computer or calculator to compute probabilities. May be approximated by the Binomial distribution under the conditions specified in footnote 17.

Chapter 4

Chapter 4 Problems

1. Suppose a die is biased. The die is rolled once. The PDF is shown below, where X = number of face on die.

X	1	2	3	4	5	6
P(X = x)	0.1	0.1	0.1	0.5	0.1	?

a. Give the range of X **b.** Find $P(X = 6)$

c. Find P(even face comes up)

d. Find $P(X \geq 4 \mid$ even face came up)

e. Find μ and explain the meaning of this number.

2. Let X = number of books purchased by students at your college during a given academic term. The PDF for X is given below.

X	1	2	3	4	5	6	7
P(X = x)	0.05	0.1	0.2	0.35	0.1	0.15	0.05

a. A student is randomly chosen from the student population. What is the probability that the student purchased 5 or more books during the current academic term?

b. How many books are expected to be purchased for a particular academic term when the enrollment is 20,000 students?

c. What is the probability that a randomly chosen student purchased 5 or more books if it is known that the student purchased 6 books?

d. What is the probability that a randomly chosen student purchased 6 books if it is known that the student purchased 5 or more books?

e. Construct a histogram for this PDF.

3. A contractor is required by a county planning department to submit one, two, three, four, or five forms (depending on the nature of the project) in applying for a building permit. Let Y = number of forms required of the next applicant. The probability that y forms are required is known to be proportional to y. That is, $P(Y = y) = ky$ for $Y = 1,2,3,4,5$.

a. Find k so that $P(Y = y) = ky$ is a PDF.

b. What is the probability that at most three forms are required?

c. What is the probability that between two and four forms, inclusive, are required?

4. The casino game of American Roulette consists of a circular wheel with 38 spots. Thirty six of the spots have the numbers 1 to 36 in them. Eighteen of those are colored red and the other eighteen are colored black. The remaining two spots are colored green with no number assignment. If you play a color (either red or black), the house will pay you even odds. That is, if you play black and wager $1, you will profit $1 if black comes up on that particular spin of the wheel.

    a. Let X = profit[18] amount when playing colors. Find μ and explain what it means.

    b. How much money is expected to be won or lost after 1,000 games where the player wagers $10 per game?

Problems **5-11** are all Binomial. For each one:

    a. Use words to define the random variable X.
    b. Give the range of the random variable.
    c. Use an appropriate notation to write the distribution and corresponding parameters. That is, write "X ~ B(n,p)" where the n and the p are numbers obtained from each problem.

5. A multiple choice test consists of 10 questions. Each question has five choices. Only one of the five choices is correct. Assume each question is answered by guessing.

    a., b., c. as above.
    d. Find the probability that 5 or more correct answers are given.
    e. Find the probability that exactly 4 correct answers are given.
    f. How many incorrect answers are expected?

6. A basketball player makes free throws with 80% accuracy. The player shoots 5 free throws.

    a., b., c. as above.
    d. Write the probability distribution.
    e. Find the probability that the player makes at least 3 free throws.
    f. How many of the 5 free throws is the player expected to make?
    g. Find the variance of X.

7. Fifteen machines are in operation. The probability that at the end of one day a machine is still in operation is 0.60. Assume the machines function independently.

    a., b., c. as above.
    d. Find the expected number of machines in operation at the end of one day.
    e. What is the probability that the number of machines in operation at the end of the day is equal to the answer from **d.** above?

---

[18] Recall that a negative profit represents a loss.

8. A manufacturer ships fuses in lots of 10,000 and guarantees that a lot will contain no more than 15% defective. A purchaser decides to sample 20 fuses from each lot and accept a lot only if the number of defective fuses does not exceed three.

    a., b., c. as above.
    d. What is the probability of accepting a lot if it contains 10% defective?
    e. What is the probability of accepting a lot if it contains 20% defective?
    f. What is the probability of rejecting a lot if it contains 20% defective?
    g. What is the probability of rejecting a lot if it contains 30% defective?

9. A sales rep for a tire manufacturer claims that her steel belted radials will last at least 40000 miles. A tire dealer decides to check this claim by testing 20 tires. If 75% or more of the 20 tires last at least 40000 miles, he will purchase all his tires from the rep.

    a., b., c. as above.
    d. In extensive tests, the tire manufacturer establishes that 90% of the tires last at least 40000 miles. What is the probability that the tire dealer will purchase from the rep?
    e. In extensive tests, the tire manufacturer establishes that 70% of the tires last at least 40000 miles. What is the probability that the tire dealer will purchase from the rep?

10. A computer manufacturer produces a certain type of ROM chip with a known defect rate of 10%. The chips are sold in packages of 15. The distributor guarantees that no more than three are defective.

    a., b., c. as above.
    d. Find the probability that a given package will violate the guarantee.
    e. Find the probability that the number of defective chips will be between 1 and 5, inclusive.
    f. How many defective chips are expected to be found in 1000 such packages?

11. A baseball player has a batting average of 0.300 (in baseball parlance, the player is said to be hitting "300"). Assume that in a particular game, the player comes to bat 4 times. Each at bat is assumed to be a Bernoulli trial.

    a., b., c. as above.
    d. What is the probability that the player will get at least one base hit?
    e. What is the expected number of base hits the player will get over a 162 game season?

12. Let X = number of deaths attributable to typhoid fever in a period of one year in the United States. Since typhoid fever deaths are rare, X may be modelled by the Poisson distribution. Suppose for the year in question, $\mu = 4$.

    a. Write the distribution for X if a 6 month period, instead of one year, is considered.

    b. Someone claims that X ~ B(52, 4/52). Explain what this person is thinking and how the person obtained n = 52 and p = 4/52.

    c. Another person claims that X ~ B(365, 4/365). Explain what this person is thinking and how the person obtained n = 365 and p = 4/365.

    d. Which of the two distributions, the one in **b.** or the one in **c.**, better approximates P(4)? Explain.

13. Consider the baseball player from problem **11.** above.

    a. Define X, in words, so that X ~ G(0.300).

    b. Give three examples of possible outcomes for this situation. Use H for base hit and N for no base hit.

    c. Find P(X = 1).

    d. Find μ and explain what this number means.

    e. Build the probability table for the distribution in **a.** and use it to approximate the 75th percentile for this distribution. What does this number mean?

For problems **14-20**:

    a. Use words to define the random variable X.

    b. Give the distribution and appropriate parameters.

    c. Set up (**do not compute**) the probability question in terms of the random variable.

14. A department store has a sales display of 1,000 light bulbs, 10 of which are defective. If you buy 20 of these bulbs, what is the probability that none of the 20 bulbs will be defective?

15. Each time you drive your car the probability is 0.001 that you will get a speeding ticket. You will lose your license once you receive 3 such tickets. Find the probability that you will drive your car 2,000 times and not lose your license?

16. An urn contains 10 blue marbles and 20 red marbles. Five marbles are chosen, one at a time and without replacement. What is the probability that exactly 3 of the 5 marbles are blue?

17. Suppose you get an average of 3 traffic tickets per month. What are the chances of getting no tickets in the coming year?

18. A committee of 5 people is to be selected from a group composed of 8 women and 12 men. Find the probability that at least 3 women are in the committee.

19. A student takes a 50 questions multiple choice exam. Each question has 4 choices, only one of which is correct. A student needs to get at least 60% of the questions correct in order to pass. What is the probability that the student will pass? Assume the student guesses at each question.

20. A gambler plays until the third win and then goes home. The probability of the gambler winning any one gamble is 40%. What is the probability the gambler will go home before the tenth gamble?

21. A student studies discrete distributions using a computer tutorial. The computer presents problems, randomly chosen from all of the discrete distributions. The student enters an answer and the computer displays hints and explanations if a wrong answer is entered. Let X = number of problems the student gets right out of 15 computer generated problems. Can it be argued that X follows a Binomial distribution? Explain.

22. According to the latest US Census, 30% of all employed women have never been married. Suppose 20 employed women are randomly chosen.

    a. Let X = number of women in the sample who have never been married. Give the range of X.
    b. Write the distribution of X with appropriate parameters.
    c. What is the probability that 5 or fewer of the women in the sample have never been married?

23. Charges of discrimination in hiring have been brought against Company ABC. The complaint claims that out of the last 20 persons hired, only 7 were men. Furthermore, the number of applicants responding to the job announcements were equally divided between men and women and with few exceptions, were considered equally qualified.

    a. Put forth a probabilistic case if you are defending the complaint.
    b. Put forth a probabilistic case if you are arguing against the complaint.

24. A commuter airline uses airplanes carrying a maximum of 12 passengers. It is known that a passenger that makes a reservation makes the scheduled flight 70% of the time. The airline wishes to minimize the probability of overbooking (i.e., making too many reservations so that over 12 passengers show up). How many reservations should be made in order to be 95% certain that an overbooking situation will not occur?

25. Suppose a certain state has 500,000 registered automobiles, of which 400,000 were manufactured domestically. A sample of 10 cars is chosen without replacement. Let X count the number of domestically manufactured cars in the sample of 10.

    a. Give the distribution of X with appropriate parameters.

    b. Give the range of X.

    c. Find the expected number of domestically manufactured cars in the sample of 10.

    d. Give another distribution, with appropriate parameters, that approximates this situation.

         Chapter 4

Chapter 5

Continuous Probability Distributions

5.1   Continuous random variables: area and probability

A discrete random variable is one whose possible values constitute a finite set or can be listed in an infinite sequence where there is a first element, a second element, etc. A random variable whose set of possible values is an entire interval is not discrete.

A random variable is said to be **continuous** if its set of possible values is an entire interval of numbers. That is, if we consider an interval [a,b] on the number line,[1] then any number between a and b, inclusive, is possible. We may also use the notation $a \leq x \leq b$ to indicate that x is some number in the interval [a,b].

Example 1

In studying a lake, ecologists make depth measurements at randomly chosen locations throughout the lake. If X = depth of the lake at such locations, then X is a continuous random variable. The range of the random variable would be an interval [a,b] where a is the minimum depth and b is the maximum depth.

Example 2

If a chemical compound is randomly selected and its pH X is determined, then X is a continuous random variable. The range of X is known to be [0,14]. If additional information is available about the particular compound chosen, then the range may be a subinterval of [0,14] such as (5.5,6.5).

If the measurement scale of X can be subdivided to any extent desired, then the variable is continuous. It may be argued that no matter how fine the measuring instruments are, the practical limitations of these instruments restrict us to a discrete, albeit very finely subdivided, world. However, the point being that continuous models approximate real world situations quite adequately, and continuous mathematics (i.e., the Calculus) is easier to handle than the mathematics of discrete random variables and their distributions.

---

[1] The notation [a,b] means that $a < b$ and both a, b, are included in the interval. The interval [a,b) includes a but excludes b. The interval consisting of all real numbers may be conveniently written as $(-\infty, +\infty)$.

Example 3

Consider a wheel 10 inches in circumference. Suppose there is a spinner right at the center of the wheel. Let X = number value, along the circumference of the wheel, pointed by the spinner. The range of X is [0,10). That is, 0 is included but 10 is excluded.

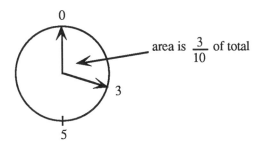

Consider the region [0,3]. The area of that region is 3/10 the area of the entire circle. That is, the probability that the spinner will land in the interval [0,3] is just 3/10. We write this as $P(0 < X < 3) = 3/10$. This may also be written in the form $P(0 \leq X \leq 3) = 3/10$. Similarly, note the following:

$P(5 \leq X < 10) = 5/10$ $\qquad$ $P(0 < X < 10) = 1$ $\qquad$ $P(3 < X \leq 5) = 2/10.$

In general, if X is a continuous random variable then $P(X = a) = 0.$[2] Therefore, if [a,b] is a subinterval in the range of X, then $P(a < X < b) = P(a \leq X \leq b)$.

We can cast the above situation in terms of a histogram where the horizontal scale is the interval [0,10) with class width = 1 and starting point X = 0. The vertical scale has a uniform height of 1/10. Note that the total area enclosed by the rectangle with base = 10 and height = 1/10 is base • height = 1.

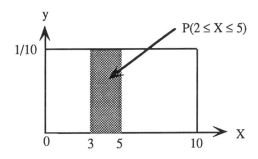

The line $y = \dfrac{1}{10}$ is the **probability distribution** (also called **density**) **function.** We again use the abbreviation PDF. Note that the PDF in case of a continuous random variable is not an equation of probabilities but an equation for the height at each value X in the range of the random variable. The

---

[2] Regions have areas. A single point doesn't determine a region; thus, there is no measurable area.

probabilities are obtained by computing the area of the corresponding region. If the region of interest is circular, rectangular or triangular, then it is easy to compute areas.[3]

Example 4

Let X = time, measured in hours, for students to return certain materials placed on reserve at the Campus Library. The range of X is (0,4]. Suppose we can model this situation by the height equation (i.e., the PDF) $y = \frac{x}{8}$. The graph of this equation is a straight line starting at the point (0,0) and ending at the point (4,1/2).[4] The PDF is graphed below.

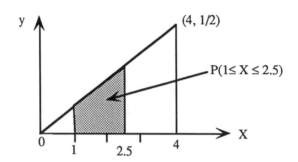

The region defined by the PDF, that is, the area enclosed by the straight line $y = \frac{x}{8}$ and the x and y axes, has a total area of 1. We can check this by realizing that the region is triangular in shape. The area of a triangle is given by, *area* = $\frac{1}{2}$ • *base* • *height*. Thus, area = $\frac{1}{2}$ • (4 – 0) • $(\frac{4}{8})$ = 1. Suppose we are interested in finding the probability that a randomly chosen student checking out materials on reserve will keep them for over 1 hour but less than 2.5 hours. That is, we wish to find P(1 < X < 2.5). To determine this probability we need to find the area under the line $y = \frac{x}{8}$ and covering the region from x = 1 to x = 2.5 (this region is shaded in the above graph). We note that it is easy to compute the area of the triangular region from x = 0 to x = 2.5 and then compute the area of the triangular region from x = 0 to x = 1. Subtracting these two areas gives the area of the desired region. This is the answer to the original probability question. That is,

area of triangular region from x = 0 to x = 2.5 = $\frac{1}{2}$ • base • height = $\frac{1}{2}$ • 2.5 • $\left(\frac{2.5}{8}\right)$ = 0.3906,

area of triangular region from x = 0 to x = 1 = $\frac{1}{2}$ • base • height = $\frac{1}{2}$ • 1 • $\left(\frac{1}{8}\right)$ = 0.0625;

thus, P(1 < X < 2.5) = 0.3906 – 0.0625 = 0.3281. Therefore, there is almost a 33% chance that a

---

[3] If the regions have other shapes, then the integral calculus is necessary. However, for those continuous random variables of interest to us, tables of areas are provided or the formula for the area computation is given.

[4] Note that when x = 0, y = 0 and when x = 4, y = 4/8 = 1/2.

randomly chosen student who checked out these reserved materials will return them 1 to 2.5 hours later.

We define y = some function of x, written y = f(x), to be a PDF, if:

- y ≥ 0 for all values of x,

- area under graph determined by y = f(x) equals 1.[5]

Again, it is important to understand that, as opposed to discrete PDF's, continuous PDF's do not give probabilities. *They only provide the height of the graph at some value x.* Probabilities are obtained by computing areas of regions defined by the graph produced by the PDF.

A continuous random variable, like a discrete random variable, has a mean and standard deviation. The mean, μ, is an average of the possible values of the random variable, weighted by their probabilities. Because a continuous random variable has infinitely many values, this idea can no longer be expressed by writing a sum of finite values. Think of μ as the mean of the density curve, the point at which the region defined by the curve would balance if made of solid material. Unless the curve is symmetrical, the standard deviation, σ, is not easy to interpret. We will come back to this in later chapters.

5.2   Area computation and Cumulative Distribution Functions

A cumulative distribution function, abbreviated CDF, is a formula giving the area under the graph of the PDF, starting at the left end point of the range of X and ending prior to reaching the right end point of the range of X. For instance, if y = f(x) is defined in the interval [c,d], the CDF is a formula giving the area in the subinterval [c,x] where x < d. Thus, CDF = P(c < X < x). If this formula is known, then the computation of probabilities and critical values (i.e., percentiles) is a fairly simple matter.[6] We illustrate by referring to Examples 3 and 4 in the previous section.

Example 3 (continued)

The CDF for the spinner problem is the area of the region from x = 0 to some x less than 10. That is,

---

[5] The graph of y = f(x) could be of any shape. In general, we will use the word "curve" to denote any shape.

[6] It should be quite clear that if x = d, then P(c < X < d) = 1.

$$CDF = P(0 < X < x) = \text{area of rectangle} = \text{base} \cdot \text{height} = (x - 0) \cdot \frac{1}{10} = \frac{x}{10}.$$

Probabilities and percentile questions are readily answered using the formula $\frac{x}{10}$.

   a. Find the probability that the spinner will land in the interval [2,8].

      The translation to a probability statement is: $P(2 < X < 8)$. We use the CDF twice as follows: (accumulate to $x = 8$ – accumulate to $x = 2$) = $\frac{8}{10} - \frac{2}{10} = \frac{6}{10} = \frac{3}{5} = 0.6.$

   b. Find the 85th percentile of the distribution.[7]

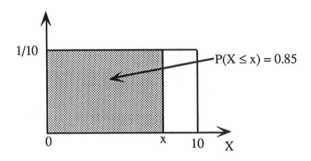

We seek the value of x between 0 and 10 such that 85% of the density is below it. In probability form this means: $P(0 < X < x) = 0.85$ or $P(X < x) = 0.85$. Think of the CDF as being set equal to 0.85 and solving for x. That is,

$$CDF = 0.85 = \frac{x}{10} \quad \rightarrow \quad x = 0.85 \cdot 10 = 8.5.$$

Thus, $x = 8.5$ is the 85th percentile since 85% of the density is found below it. This also means that 15% of the density is found above $x = 8.5$.

Example 4 (continued)

    The CDF for the time to return materials on reserve is obtained by considering the region from $x = 0$ to some x less than 4. That is,

$$CDF = P(0 < X < x) = P(X < x) = \frac{1}{2} \cdot \text{base} \cdot \text{height} = \frac{1}{2} \cdot (x - 0) \cdot \frac{x}{8} = \frac{x^2}{16}.$$

---

[7] Finding percentiles or critical values is equivalent to finding the "inverse CDF". That is, the CDF is given and we seek the value of x, in the range of X, that will yield the given area (i.e., the specified percent.)

Note that if $x = 4$ then the CDF $= 1$, as it should. Thus, probabilities and percentile questions for this situation are found using the expression $\dfrac{x^2}{16}$.

a. Find the probability that a randomly chosen student will return the materials sometime between 2 and 3.5 hours after checking them out.

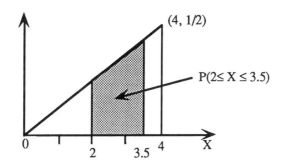

The probability statement is: $P(2 < X < 3.5)$. We use the CDF twice as follows:

(accumulate to $x = 3.5$ − accumulate to $x = 2$) $= \dfrac{3.5^2}{16} - \dfrac{2^2}{16} \approx 0.5156$. That is, there is almost a 52% chance that this particular student will keep the materials for at least 2 hours but less than 3.5 hours.

b. Find the 3rd quartile of the distribution of X.

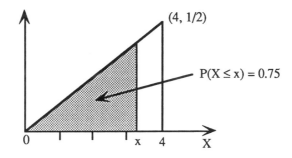

Recall that the 3rd quartile = 75th percentile. Thus, we seek a value x such that:

$$P(X < x) = 0.75. \text{ Since } CDF = P(X < x) = 0.75 = \dfrac{x^2}{16}, \text{ then}$$

$$x^2 = 0.75 \cdot 16 \rightarrow x = \sqrt{12} \approx 3.464.$$

Thus, 75% of students checking materials on reserve return them within 3.464 hours.

Chapter 5

5.3 The Uniform, Exponential, and Triangular Distributions

Uniform (also called *Rectangular*)

Suppose you take a bus to school. A bus arrives at your stop every 5 minutes. Because of variations at the time you leave your house for the bus stop, you don't always arrive at the bus stop at the same time. Let X = waiting time until the next bus arrives. The range of X is any number in the interval [0,5]. A possible PDF for X is:

$$y = f(x) = \frac{1}{5} \quad \text{for } 0 \le x \le 5 .$$

The histogram for this PDF is given below.

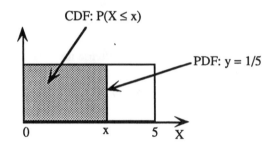

Note that the total area under the region enclosed by the line $y = \frac{1}{5}$, $x = 0$ on the left, and $x = 5$ on the right, is: base • height = $5 \cdot (\frac{1}{5}) = 1$. The probability that you will wait between 1 and 3 minutes for the bus to arrive is:

$$P(1 < X < 3) = \text{area of rectangular region} = \text{base} \cdot \text{height} = (3 - 1) \cdot \frac{1}{5} = \frac{2}{5} = 0.4 .$$

Note that the above probability depends only on the length of the subinterval of interest in [0,5] and not on the height. That is, the height remains $\frac{1}{5}$ no matter what value X takes in [0,5]. For this reason we say that X follows a **Uniform** (also called **Rectangular**) **Distribution**.

The following are important facts of a uniformly distributed random variable X defined on the interval [a,b]:

• Notation used: X ~ U(a,b) or X ~ R(a,b).

• PDF is given by $y = \frac{1}{b - a}$.

- CDF $= P(a < X < x) = P(X < x) = \dfrac{x - a}{b - a}$ for $x \le b$.

- The Pth percentile is given by: $x = P(b - a) + a$.

- $\mu = \dfrac{a + b}{2}$; $\sigma^2 = \dfrac{(b - a)^2}{12}$.

- Graph:

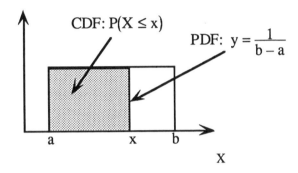

Exponential

The Exponential distribution models the length of life of certain materials or equipment. For example, if X = useful life, in months, of car batteries, then X has an Exponential distribution. The PDF is defined for $X \ge 0$. The PDF and graph for this distribution are given below.

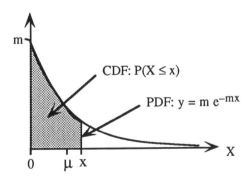

The parameter m depends on the quantity being measured and is assumed to remain constant over the life of the variable under study. The following graphs indicate how the magnitude of m controls the behavior of the graph for this PDF.

Chapter 5

Example 5

Exponential graphs for: **a.** m = 1;   **b.** m = 0.5;   **c.** m = 0.1

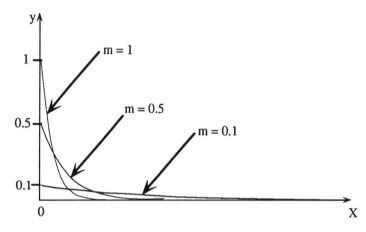

Note how a small decay rate causes a very long right tail while a large decay rate causes a quick drop in the graph. The graph of this distribution is always skewed to the right.

Here are the most useful facts about this distribution:[8]

- Notation: $X \sim Exp(m = decay)$.

- PDF is $y = m \, e^{-mx}$ for $X \geq 0$.

- CDF = $P(X < x) = 1 - e^{-mx}$.

- The Pth percentile: $x = \dfrac{\ln(1 - P)}{-m}$. That is, x is a critical value corresponding to the Pth percentile.

- $\mu = \dfrac{1}{m}$, $\sigma^2 = \mu^2$.

Example 6

Assume the average useful life for the type of car battery under study is $\mu = 60$ months. Then, the decay rate is assumed to be fixed at $\dfrac{1}{60}$ per month. That is, for each additional month, the life of the

---

[8] The letter "e" stands for the base of the natural logarithm. It is the famous Euler constant. Its numerical value is approximately 2.7183. The symbol "ln" stands for the natural logarithm. That is, the logarithm whose base is e. We assume that students are well versed in using the "e" and "ln" keys in their calculators.

battery decays by $\frac{1}{60}$. We write, $X \sim \text{Exp}\left(\frac{1}{60}\right)$.

a. What is the probability that the car battery you recently bought will last over 80 months?

We want: $P(X > 80) = 1 - P(X < 80)$. Note that $P(X < 80) = \text{CDF}$ with $x = 80$.
Thus, $P(X > 80) = 1 - \left(1 - e^{-80/60}\right) = e^{-80/60} = 0.2636$.

Therefore, there is about a 26% chance that the car battery you recently bought will last over 80 months.

b. What is the median of the distribution of X?

The median is the 50th percentile. Use the formula for the Pth percentile:

$$x = \frac{\ln(1 - 0.50)}{-1/60} = \frac{-0.69315}{-1/60} \approx 41.589.$$

Thus, about half of such batteries will have a useful life exceeding about 41.589 months.

Triangular

The situation illustrated in Example 4, section **5.1**, may be generalized by considering a broader class of distributions that we call Triangular. A triangularly distributed random variable is denoted by $X \sim T(a,b)$ where a and b are the beginning and end points respectively.

Here are the major characteristics of this distribution:

- PDF: $y = \dfrac{2(x-a)}{(b-a)^2}$ for x in [a,b].

- CDF $= P(a < X < x) = P(X < x) = \frac{1}{2} \cdot \text{base} \cdot \text{height} = \frac{1}{2} \cdot (x-a) \cdot \dfrac{2(x-a)}{(b-a)^2} = \dfrac{(x-a)^2}{(b-a)^2}$.

- The Pth percentile is given by: $x = a + (b-a)\sqrt{P}$.

- $\mu = \dfrac{a + 2b}{3}$ and $\sigma^2 = \dfrac{(b-a)^2}{18}$.

Chapter 5

- Graph:

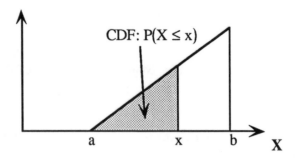

CDF: $P(X \leq x)$

Example 7

We return to Example 4, section **5.1**. The PDF was defined by $y = \dfrac{x}{8}$ for x in the interval [0,4]. Note that $a = 0$ and $b = 4$. Thus, using the general formula for the PDF of a triangular distribution, we obtain:

$$y = \frac{2(x-0)}{(4-0)^2} = \frac{x}{8}, \text{ as given.}$$

In a similar manner, $P(1 < X < 1.5)$ may be calculated using the CDF twice as follows:

$$P(1 < X < 1.5) = P(X < 1.5) - P(X < 1) = \frac{(1.5-0)^2}{(4-0)^2} - \frac{(1-0)^2}{(4-0)^2} = \frac{1.25}{16} = 0.078125.$$

Chapter 5 Problems

1. Let $X \sim U(25,60)$. Find:

    a. $P(30 < X < 50)$ **b.** $P(X < 44.2)$

    c. $P(X = 45)$ **d.** median of X

    e. mean of X **f.** 90th percentile

    g. variance of X

2. Let $X \sim Exp(decay = 0.02)$

    a. $P(30 < X < 70)$ **b.** $P(X > 65)$

    c. $P(X = 43.75)$ **d.** median of X

    e. mean of X **f.** 99th percentile

    g. standard deviation of X

3. Let $X \sim T(0,50)$

    a. $P(30 < X < 40)$ **b.** $P(X < 23)$

    c. $P(X = 45)$ **d.** median of X

    e. mean of X **f.** 90th percentile

    g. standard deviation of X

For problems **4–10**, which of the three continuous distributions studied in this chapter (Uniform, Exponential, Triangular) fits the situation best? Explain.

4. X = distance between cars (from the front bumper to the back bumper of the car in front), in feet, during commute hours at a very busy freeway.

5. Y = length of a long distance business phone call, measured in minutes.

6. W = length of wait, in minutes, at a supermarket cash register.

7. X = amount of money, in coins, students carry in their wallets/purses.

8. Y = distribution of wealth, measured in dollars, for the population of Kuwait

9. W = time of day in which women give birth.

10. X = number chosen by the random number generator found in a popular calculator.

11. Assume the distribution of scores for a midterm examination is Uniform with a low of 25 and a high of 95.

    a. Let X = scores. Write the distribution for X with appropriate parameters.

    b. Find the probability that a randomly chosen student obtained a score between 60 and 80.

    c. What is the mean score?

    d. Find the percentile corresponding to the mean score.

    e. A randomly chosen student scored 75. What percent of the students taking the examination scored above 75?

    f. Find the probability that a randomly chosen student obtained a score above 70 if it is known that the student scored above the mean.

12. A batch of neon light bulbs has a mean useful life of 1,000 hours. The hours that a bulb lasts is known to be exponentially distributed.

    a. Let X = time, in hours, a bulb will last. Write the distribution of X with appropriate parameters.

    b. Find the probability that a randomly chosen bulb from the batch will last at least 1,200 hours.

    c. Find the probability that a randomly chosen bulb from the batch will last at most 1,200 hours.

    d. Find the median of the distribution of X.

    e. If the batch consists of 5,000 bulbs, how many bulbs are expected to last over 1,000 hours?

    f. Find the 90th percentile of the distribution of X and explain what this number means.

13. During World War II, the allied forces intelligence unit based in England, estimated the number of tanks the Germans had in operation using statistics and probability. The Germans numbered each tank built with a positive integer. The allies assumed that the Germans had done this sequentially, beginning with the number 1. As it turned out, this was a valid assumption. As the allied forces encountered tanks in the field of battle, they would convey the corresponding serial number to headquarters. Suppose the following numbers had been cited: 1, 10, 15, 156, 225, 180, 75.

    a. Of the three distributions studied in this chapter, which one reasonably approximates the distribution of serial numbers on German tanks?

    b. Using the available serial numbers, give two estimates of the maximum number of tanks the Germans had in operation. Which one do you think is the most likely estimate?

    c. Suppose a wave of new information arrives from the field and the following new serial numbers are reported: 185, 200, 220, 190. How would your answer to **b.** above change? Explain.

14. Refer to Example 4 section **5.1.**

    a. Use the formula for the CDF of a Triangular distribution to verify that the CDF for X is $\dfrac{x^2}{16}$.

    b. On average, how long will it be before a randomly chosen student returns the materials?

    c. Find the median of the distribution and explain what this number means.

    d. Find $P(X > 2 \mid X > 1)$.

Chapter 6

The Normal Distribution

6.1   The Normal random variable

A particularly important class of probability density functions is the so called **Normal** distribution. The graphs of these curves are symmetric about the mean, single-peaked, and bell-shaped. All Normal distributions have the same overall shape. A particular curve is completely determined by the mean and standard deviation parameters. The mean is at the center of the curve and is the same as the median. A change in the mean simply shifts the curve right or left on the horizontal axis (see Figure 1 below). A change in the standard deviation makes the curve more or less spread about its mean (see Figure 2 below). The larger the standard deviation the more spread out the curve is.

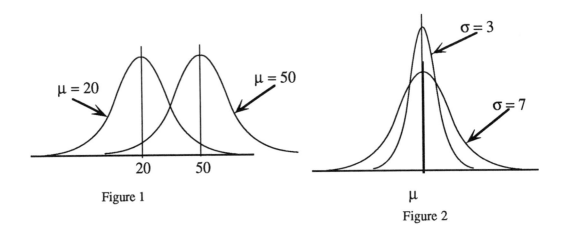

Figure 1

Figure 2

Any random variable that can be expressed as the sum of other variables can be well approximated by the normal. For instance, height of people is approximately normal. The variable "height" is the result of other variables such as: genetics, diet, bone composition and structure, etc. The effect of these other variables seems to "add up" to a normally distributed variable called "height". Here are other random variables that follow Normal distributions: SAT scores; characteristics of biological populations; stock market returns; baseball batting averages for major league players. However, there are many other random variables that do not follow a Normal distribution. For instance, income distributions are skewed right.

Even though such smooth, perfectly symmetrical curves are idealizations of phenomena in the real world, they are almost always reasonable approximations of such phenomena. For instance, if we consider the theoretical histogram for $X \sim B(20, 0.5)$, we realize that it is "bell-shaped" and symmetrical about $\mu = 10$. Furthermore, $\sigma^2 = np(1-p) = (20) \cdot (0.5) \cdot (1-0.5) = 5$. That is, $\sigma = \sqrt{5} \approx 2.2361$. With the help of a computer, we superimpose a bell-shaped curve, with $\mu = 10$ and $\sigma = 2.2361$, on the histogram for the above Binomial.

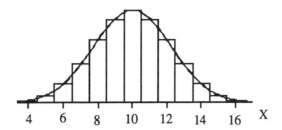

It is clear that the smooth curve drawn through the tops of the histogram bars is a very good description of the overall pattern of the discrete data. It is almost always easier to work with smooth curves than with histograms. For one, as we have seen in Chapter 2, the shape of a histogram depends on the choice of the class width, while smooth curves do not depend on such a choice. Since the total area under the histogram is 1, so is the total area under the approximating curve.

The notation we will use to denote a normally distributed random variable is: $X \sim N(\text{mean, variance})$ or, in symbols, $X \sim N(\mu, \sigma^2)$. The standard deviation is the natural measure of spread for normal curves. In fact, we can easily locate σ by eye on the curve. As we move out from the center of the curve, the curve changes from falling quickly to falling slower. Make sure you can visualize this in the graph below.

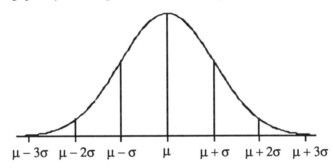

Although there are many normal curves,[1] they all have common properties. In particular, they all follow the so called **68-95-99 rule**. That is, if $X \sim N(\mu, \sigma^2)$, then:

- $P(\mu - \sigma < X < \mu + \sigma) \approx 0.68$

- $P(\mu - 2\sigma < X < \mu + 2\sigma) \approx 0.95$

- $P(\mu - 3\sigma < X < \mu + 3\sigma) \approx 0.99$.

The following graphs illustrate the above conditions:

---

[1] Each μ and σ define a different curve.

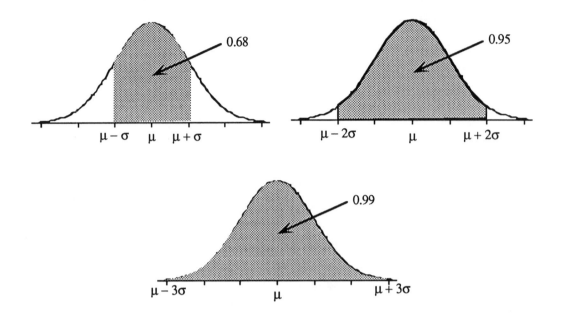

Areas under Normal curves are found by using tables. Computers and some calculators can easily do the calculations and only require the user to input the mean and the variance (or standard deviation). Using tables is a bit more laborious but just as easy.

6.2   Probability and Percentile computations: the Standard Normal Distribution and use of Tables.

In order to use just one table to find areas or percentiles for any normally distributed random variable, it is necessary to standardize the original observations in order to express them in a common scale. The most convenient way of carrying out the standardization is to change the data via the z-score formula studied in Chapter 2. This result is so important that we will name it: the **Standard Normal Distribution.** This is how it works:

> if $X \sim N(\mu, \sigma^2)$ and for each x in the distribution we obtain a corresponding z via the formula $z = \frac{x - \mu}{\sigma}$, the distribution of all these z's is also Normal but with mean = 0 and variance = 1. That is, $Z \sim N(0,1)$.[2]

Thus, every time we refer to the "Standard Normal" it is understood that what is meant is a Normal distribution with mean = μ = 0 and variance = σ^2 = 1.

---

[2] The letter Z is reserved to denote the Standard Normal Distribution. It is not difficult to algebraically prove that the distribution of z's has mean = 0 and variance = 1. Ambitious students may want to try the proof.

Reading the Standard Normal Table

This is a table of cumulative areas under the standard normal curve. That is, the table entry for each value of z is the area under the curve **to the left** of z. The top row of the table is the second decimal in z.

Example 1

The table entry corresponding to $z = -0.65$ reads 0.2578. This means that the area to the left of $z = -0.65$ is 0.2578. Another way of writing this is:

$$P(Z < -0.65) = 0.2578.$$

The graph for this situation is given below.

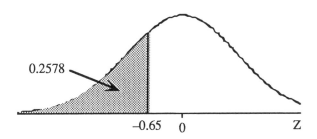

In fact, drawing graphs, with appropriate labels and scaling, and shading appropriate regions, will go a long way towards mastering the use of this table.

Example 2

Let $Z \sim N(0,1)$. What is the probability that a randomly chosen value of z will fall between –2 and 2?

- Translate the problem into symbols. That is, $P(-2 < Z < 2) = ?$
- Draw a graph like the one below.

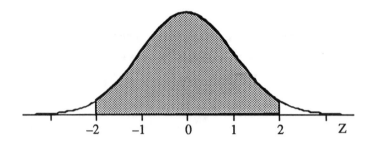

- To answer the question, either recall the 68-95-99 rule; that is, $P(-2 < Z < 2) \approx 0.95$, or use the table as follows: the table entry for $z = 2.0$ is 0.9772 and the table entry for $z = -2.0$ is 0.0228. The area of interest is the difference between these two numbers. That is, $0.9772 - 0.0228 = 0.9544$. The table answer is exact to four decimal places, while the 0.95 is just an approximation.

Example 3

Find the value of z so that the area above it is 0.21.

- In symbols, this translates to: $P(Z > z) = 0.21$. We wish to find z.
- Draw a graph, like the one below, labelling all the pertinent information.

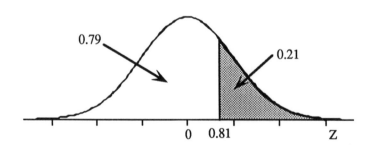

- In terms of the table, it might be easier to look at the problem as: $P(Z < z) = 0.79$. In this way, z can be readily thought of as the 79th percentile. To obtain the value of z we read the table from the "inside to the outside". That is, we are reversing what we did in the above examples. Thus, look in the body of the table until you find the closest number to 0.79 (in general, we will avoid interpolating). The closest number is 0.7910, corresponding to a z value of 0.81.

<u>Example 4</u>

IQ scores on the Stanford-Binet Intelligence Test are known to be normally distributed with mean = 100 and standard deviation = 15. What is the probability that a randomly chosen person scores between 88 and 115 on this test?

- Let's translate the words into symbols. Letting X = IQ scores, we write $X \sim N(100,15^2)$. The question may now be expressed as: find $P(88 < X < 115)$.

- Draw a graph. Note that both, the X and Z scales should be marked on the horizontal axis.

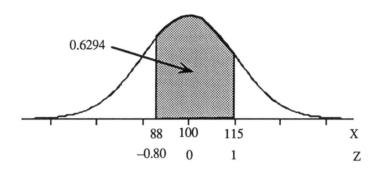

- In order to use the standard normal table, we must transform the X values into Z values using the z-score formula twice. That is,

$$\text{when } x = 88, \quad z = \frac{x - \mu}{\sigma} = \frac{88 - 100}{15} = -\frac{12}{15} = -0.80;$$

$$\text{when } x = 115, \quad z = \frac{x - \mu}{\sigma} = \frac{115 - 100}{15} = \frac{15}{15} = 1.$$

Thus, $P(88 < X < 115) = P(-0.80 < Z < 1)$. To evaluate this probability, we read two values from the table and subtract. That is,

$$P(-0.80 < Z < 1) = P(Z < 1) - P(Z < -0.80) = 0.8413 - 0.2119 = 0.6294.$$

Thus, there is a 62.94% chance that someone chosen randomly from the population at large will have an IQ, as measured by the Stanford-Binet IQ Test, between 88 and 115.

Chapter 6

Example 5

For X as in example 4, find the 95th percentile of the distribution of IQ's.

- Since $X \sim N(100, 15^2)$, we translate the problem to: $P(X < x) = 0.95$, find x. That is, we seek an IQ score so that 95% of all of the IQ scores fall below it.

- Draw a graph. Label the axis and mark an appropriate region.

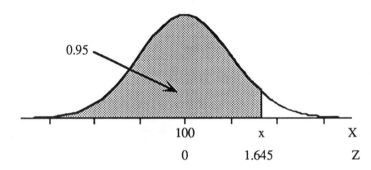

- In order to find x, we must first find the z associated with the 95th percentile. Reading the table from the inside to the outside, we see that z = 1.64 or 1.65 or 1.645 (any of the three numbers are acceptable: they correspond to a cumulative area of 0.9495, 0.9505, or right in the middle[3]). Using the z-score formula and solving for x, gives:

$$z = \frac{x - 100}{15} = 1.645 \rightarrow x = 1.645 \cdot 15 + 100 = 124.675.$$

That is, 95% of all the people have IQ's below 124.675.

Example 6

From a notation point of view, we will denote percentiles or critical values for the standard normal by $z(\alpha)$ where α is the area **to the right** of the z value. Draw graphs and verify each of the following:

- $z(0.05) = 1.645$ since 5% of the area under the standard normal is to the right of 1.645. That is, the 95th percentile of the Z distribution is 1.645.

- $z(0.90) = -1.28$ since 90% of the area under the standard normal is to the right of -1.28.

---

[3] Note that the exact z value of 1.645 is an interpolation. In this case; however, since 0.95 area corresponds to the midpoint between 0.9495 and 0.9505, the results of interpolation bears out our intuition.

That is, the 10th percentile of the Z distribution is –1.28.

- z(0.025) = 1.96 since 2.5% of the area under the standard normal is to the right of 1.96. That is, the 97.5th percentile of the Z distribution is 1.96.

Similarly,

- if z(α) = 1 then α = 1 – 0.8413 = 0.1587 (i.e., α is the area to the right of z = 1).

- if z(α) = –3 then α = 0.9987 (i.e., 0.9987 is the area to the right of z = –3).

The two important things to remember about the notation z(α) = k are:

- α represents the area to the right of k.

- k is also called the critical value corresponding to the 100 • (1 – α)th percentile. Note that k is a value of z. It is NOT an area.

6.3   The Normal approximation to the Binomial distribution

In Chapter 4 we mentioned that the Binomial may be approximated by the Normal under certain circumstances. In section 6.1, we graphed a B(20,0.5) and superimposed the corresponding Normal (μ = 10 and σ^2 = 5). Here are the conditions under which the Normal adequately fits the Binomial:

- $n \geq 20$ and np, n(1 – p) are both 5 or larger.

Example 7

Let X ~ B(20,0.4). Note that: n = 20, np = 8, and n(1 – p) = 12; thus, the conditions for an adequate Normal fit are all met. The corresponding Normal has mean = μ = n•p = 20•0.4 = 8, and variance = σ^2 = n•p•(1 – p) = 20•0.4•0.6 = 4.8.

a.   First we graph the Binomial and superimpose the corresponding Normal.

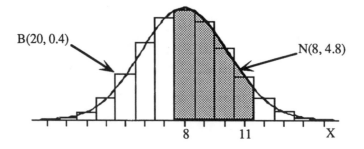

B(20, 0.4)

N(8, 4.8)

8   11   X

b. Compute $P(8 \leq X < 12)$ using the Binomial Table and then the Normal approximation.

From the Binomial Table, we find: $P(X = 8) + P(X = 9) + P(X = 10) + P(X = 11) = 0.5275$. This answer is exact to four decimal places.

We will now use the corresponding Normal to approximate this probability. Let's pay closer attention to the graph from part **a.** above. Note that the Normal curve crosses the rectangles generated by the Binomial in the center. For instance, if the value of the Binomial random variable is 8, this corresponds to the region between 7.5 and 8.5 under the Normal. This suggests that if we look at x under the Binomial then we must look at the interval $(x - 0.5, x + 0.5)$ under the corresponding Normal.[4] Thus, we translate the probability problem from $P(8 \leq X < 12)$ to $P(7.5 < X < 11.5)$. It would be incorrect to start at 8.5 and end at 12.5 (why?). We now proceed with the Normal computation to the probability question by first finding the corresponding z-scores and looking up the areas in the standard normal table:

$$P(7.5 < X < 11.5) = P\left(\frac{7.5 - 8}{\sqrt{4.8}} < Z < \frac{11.5 - 8}{\sqrt{4.8}}\right)$$

$$= P(-0.23 < Z < 1.60) = 0.9452 - 0.4090 = 0.5362.$$

That is, 0.5362 approximates the exact answer of 0.5275.

c. Additional cases in translating from Binomial to Normal

The table below gives the correct probability formulation when using the Normal approximation to the Binomial. Note the use of the continuity correction factor (i.e., refer to footnote 4 below.)

---

[4] The number 0.5 is called the *continuity correction*. That is, adding or subtracting 0.5 "corrects" for the fact that a discrete variable is being treated as continuous.

Binomial question	Corresponding Normal Approximation
$P(X \geq 9)$	$P(X > 8.5)$
$P(X = 10)$	$P(9.5 < X < 10.5)$
$P(X \leq 6)$	$P(X < 6.5)$
$P(X \geq x)$	$P(X > x - 0.5)$
$P(X > x)$	$P(X > x + 0.5)$
$P(X \leq x)$	$P(X < x + 0.5)$
$P(X < x)$	$P(X < x - 0.5)$
$P(a < X \leq b)$	$P(a + 0.5 < X < b + 0.5)$
$P(a \leq X < b)$	$P(a - 0.5 < X < b - 0.5)$

The approximation is most useful when we deal with Binomial distributions for which tables do not exist. This will be better illustrated in the problem set for this chapter.

Chapter 6 Problems

For problems **1–10**:

      a. Sketch a graph representing the Standard Normal Distribution and clearly mark the mean. Label the horizontal axis Z.

      b. Shade the region defined by each statement and write the area of the shaded region.

      c. Mark the appropriate z-value on the horizontal axis.

1. $z(0.5) = 0$

2. $z(0.05) = z$. Find z.

3. $z(\alpha) = 2$. Find α.

4. $z(\alpha) = -1.5$. Find α.

5. Find $P(-2 < Z < 3)$

6. Find the 90th percentile of the Z distribution.

7. If $P(Z < z(\alpha)) = 0.99$, find α and $z(\alpha)$.

8. If $P(Z > z(\alpha)) = 0.98$, find α and $z(\alpha)$.

9. Find $P(Z < -2$ or $Z > 1)$

10. Find $P(Z > -2$ and $Z < 1)$

11. Let $Z \sim N(0, 1)$

      a. $P(Z < -0.94) =$ **b.** $P(Z = 1.2) =$

      c. $P(1.23 < Z < 2.09) =$ **d.** median $=$

      e. mean $=$ **f.** 85th percentile $=$

12. Let $X \sim N(10, 25)$

      a. $P(X > -8.88) =$ **b.** $P(X = 10) =$

      c. $P(9.2 < X < 12.3) =$ **d.** $\sigma =$

      e. mean $=$ **f.** 45th percentile $=$

13. Let $X \sim N\left(15, \frac{1}{4}\right)$

      a. $P(X < 15.3) =$ **b.** $P(X > 15.3) =$

      c. $P(X = 15) =$ **d.** $P(14.5 < X < 14.8) =$

      e. mean $=$ **f.** 7th percentile $=$

14. For each of the following, sketch the region corresponding to α as well as solve.

    a. If $z(\alpha) = 1.79$, $\alpha =$ **b.** If $z(\alpha) = -1.43$, $\alpha =$

    c. If $z(\alpha) = 0$, $\alpha =$ **d.** If $z(\alpha) = -4$, $\alpha =$

    e. If $z(\alpha) = 4$, $\alpha =$ **f.** $z(0.06) =$

    g. $z(0.96) =$ **h.** If $P(Z < z(\alpha)) = 0.9$, find α and z_α.

    i. If $P(Z < z(\alpha)) = 0.01$, find α and $z(\alpha)$.

    j. If $P(|Z| < z(\alpha)) = P(-z(\alpha) < Z < z(\alpha)) = 0.92$, find α and $z(\alpha)$.

    k. $P(|Z| > z(\alpha)) = P(Z < -z(\alpha) \text{ or } Z > z(\alpha)) = 0.80$, find α and $z(\alpha)$.

15. The scores for a certain exam are distributed normally with $\mu = 74$ and $\sigma = 6$.

    a. If $X =$ students' scores, then $X \sim$

    b. Find the probability that a randomly chosen student score is between 70 and 80.

    c. Find the 94th percentile for the distribution of scores.

    d. What fraction of the scores are less than 68?

    e. A student scores 80. What fraction of the scores are greater than the student's score?

16. An auto parts retailer sells a car battery with a mean life of 3.4 years and a standard deviation of 0.8 years. He offers the following guarantee: If the battery fails before x years, it can be returned for a full refund. Assume the time to failure is normally distributed.

    a. Define in words the random variable $X =$

    b. $X \sim$

    c. Find the probability that the battery lasts between 3 and 4 years.

    d. Find the probability that the battery lasts more than 4 years.

e. Find the probability that the battery lasts less than two years.

f. Find the 95th percentile for the life of the batteries.

g. Find the 5th percentile for the life of the batteries.

h. Find the guarantee x if the retailer wants only 5% returned.

i. Find the guarantee x if the retailer wants only 10% returned.

j. If the retailer is willing to accept 60% returned, find the guarantee.

17. Let $X \sim N(100,144)$. For each of the following problems, find:

    i.   z value associated with each x value.

    ii. sketch a graph, scaling the horizontal axis in terms of both, X and Z.

    iii. shade the appropriate region of the graph and use the standard normal table to compute the indicated probability or critical value.

    a. $P(X > 110)$ **b.** $P(90 < X < 105)$

    c. $P(X < x) = 0.95$. Find x.   **d.** Find the median of X.

    e. Find the 90th percentile. Explain what this number means.

    f. $P(X < 88)$

18. The automatic opening device of a military cargo parachute is designed to open at an altitude of 200 meters above the ground. Suppose opening altitude actually is normally distributed with a mean of 200 meters and a standard deviation of 30 meters. Cargo damage will occur if the parachute opens at an altitude of less than 110 meters.

    a. What is the probability that there is damage to the cargo of one dropped parachute?

    b. What is the probability that there is damage to the cargo of at least one of five independently dropped parachutes?

19. A particular type of gasoline tank for a compact passenger car is designed to hold 15 gallons. Suppose that the actual tank capacity for this type of car is normally distributed with mean = 15 gallons and standard deviation = 0.20 gallons.

    a. What is the probability that a randomly selected tank will hold at most 14.8 gallons?

    b. Find the tank capacity representing the 90th percentile of all such tanks.

20. Suppose 60% of all drivers in a certain state regularly wear a seatbelt. A random sample of 500 drivers is selected. Let X = number of drivers who regularly wear a seatbelt. It is clear that X ~ B(500, 0.60).

    a. Verify that the conditions for approximating the Binomial with the Normal are met.

    b. Use the Normal approximation to the Binomial to find the probability that between 280 and 330, inclusive, of the drivers in the sample regularly wear a seatbelt.

    c. Find the 90th percentile of the distribution of X and explain what this number means in terms of drivers wearing seatbelts.

21. The rate of return on stock indexes (combining many different stocks) is approximately normal. Since 1945, the Standard & Poor's 500 index has produced an average annual return of 12%, with a standard deviation of 17%. Assume this normal distribution is the distribution of stock returns over a long time period.

    a. In what range do the middle 95% of all stock yearly returns lie?

    b. The stock market is said to be down on any year if the return on the S & P index is below zero. In what percent of years is the market down?

    c. Investors have "something to cheer about" if in any one year the stock index returns in excess of 25%. In what percent of years does the index gain over 25%?

22. In 1941, Ted Williams of the Boston Red Sox, was the last player to hit for an average of over 0.400 in a season. In fact, his batting average that season was 0.406. Compute the probability that Williams would get 20 or less hits in 40 times at bat during that season.

23. Final exam scores for Elementary Statistics are normally distributed with a mean of 67 and a variance of 100. If a randomly chosen student scores on the top quartile on the final exam, find the minimum possible score for the student.

24. Diagnosing stroke strictly on the basis of clinical symptoms is difficult. A standard diagnostic test used in clinical medicine to detect stroke in patients is the angiogram. Angiograms are risky for patients and several noninvasive techniques have been developed that are currently believed to be as effective as angiograms. One of these techniques is to measure the Cerebral Blood Flow (CBF) in the brain region. Stroke patients tend to have lower levels of CBF than healthy people. Assume that in the general population CBF is normally distributed with mean 75 and standard deviation 15. A patient is classified as being at risk for stroke if the CBF is less than 40. What proportion of healthy people will be mistakenly classified as being at risk for stroke?

25. The length of human pregnancies from conception to birth varies according to a roughly normal distribution with mean 266 days and standard deviation 16 days.

    a.   What percent of pregnancies last less than 240 days?

    b.   How long do the longest 10% of pregnancies last?

26. You are planning to move to a certain part of the country but are concerned with the temperature during the summer months. Literature sent to you by the Chamber of Commerce indicates that during the summer months, the daily temperature, measured at 12 noon, is normally distributed with mean 80 degrees Fahrenheit and standard deviation 4 degrees Fahrenheit.

    a.   If summer lasts exactly 90 days, how many summer days are expected to have a temperature exceeding 90 degrees Fahrenheit?

    b.   Find the 90th percentile of the distribution of daily temperatures and explain what this number means.

    c.   How many summer days are expected to have a temperature below 80 degrees Fahrenheit?

    d.   If you are really concerned with extremely hot days, what information would you like to receive from the Chamber of Commerce or the local weather bureau?

Chapter 7

Sampling Distributions, the Central Limit Theorem and the Law of Large Numbers

7.1 Sampling Distributions

In Chapter 2, we defined a *statistic* as being a measurable characteristic of those observations contained in a sample. More often that not, a statistic is simply a number computed from sample data. A statistic is used to estimate the value of the corresponding unknown population parameter. For instance, the sample mean, $\bar{x}$, estimates the corresponding (unknown) population mean, μ.

Whenever we estimate an unknown population parameter from a sample statistic, we must be aware of existing sampling variability. That is, if we take many independent samples from a population and each time we compute a particular sample statistic, we expect this sample statistic to vary from sample to sample. This phenomenon is called **sampling variability**. In practice, it is way too costly and time consuming to take repeated samples from a population; however, we can imitate the process of repeated samples by simulation. Computers are the most practical tool to use in carrying out simulations.

Suppose we wish to estimate the proportion of the population of adult Americans who are currently invested in at least one Mutual Stock Fund. Call this population proportion p. It is a parameter. A scientifically designed poll finds that 1200 out of 2500 adults own at least one Mutual Stock Fund. The proportion of the sample is

$$p' = \frac{1200}{2500} = 0.48.$$

This sample proportion p′ is a statistic. We use it to estimate the unknown population parameter p. Thus, we ask, how is it possible that we can reasonably estimate p based on a sample of only 2500 adult Americans?[1] After all, if we take a different sample of 2500 adult Americans we expect to obtain a different p′. This is the core of sampling variability: the statistic (p′ in this case) is expected to vary from sample to sample. However, sampling variability is not a hopeless situation. In fact, we seek to understand it. Thus, we ask, "What would be the behavior of the sample statistic if we take many samples?" Here are guidelines in attempting to answer that question:

---

[1] As of the 1990 census, there are about 180 million adult Americans.

- Take a large number of samples from the same population.

- Calculate the sample proportion, p′, for each sample.

- Make a histogram of the values of p′.

- Examine the distribution drawn in the histogram for overall pattern, center, spread, and any deviant observations.

Example 1

We use a computer to simulate the above situation. However, instead of taking samples of size 2500, we take samples of size 100. The computer will do this 1000 times. The computer is assuming that the true proportion of adult Americans who own at least one Mutual Stock Fund is 0.60. That is, if X = number of adult Americans who own at least one Mutual Stock Fund, then X ~ B(100,0.60). The table and histogram below show the result:

Class interval for p′	Frequency
0.445 – 0.475	5
0.475 – 0.505	10
0.505 – 0.535	52
0.535 – 0.565	124
0.565 – 0.595	190
0.595 – 0.625	235
0.625 – 0.655	200
0.655 – 0.685	125
0.685 – 0.715	48
0.715 – 0.745	7
0.745 – 0.775	4

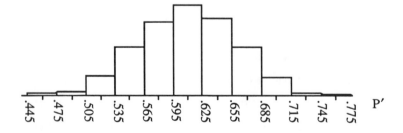

Note how the sample statistic p′ varies. Depending on which one of the 1000 samples we obtain, the estimate for p would differ. The distribution of p′ shows what would happen if we were to take many samples of size 100 from the population. It displays the *sampling distribution* of p′.

We define the **sampling distribution of a statistic** as:

the distribution of values taken by the statistic in all possible samples of the same size from the same population.

It is important to understand that the sampling distribution of a statistic is the theoretical or idealized pattern that would emerge if we took all possible samples of a given size from the population under study. Of course, a sampling distribution like the one in example 1 above, obtained by taking 1000 samples, is an approximation to the theoretical sampling distribution. One of the uses of probability when studying statistics is to obtain exact sampling distributions without a need to simulate. However, this is difficult to accomplish. It is precisely the access to simulation that allows us to illustrate and gain insight into the very difficult mathematics involved in theoretical probability and statistics.

Because of this inherent sample variability, sample statistics are considered to be random variables. We know that random variables have underlying distributions. We seek knowledge of the underlying distribution (i.e., the population). Thus, we can think of P' as being a random variable while p' represents specific values P' takes (i.e., the range of P'). Likewise, we can think of $\overline{X}$ as being a random variable with $\overline{x}$ representing values in its range. The same can be said of σ^2 and s^2, and of any other population parameter and the corresponding sample statistic.

7.2   The Central Limit Theorem

Sample proportions, like in Example 1 above, come up most often when we are interested in categorical variables. It is customary to then ask questions like: "What proportion of the adult American population is invested in at least one Mutual Stock Fund?", or "What percent of the student population favors the recent University of California Regents decision to abolish ethnicity from its admission policy?". On the other hand, when we are interested in strictly quantitative variables based on measurements rather than counts - income of households, heights of people, the circumference of a certain bolt, the blood pressure of heart patients - we then compute statistics other than proportions, such as the mean or median or standard deviation. Because sample means are just arithmetic averages of a set of numbers, they are among the most frequently used of all statistics. We now turn our attention to the sampling distribution of sample means.

Example 2

One of the most fundamental principles of investing in financial markets is that diversification reduces risk. That is, buying a basket of stocks, rather than just a single stock, reduces the variability of the investment return. The histogram below illustrates this idea. It shows the return of all 1815 stocks listed on the New York Stock Exchange (NYSE) for all of 1987. This was a year of extreme volatility in the financial markets. In fact, on the infamous Black Monday (October 19, 1987), the stock market had a record loss of over 20%. However, the average return for all 1815 stocks on the NYSE for all of 1987 was –3.5%.

Rates of return (in percent)	Percent of stocks
–80 to –70	1
–70 to –60	2
–60 to –50	4
–50 to –40	5
–40 to –30	6
–30 to –20	12
–20 to –10	14
–10 to 00	15
00 to 10	14
10 to 20	8
20 to 30	7
30 to 40	5
40 to 50	4
50 to 60	2
60 to 70	1

rate of return for individual stocks

The histogram below shows the average distribution of returns for all possible portfolios consisting of 5 randomly chosen stocks from the NYSE with equal dollar amounts invested on each of the 5 stocks.[2]

------

[2] This is another way of saying that 5 stocks have been sampled from the 1815 stocks on the NYSE and all such possible samples have been considered. The return on the portfolio is the average return of the 5 stocks chosen. The mean return for all the portfolios is still –3.5%. In case you are curious, there are over $1.6 \cdot 10^{14}$ porfolios being considered (fast work for a computer). The stock data are found in the *American Association of Individual Investors Journal*, March 1988, pages 16-17.

Rates of return (in percent)	Percent of portfolios
–50 to –40	2
–40 to –30	4
–30 to –20	10
–20 to –10	18
–10 to 00	25
00 to 10	22
10 to 20	13
20 to 30	6

average rate of return

We notice that the average return on a portfolio of 5 stocks is a lot less variable than the return based on individual stocks. Also, averages seem to be normally distributed (a lot more so than individual stocks). These two facts go a long way towards contributing to the enormous popularity of averages.

We summarize what has been observed in Example 2 above as follows.

Central Limit Theorem (CLT)

We consider a population, denoted by X, with any distribution, and with a certain mean, μ_X, and variance σ_X^2 . We form all possible samples of a given size, say, size n, and compute the average for each sample.[3] We denote this sampling distribution of averages by $\overline{X}$. Then,

---

[3] If the original distribution is unknown or it is not Normal, in order for the distribution of averages to be reasonably approximated by the Normal, the sample size should be at least 20. A more precise rule for the sample size (assuming the population we are sampling from is finite and not normal) is: the sampling distribution of averages is approximately Normal if the size of the entire population is at least 10 times the size of the sample.

- $\overline{X}$ *is normally distributed,*

- *The mean of* $\overline{X}$ *, denoted by* $\mu_{\overline{X}}$ *, is equal to* μ_X,

- *The variance of* $\overline{X}$ *, denoted by* $\sigma_{\overline{X}}^2$ *, is equal to* $\dfrac{\sigma_X^2}{n}$ *.*

In other words, if X has any distribution with mean $= \mu_X$ and variance $= \sigma_X^2$, and samples of size n are taken from X and the average of each sample is computed, the distribution of these averages, represented by $\overline{X}$, is $N\left(\mu_X, \dfrac{\sigma_X^2}{n}\right)$. We note that the standard deviation of $\overline{X}$, $\sigma_{\overline{X}}$, is given by the expression $\dfrac{\sigma_X}{\sqrt{n}}$. This is also called the *standard error of the mean*.

Example 3

The height of adult women is distributed with mean = 64 inches and standard deviation = 3 inches. Suppose a random sample of 36 women is taken and the average height of the women in the sample is computed.

   a.   What is the standard deviation of the distribution of average heights?
   b.   What is the probability that the average height of the women in the sample exceeds 65 inches?
   c.   What is the 90th percentile of the sampling distribution of these averages?

We formulate the solution to the questions using the Central Limit Theorem. We strongly suggest the use of appropriate notation, in terms of the pertinent random variable, in order to summarize the information contained in the problem. We proceed according to these guidelines.

Let X = height, in inches. Note that $\mu_X = 64$ and $\sigma_X = 3$. We are interested in the distribution of $\overline{X}$ when samples of size = n = 36 are taken. The CLT provides the key to the solution. That is,

$$\overline{X} \sim N\left(\mu_X, \dfrac{\sigma_X^2}{n}\right) \quad \text{or} \quad \overline{X} \sim N\left(64, \dfrac{9}{36}\right).$$

   a.   The standard deviation of the mean = standard error of the mean = $\sqrt{\dfrac{9}{36}} = \dfrac{1}{2}$.

b. We wish to find $P(\overline{X} > 65)$. Just like we did in Chapter 6, we transform from $\overline{X}$ to the Z in order to use the standard normal table. That is,

$$P(\overline{X} > 65) = P\left(Z > \frac{65 - 64}{1/2}\right) = P(Z > 2) = 1 - 0.9772 = 0.0228.$$

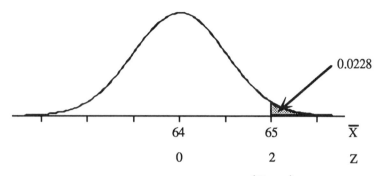

c. The 90th percentile is the critical value, $\overline{x}$, so that $P(\overline{X} < \overline{x}) = 0.90$. We read the table in reverse (from the inside to the outside), to find the value of z associated with an area to its right of 10%. Using the notation of Chapter 6, we find that $z(0.10) = 1.28$. The graph below illustrates this situation. Thus, using the z-score equation:

$$1.28 = \frac{\overline{x} - 64}{1/2} \Rightarrow \overline{x} = 1.28 \cdot \left(\frac{1}{2}\right) + 64 = 64.64.$$

That is, 90% of the samples consisting of 36 randomly chosen women will have an average height below 64.64 inches.

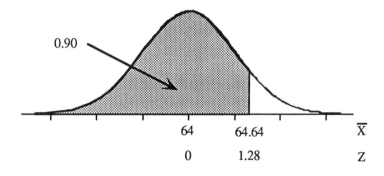

Example 4

The team score in gymnastics competition is the sum of the scores for each individual gymnast. Suppose it is known that the score for an individual gymnast at your school, on the floor exercise, is normally distributed with average = 9 and standard deviation = 0.4. There are 4 gymnasts in your school gymnastics team.

    a. What can be said about the distribution of the team score on the floor exercise?

    b. What is the probability that on the next gymnastics meet the team will score fewer than 35 points on the floor exercise?

    c. At lunch the other day, your friend gymnast was bragging about the team scoring over 39.5 points, on the floor exercise, in their last gymnastic meet. What did you respond to this claim?

Solution (hint: provide an appropriate graph as you read through these solutions)

    a. Let X = individual scores on floor exercise. Note that $X \sim N(9, 0.16)$. Of interest is the sum of the X's, rather than $\overline{X}$. Let $\sum X$ = sum of the X's. Since averages and sums are equivalent, we derive the distribution of $\sum X$ from that of $\overline{X}$.[4] Since $n = 4$, we note that $4 \cdot \overline{X} = \sum X$. Thus,

$$\overline{X} \sim N(9, 0.16/4) \Rightarrow \sum X = 4 \cdot \overline{X} \sim N\left(4 \cdot 9, \ 4^2 \cdot 0.16/4\right) \text{ or } \sum X \sim N(36, 0.64).$$

    b. Need to compute $P\left(\sum X < 35\right)$. We use the standard normal. Thus,

$$P\left(\sum X < 35\right) = P\left(Z < \frac{35 - 36}{\sqrt{0.64}}\right) = P(Z < -1.25) = 0.1056.$$

    c. Let's compute $P\left(\sum X > 39.5\right)$. That is,

$$P\left(\sum X > 39.5\right) = P\left(Z > \frac{39.5 - 36}{\sqrt{0.64}}\right) = P(Z > 4.357) \approx 0.$$

From a probability standpoint, a total score exceeding 39.5 is practically impossible. However, perhaps the judges were quite generous or your friend reversed the digits 5 and 9!

---

[4] By this we mean that averages are obtained by first computing the sum of all the data. Thus, sums are obtained by multiplying an average by the corresponding sample size. This allows us to apply the results of the CLT to sums. That is, $\sum X \sim N\left(n \cdot \mu_X, n \cdot \sigma_X^2\right)$.

Example 5

Let $X \sim N\left(\mu_X, \sigma_X^2\right)$ and suppose we take samples of size n. Furthermore, of interest is the sampling distribution of the sample means.

a. By the CLT, we know that $\overline{X} \sim N\left(\mu_X, \dfrac{\sigma_X^2}{n}\right)$; thus, for n > 1, the graph of the distribution of $\overline{X}$ is tighter (i.e., smaller variance) than that for X. The graph below illustrates this point.

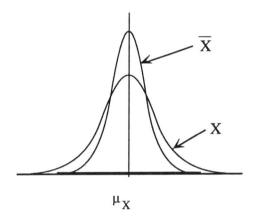

b. Suppose the original population, X, is very large or infinite. What happens to the distribution of $\overline{X}$ as the sample size increases without bounds?

As n grows without bounds, the variance of $\overline{X}$ gets smaller and smaller. In fact, as n approaches infinity, the ratio $\dfrac{\sigma_X^2}{n}$ approaches zero. That is, the *variance* of the $\overline{X}$ distribution goes to zero. Thus, the mean of any one such sample should equal the population mean. This is the only time when we can write $\overline{x} = \mu_X$ with complete certainty. The graph of the distribution of $\overline{X}$ would be just a vertical line right at μ_X.

Example 6

Suppose the distribution of X is extremely skewed, like an Exponential distribution. Will the sampling distribution of sample means still approach the Normal?

According to the CLT, the shape of the distribution of X doesn't matter at all. What matters is that X have a mean and a variance. Extreme skewness necessitates a large sample size in order to reasonably approximate the Normal. We illustrate this point by letting X ~ Exp(decay = 1) and graphing the sampling distribution of sample means for sample sizes n = 2, 10, 50, superimposed with the corresponding Normal.

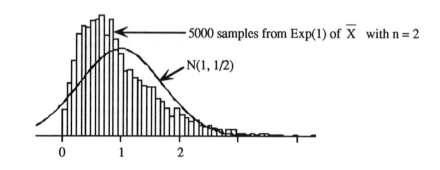

5000 samples from Exp(1) of $\overline{X}$ with n = 2

N(1, 1/2)

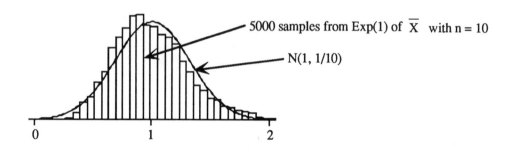

5000 samples from Exp(1) of $\overline{X}$ with n = 10

N(1, 1/10)

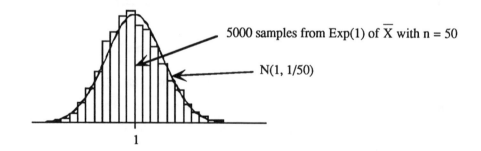

5000 samples from Exp(1) of $\overline{X}$ with n = 50

N(1, 1/50)

7.3   The Law of Large Numbers

The CLT basically says that for large sample sizes, the sample mean $\overline{x}$ must be close to the population mean μ_X. Example 5 above provides the justification for this fact. That is, as the sample size gets larger and larger, the variance of $\overline{X}$ gets smaller and smaller. We now turn this fact around to help us better understand the population mean μ_X.

The Law of Large Numbers states that:

> *if observations are randomly drawn from any population with finite mean* μ_X, *as the number of observations drawn increases, the mean* $\bar{x}$ *of these observations gets closer and closer to* μ_X.

Note that this is very similar to the idea of a long run probability. That is, the proportion of outcomes taking any particular value gets close to the probability of that value, and the average outcome gets closer to the population mean. The Law of Large Numbers is the foundation of gambling casinos and insurance companies. We discussed two such examples in Chapter 4.

Misuses of the Law of Large Numbers are plentiful. To most people, the Law of Large Numbers is synonymous with what is commonly called the "Law of Averages". Here are some of the most frequently encountered situations about the bogus "Law of Averages".

- If a baseball player with a batting average of about 0.300 encounters a hitless streak, most people believe that on the next at bat, the player is "due". That is, the absence of any base hits on however many previous at bats, is almost a "guarantee" of a base hit on the next at bat. The fact of the matter is that the chances of a base hit on the next at bat is predicated by the player's long run batting average (about 0.300) and not by the length of a previous hitless streak.

- The above situation is analogous to rolling a fair die and a "5" not coming up on the first 36 rolls. This doesn't mean that a "5" is imminent on the next roll of the die. In fact, the chances of obtaining a 5 on the next roll is the familiar 1/6. The Law of Large Numbers states that if we roll the die a very large number of times, the proportion of 5's that come up will approach 1/6.

- A disgruntled mother once wrote to Ann Landers: "...my husband and I just had our sixth child, another girl. What a disappointment. We were so certain that a boy was due. Even the doctor told us that the Law of Averages were in our favor with odds of 100 to 1..." Here again, the Law of Large Numbers says that over many births, the proportion of male births approaches 0.50. Unfortunately for this particular couple, their doctor was inexcusably misinformed.

Chapter 7

Chapter 7 Problems

1. This problem will verify the CLT for a finite population.

Consider a population, denoted by X, consisting of the numbers $\{1,3,5\}$. That is, X is finite. It is easy to verify that $\mu_X = 3$ and $\sigma_X^2 = \frac{8}{3} \Rightarrow \sigma_X = 1.633.$[5]

      a. Write down all possible samples of size n = 2 that can be drawn from this population (i.e., there are 9 of them). Since we assume independence, the sampling is assumed to be done with replacement. That is, the set $\{1, 1\}$ is one of the nine possible samples.

      b. Compute the mean for each of the nine samples from **a.** above. These nine means constitute the sampling distribution of sample averages.

      c. Verify that the average of these nine means = 3. That is, $\mu_{\overline{X}} = \mu_X$.

      d. Compute the variance of the nine sample means and verify that $\sigma_{\overline{X}}^2 = \dfrac{\sigma_X^2}{2}$.

      e. Draw a histogram of the nine means from **b.** above. Comment on the shape of the histogram.

2. Test scores for an Elementary Statistics course are normally distributed with mean 100 and standard deviation 6. Let X = individual test scores; $\overline{X}$ = average for sample of 9 test scores; $\sum X$ = sum for sample of 10 test scores.

      a. $X \sim$ _____   **b.** $\overline{X} \sim$ _____   **c.** $\sum X \sim$ _____

      d. Find each of the following:

            $P(X > 103) =$ $P(\overline{X} > 103) =$

            $P(X < 100) =$ $P(\overline{X} < 100) =$

            $P(X < 96) =$ $P(\overline{X} < 96) =$

            $P(96 < X < 103) =$ $P(96 < \overline{X} < 103) =$

---

[5] Since we are dealing with the population, recall that $\sigma_X^2 = \dfrac{\sum\limits_{all\ x} (x - \mu_X)^2}{n}$

$P(X < 96 \text{ or } X > 103) =$ $P(\overline{X} < 96 \text{ or } \overline{X} > 103) =$

40th % for X =   40th % for $\overline{X} =$

75th % for X =   75th % for $\overline{X} =$

$P(\sum X < 1000) =$ $P(\sum X < 960) =$

$P(960 < \sum X < 1030) =$ $P(\sum X < 960 \text{ or } \sum X > 1030) =$

40th % for $\sum X =$ 75th % for $\sum X =$

3. The scores of all students taking the SAT in a recent year are normally distributed with mean 840 and standard deviation 100.

    a. Find the probability that a single student randomly chosen from all those taking the SAT scores higher than 820.

    b. Consider a random sample of 100 students who took the test. What is the probability that the mean score of these students exceeds 820?

    c. Explain why the answer to **b.** is considerably larger than the answer to **a.**

4. High school dropouts account for 15% of all Americans between the ages of 18 and 24. An Alternative School that wants to attract dropouts mails an advertising brochure to 50,000 persons between the ages of 18 and 24.

    a. Assuming that the mailing list was composed by random selection from the population of 18 to 24 year olds, what is the average number of high school dropouts who will receive the brochure?

    b. What is the probability that at least 8,000 high school dropouts will receive the brochure?

5. Let X = time to blood coagulation on certain types of surgical incisions. It is known that the distribution of X is Exponential with mean = standard deviation = 60 seconds.

    a. What is the probability that in a sample of 36 surgical patients the average coagulation time exceeds 70 seconds?

    b. If coagulation has not occurred within 100 seconds, a blood transfusion is started. In a sample of 64 surgical patients, how many blood transfusions would have been started? (hint: think about this. You might need to refer to the appropriate material in Chapter 5).

    c. In a sample of 49 surgical patients, what is the 90th percentile for $\overline{X}$? Explain what this number means.

6. A TV manufacturer guarantees that his TV sets will last at least 5 years. Suppose that X = life of single TV's in years. It is known that $X \sim Exp(decay = 0.25)$. Thus, $\mu_X = \sigma_X = 4$ years.

    a. Find the probability that a single TV will not satisfy the guarantee.

    b. Find the 80th percentile for the distribution of X.

    c. Find the probability that the average life of a random sample of 36 TV's will not satisfy the guarantee.

    d. Find the 80th percentile for the average life of a random sample of 36 TV's.

7. A nursery sells shrubs that grow to an average height of 6 feet with a standard deviation of 3 feet. The nursery sells the shrubs in packages of 50. A landscape designer needs a guarantee on the minimum average height of the 50 shrubs in a package.

    a. The nursery owner sets the guarantee at 7 feet. What is the probability that a given package will violate the guarantee?

    b. Clearly, the answer to **a.** indicates a very high return rate. At what height should the nursery set the guarantee in order to reduce the return rate to no more than 2%?

8. The weight of hardbound college textbooks has an unknown distribution with mean = 3 lbs. and standard deviation = 1 lb. Hardbound books are shipped to bookstores in cartons of 100 books. Think of these cartons as random samples from the population of all hardbound college textbooks. What is the probability that the total weight of one randomly selected carton exceeds 320 lbs?

9. While he was a prisoner of the Germans during World War II, the British mathematician John Kerrich flipped a coin 10,000 times. He meticulously recorded 5,067 heads. Let p = probability of heads on a single toss of the coin. For a fair coin, $p = 0.50$. Is there sufficient reason to believe that Kerrich's coin is not fair? Explain your conclusion. Hint: consider the probability of a fair coin coming up heads 5,067 or more times in 10,000 flips.

10. For a certain bank, X = dollar amount in an individual savings account. Suppose that X is normal with mean $12,000 and standard deviation $1,000. Let $\overline{X}$ = average dollar amount in random samples of 25 accounts and $\sum X$ = total dollar amount in random samples of 25 accounts.

    a. $X \sim$ _____   **b.** $\overline{X} \sim$ _____   **c.** $\sum X \sim$ _____

    d. Find the probability that one randomly selected account exceeds $12,400.

e. Find the probability that the average dollar amount of a randomly selected group of 25 accounts exceeds $12,400.

f. Find the probability that the total dollar amount of a randomly selected group of 25 accounts exceeds $124,000.

g. Find the 90th percentile for the dollar amount in a single randomly chosen account. Explain what this number means.

h. Find the 90th percentile for the average dollar amount in a randomly chosen group of 25 accounts. Explain what this number means.

i. Find the 90th percentile for the total dollar amount in a randomly chosen group of 25 accounts. Explain what this number means.

j. There is a 1% probability that the dollar amount in a single randomly chosen account will exceed what value?

k. There is a 1% probability that the average dollar amount of a randomly selected group of 25 accounts will exceed what value?

l. There is a 1% probability that the total dollar amount in a randomly selected group of 25 accounts will exceed what value?

11. Among financial professionals there is a saying (referring to stocks) that goes like this: "every dog has its day". Explain what this could possibly mean in light of the Law of Large Numbers.

12. In actor Marlon Brando's biography and autobiography,[6] there is a passage referring to the Law of Averages: "Brando has had so many lovers, it would only be surprising if they were all of one gender; the law of averages makes him bisexual". What Law of Averages can the passage refer to?

13. From time to time, financial publications make reference to the fact that the return on a stock portfolio chosen by throwing darts at the financial pages of any publication frequently exceeds the return of professionally managed ones. Is there an explanation in light of the Law of Large Numbers?

14. An elementary statistics teacher gives a standardized final. The test scores are normal with a mean of 60 and a standard deviation of 8. For parts **a., b.,** and **c.,** assume 30 students took the final exam.

a. Find the probability that a randomly chosen student scores at least 65.

b. Find the probability that the class average is at least 65.

c. Find the 40th percentile for the class average.

d. At another school, all the classes are the same size. If the 80th percentile at this school is 60.95, what is that class size?

---

[6] *Los Angeles Times*, 16 September 1994; Book Reviews, page 13.

Chapter 8

Estimation and Confidence for Means and Proportions

8.1   Estimation of Population Parameters

Estimating the value of a population parameter from the corresponding sample statistic is a very important problem in statistics. In fact, it is the basis of an entire field of statistics known as *inference*. That is, from the value of the sample statistic we infer something about the corresponding population parameter. For instance, from a computed sample mean we would like to make inferences about the unknown value of the population mean.

Not every sample statistic is an adequate estimate of the population parameter of interest. For example, the midrange of a data set is not as good an estimate of the center of the population as the average of the data set. In general, there are two characteristics about sample statistics that are most desirable. First, sample statistics must provide unbiased estimates of the corresponding population parameter. Avoiding biases is a function of two things: the sample data must constitute a representative random sample from the underlying population, and the average of the sample statistic taken over repeated samples must equal the unknown parameter. Fortunately, for means and proportions, the Central Limit Theorem guarantees the latter. The question of collecting representative data from the population is one that requires constant attention and care. Sound sampling procedures are an integral part of estimation. We talked about sampling back in Chapter 1; however, there are entire courses devoted to the study of sampling. Secondly, sample statistics must be computed in such a way that they represent the most likely value the unknown population parameter may take. In other words, the most likely center of the unknown population is the arithmetic mean computed from sample data, and the most likely value of the unknown population proportion is the ratio of the number of successes to the total number of trials computed from sample data. This may not sound like much, but in the case of the sample mean, it rules out other competing statistics as the most likely center.[1]

Because of their computational simplicity, the population mean, μ, and the population proportion, **p**, are the two parameters that attract the most attention. Newspapers and the media at large bombard us with statistics where a sample average or a sample proportion are quoted. We constantly hear about average test scores, average income, average age, proportion of adult unemployment, proportion of baby boomers buying luxury automobiles, proportion of voters favoring such-and-such candidate, etc. There seems to be a

---

[1] For instance, neither the median or mode or midrange are the most likely center.

never ending plethora of statistical information derived from averages and proportions.

The Central Limit Theorem and the idea of a sampling distribution go a long way towards dispelling most of the mystery surrounding the estimation of a population mean and a population proportion. That is, once we have obtained a sample mean or a sample proportion, what can we say about the corresponding population mean or population proportion? To put it another way: how can we use the sample statistic and any additional information contained in the sample data, to gain a better understanding of the corresponding population parameter?

8.2   Estimating μ and p with confidence

Population mean, μ.

We estimate the value of μ by first computing the mean value of the data in the sample. In practicality, we usually have access to only one sample of a certain size n. That is, we do not have access to the entire sampling distribution of sample means.[2] So, we have a single $\bar{x}$. To claim that $\bar{x} = \mu$ would be misleading. However, we hope that the value of the unknown μ is close to the computed $\bar{x}$. That is, we hope that an interval of the form $(\bar{x}$ – *margin of error*, $\bar{x}$ + *margin of error)* would include the unknown μ with a certain probability. We proceed to quantify *margin of error* denoted by EB for **error bound**.

First, $\bar{x}$ is obtained from a distribution with mean μ and standard deviation σ. We want to know if the interval $\bar{x} \pm EB$ includes the unknown population mean μ. The diagrams below indicate that:

* μ included in $\bar{x} \pm EB$ is equivalent to $\bar{x}$ included in $\mu \pm EB$,
*   a large EB is more likely to trap μ (or equivalently, $\bar{x}$) than a small EB.

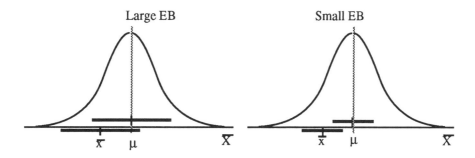

In order to quantify the concept of confidence, we will consider the random variable $\overline{X}$. From the above diagrams, $P(\overline{X} - EB < \mu < \overline{X} + EB) = P(\mu - EB < \overline{X} < \mu + EB)$ which we call the *level of confidence.* That is,

_____

[2] If we did, we would then know μ exactly.

$$\boxed{\text{Level of Confidence} = 1 - \alpha = P\left(\mu - EB < \overline{X} < \mu + EB\right)}$$

as shown below.

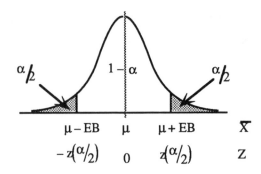

From the CLT, we know that the sampling distribution of sample means, $\overline{X}$, has a Normal distribution with mean μ and standard deviation $\frac{\sigma}{\sqrt{n}}$. We may now use the z-score formula to transform to the standard normal. That is, $z\left(\alpha/2\right) = \frac{EB}{\sigma/\sqrt{n}}$. Solving this equation for EB gives:

$$\boxed{EB = z\left(\alpha/2\right)\left(\frac{\sigma}{\sqrt{n}}\right)}$$

The exact value of $z\left(\alpha/2\right)$ is determined by the probability or confidence level $= 1 - \alpha$ that we desire.

Interpretation

$(1 - \alpha)$ is the fraction of samples that we expect μ to fall in the interval $\left(\overline{X} - EB, \overline{X} + EB\right)$. Thus, we are $1 - \alpha$ confident that μ is in $\left(\overline{x} - EB, \overline{x} + EB\right)$ for the fixed sample $\overline{x}$.

Example 1

A random sample of 100 freshman students at the University of California at Berkeley (UCB), shows an average SAT score of 1180. We wish to estimate, with 95% confidence, the average SAT score of all freshman students at UCB. It is known that the standard deviation for SAT scores is 100.

Solution

From the CLT, we know that $\overline{X} \sim N\left(\mu, \frac{100^2}{100}\right)$. The point estimate for the unknown μ is 1180. However, we also know that we can not be 95% confident in claiming that $\mu = 1180$. In order to create the 95% confidence interval about μ, we proceed to find the error bound, EB.

We note that since confidence level = 0.95 then $\alpha = 0.05$ and $\alpha/2 = 0.025$. From the standard normal table, $z\left(\dfrac{\alpha}{2}\right) = 1.96$. Thus,

$$EB = z\left(\frac{\alpha}{2}\right) \cdot \left(\frac{\sigma}{\sqrt{n}}\right) = 1.96 \cdot \frac{100}{\sqrt{100}} = 19.6.$$

Therefore, the 95% confidence interval about the unknown μ is:

$$\overline{x} \pm EB \quad \text{or} \quad 1180 \pm 19.6 \Rightarrow \text{confidence interval is } (1160.4, 1199.6).$$

The interpretation is that μ will be in $\left(\overline{X} - 19.6, \overline{X} + 19.6\right)$ 95% of the time; thus, we are 95% confident that μ is in $(1160.4, 1199.6)$

Example 2

For a fixed confidence level, as n increases, what happens to the error bound?

Solution

For simplicity, we refer to Example 1 above where confidence level = 95%. Suppose a sample of 900 freshman is taken. The EB computation follows:

$$EB = 1.96 \cdot \frac{100}{\sqrt{900}} = \frac{19.6}{3} = 6.533.$$

Thus, as long as the confidence level remains fixed, a larger n reduces the error bound. This follows from the fact that a larger n reduces the variance of $\overline{X}$.

Example 3

Suppose instead we wish to create a confidence interval so that we are 99% confident that μ lies in the interval. Again, we take the information in Example 1 above. However, this time we would like μ to fall within 5 units of the sample mean. What is the necessary sample size?

Solution

Since a larger confidence is called for and the error bound is smaller than in either Examples 1 or 2, we expect a rather large n (i.e., larger than the 900 from Example 2). We work with the EB formula as follows.

$EB = z\left(\frac{\alpha}{2}\right) \cdot \left(\frac{\sigma}{\sqrt{n}}\right) \Rightarrow 5 = z(0.005) \cdot \frac{100}{\sqrt{n}}$. From the standard normal table, $z(0.005) = 2.58$;

thus, $5 = 2.58 \cdot \frac{100}{\sqrt{n}} \Rightarrow \sqrt{n} = \frac{258}{5} = 51.6 \Rightarrow n = (51.6)^2 \Rightarrow n = 2663.$

This is a very large n. In fact, it might not be possible to have a sample of 2663 freshman because there may not be that many new freshman accepted at any one time. If that is the case, then a smaller confidence or a larger error bound will be necessary.

Example 4

For a fixed sample size and pre-determined error bound, what is the confidence level?

Solution

Continuing to work with the data from Example 1, suppose $EB = 10$ and $n = 625$. We wish to find the confidence level. That is, confidence level $= 1 - \alpha$. From the EB formula, we find α as follows.

$$EB = z\left(\frac{\alpha}{2}\right) \cdot \left(\frac{\sigma}{\sqrt{n}}\right) \Rightarrow z\left(\frac{\alpha}{2}\right) = \frac{EB}{\frac{\sigma}{\sqrt{n}}} \Rightarrow z\left(\frac{\alpha}{2}\right) = \frac{10}{\frac{100}{\sqrt{625}}} \Rightarrow z\left(\frac{\alpha}{2}\right) = 2.5.$$

Reading the standard normal table in reverse and solving for α gives:

$\frac{\alpha}{2} = 1 - 0.9938 = 0.0062 \Rightarrow \alpha = 2 \cdot 0.0062 = 0.0124 \Rightarrow$ confidence level $= 1 - 0.0124 = 0.9876.$

Thus, the confidence level is about 98.76% that μ will lie within 10 units of $\bar{x}$.

Population proportion, p

Just as $\bar{x}$ estimates μ, so does p' estimates p. In fact, it makes sense to think of p as if it were a mean. The confidence interval about p is built in a manner similar to the one for μ. The only unresolved issue is the exact form of the EB term. We derive the formula for EB as follows.

Let X = number of successes in a sample of size n. Thus, $X \sim B(n,p)$. Recall that the Binomial distribution may be approximated by the Normal under certain conditions [i.e., $n \geq 20$ and both, np and $n(1 - p) \geq 5$]. Under such conditions the distribution of X is approximately $N(np, np(1 - p))$. Since we are interested in the random variable P', we obtain its distribution by considering the ratio $\frac{X}{n}$, so that $P' \sim N\left(p, \frac{p(1 - p)}{n}\right)$.[3] Thus,

$$EB = z\left(\alpha/2\right) \cdot \sqrt{\frac{p'(1 - p')}{n}}$$

---

[3] Dividing X by n causes the variance of X to be divided by n^2.

The graph below illustrates these ideas.

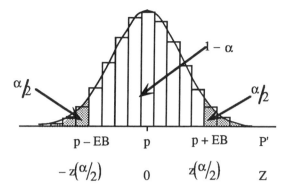

Example 5

A Gallup poll on President's Clinton popularity interviewed 1000 people randomly selected from the United States population. The poll found that 45% of the people said they like Clinton. At a 95% confidence level, the poll announced an error bound of about 3%.

a. How was the error bound of 3% obtained?

From the EB formula and with $\alpha = 0.05$, we have:

$$EB = z(0.025) \cdot \sqrt{\frac{0.45\,(1-0.45)}{1000}} = 1.96 \cdot 0.01573 \approx 0.03.$$

b. What is the 95% confidence interval about the true proportion p of people who think Clinton is popular?

$$95\% \text{ confidence interval} = (p' - EB,\ p' + EB) = (0.45 - 0.03,\ 0.45 + 0.03) = (0.42,\ 0.48).$$

c. Explain to someone who doesn't know statistics why we can't quite claim that 45% of the people in the United States like Clinton.

The sample proportion of people who like Clinton will vary from sample to sample. The 45% comes from only one such sample. The variation in the response is about 3%; thus, it is more precise to claim that the actual proportion of people who like Clinton would fall in the interval $45\% \pm 3\%$.

d. Clearly explain what "95% confidence" means.

It means that in 95% of all samples of 1000 people, the unknown p lies between $p' - 0.03$ and $p' + 0.03$.

Example 6

Suppose that attendance at major league baseball games during the current season is drastically down. Wanting to know the sentiment of the people at large about the state of baseball, the Major League Office of Public Relations conducts a poll in order to estimate to within 0.01 the proportion of people who are not attending baseball games because of the recent player's strike. How large a sample should be taken in order to achieve a confidence level of 95%?

Solution

We need to solve for n given $\alpha = 0.05$ [i.e., $z(\alpha/2) = 1.96$] and EB = 0.01. The EB formula, EB = $z(\alpha/2) \cdot \sqrt{\dfrac{p'(1-p')}{n}}$, calls for knowledge of p'. Since p' is not given, we set it at 0.5. [4] Thus,

$$0.01 = 1.96 \cdot \sqrt{\frac{0.5(1-0.5)}{n}} \Rightarrow \sqrt{n} = 1.96 \cdot \frac{\sqrt{0.5 \cdot 0.5}}{0.01} = 1.96 \cdot 50$$

$$\Rightarrow n = (1.96 \cdot 50)^2 = 9604.$$

Therefore, a sample size of 9,604 people will produce the required result.

8.3 Words of caution.

The reader should be aware that the following probability notation for a confidence interval, with confidence level = $1 - \alpha$,

$$\text{for } \mu: \ P\!\left(\overline{X} - EB < \mu < \overline{X} + EB\right) = 1 - \alpha \, ,$$

$$\text{for } p: \ P\!\left(P' - EB < p < P' + EB\right) = 1 - \alpha \, ,$$

is correct in the sense that the probability statement involves the random variables $\overline{X}$ or P'. Once the numbers are substituted, ($\overline{x}$ for $\overline{X}$ and p' for P') the above probability statements are incorrect. This is so, because a statement like $P(20 < \mu < 30) = 0.95$ has no probability meaning since μ is assumed fixed, albeit unknown.[5] Since 0.95 is our expectation of inclusion with repeated sampling, it is a reasonable

---

[4] Setting $p' = 0.5$ maximizes the variance term. This in turn produces the largest possible n. That is, this it a worst case scenario.

[5] In other words, the statement can only be made with probability 0 or 1.

measure of our uncertainty about the inclusion of the unknown but fixed quantity μ in the interval (20, 30).

The two confidence interval formulas used in this chapter,

$$\bar{x} \ \pm \ z\left(\frac{\alpha}{2}\right) \cdot \frac{\sigma}{\sqrt{n}} \quad \text{and} \quad p' \ \pm \ z\left(\frac{\alpha}{2}\right) \cdot \sqrt{\frac{p' \cdot (1 - p')}{n}}$$

for estimating a population mean μ and a population proportion p should be used with caution. As with any statistical procedure, there are always some caveats.

- The data for calculating $\bar{x}$ or p' must come from a random sample. Think of the data as observations taken at random from a large population.

- For complex sampling situations these formulas are not adequate. For instance, for stratified sample designs or multistage designs the above formulas do not produce adequate results.

- If the data are collected in a non-random manner, there are no correct procedures or formulas that will produce the required result. We must recognize that neither powerful mathematics nor fancy formulas can substitute for an ill conceived sampling plan or unreliable data.

- If the underlying population is non-normal and the sample size is small, then the Central Limit Theorem becomes a gross approximation rather than a reliable result. It is true that the confidence interval relies only on the sampling distribution of $\overline{X}$ or P', which even for fairly small samples is fairly close to the Normal. The danger of small sample sizes is accentuated by the presence of extremely deviant data. Whenever possible, examine the individual observations carefully and proceed accordingly.

- The formula for the confidence interval about a population mean μ assumes that we have knowledge of the population standard deviation σ. This is totally unrealistic. After all, if we knew σ then we should also know μ and we don't need to bother with any confidence interval. The confidence interval formula $\bar{x} \ \pm \ z\left(\frac{\alpha}{2}\right) \cdot \frac{\sigma}{\sqrt{n}}$ has little practical use. The

  more realistic situation of not knowing σ will be covered in later chapters. However, familiarity with this formula will expedite future developments. Also, note that if the sample size is large, then s should be very close to σ and the formula $\bar{x} \ \pm \ z\left(\frac{\alpha}{2}\right) \cdot \frac{s}{\sqrt{n}}$ provides an adequate confidence interval for μ. However, in the binomial case, μ and σ are related so the estimate of p also gives an estimate of σ.

Chapter 8 Problems

1. Let $\bar{x} = 100$ and $\sigma = 3$.

    a. Find a confidence interval for μ if $1 - \alpha = 0.95$ and $n = 1$.

    b. Find a confidence interval for μ if $1 - \alpha = 0.95$ and $n = 36$.

    c. Why is the confidence interval in **b.** tighter than the one in **a.**?

2. What sample size is needed in order to estimate μ within 2 units? Let confidence level = 90% and $\sigma = 9$.

3. What sample size is needed in order to estimate μ within 1/2 of a standard deviation and with confidence level = 0.90? Hint: let $EB = \dfrac{\sigma}{2}$.

4. How confident are we that μ lies between $\bar{x} - 2.5$ and $\bar{x} + 2.5$ if $\sigma = 5$ and $n = 25$?

5. A poll indicates that 65 out of 100 voters favor a certain candidate. Let X = number of voters who favor the candidate. Then, for each voter, $X = 1$ if the voter prefers the candidate or $X = 0$ if the voter does not prefer the candidate. Assume $X \sim B(1,p)$. Hint: let $Y = \sum X$; thus, $Y \sim B(100,p)$ and proceed as in Example 5.

    a. What is the estimate of p? Hint: p = proportion of voters who favor the candidate.

    b. Find the 90% confidence interval for p.

    c. Find the 98% confidence interval for p.

    d. How confident are we that p is within 0.05 of the estimate?

6. The candidate from problem **5.** wishes to know how many voters must be sampled in order to be 95% confident of being within 0.05 of the true proportion of voters in favor.

7. The probability that a four is rolled on a six-sided die is p. Suppose the die is rolled 100 times and a four appears 30 times.

    a. Find the 90% confidence interval for p.

    b. How confident are we that p lies within the interval 0.3 ± 0.08?

    c. What sample size is needed to be 99% confident that a future sample p' will be within 0.09 units of the true population proportion p?

8. The lengths of 196 fish caught in Cayuga Lake has a mean of 14.5 inches. The population standard deviation for the length of fish is known to be 2 inches.

    a. Find the 90% confidence interval for the average length of the fish population at Cayuga lake.

    b. Find the 98% confidence interval for the average length of the fish population at Cayuga lake.

    c. How confident are we that the average length of the fish population is within 0.2 inches of the sample mean of 14.5 inches?

    d. How many fish must we sample if we wish to be 95% confident of being within 0.2 inches of the true mean?

9. The National Reading Assessment Test is annually given to 5th grade children throughout the United States. A random sample of 1600 children is taken. Their mean score was 300. Suppose we know that the standard deviation of all individual scores is $\sigma = 40$.

    a. Give a 95% confidence interval for the mean score in the population of all 5th graders.

    b. Suppose the same sample mean had come from a sample of 400 fifth graders. Give the 95% confidence interval for the population mean of all 5th graders.

    c. Then suppose that the same sample mean had come from a sample of 100 fifth graders. Give the 95% confidence interval for the population mean of all 5th graders.

    d. What are the error bounds for **a.**, **b.**, and **c.**? How does decreasing the sample size from 1600 to 400 to 100 affect the error bound for a fixed confidence level and fixed σ?

10. The last closely contested presidential election in the United States took place in 1976 when Gerald Ford, the incumbent, ran against Jimmy Carter. A Gallup poll taken days prior to election day in November 1976 showed that 51% of the sample intended to vote for Carter. The Gallup people announced that they were 95% confident this result was within 2 percentage points of the true proportion of all voters who favored Carter.

    a. Explain to someone who doesn't know statistics what it means to have "95% confidence" in the Gallup announcement.

    b. According to the results of the poll, Carter was leading. Yet, the Gallup organization said the election was "too close to call". Explain why.

    c. Upon hearing of the poll, President Ford summoned his chief statistician. "What is the probability that over half of the voters prefer Carter?", he asked. The statistician replied that this question can't be answered from the poll results. In fact, it doesn't even make sense to talk about such a probability. Explain why. (Needless to say, President Ford was in a foul mood).

11. How satisfied are pharmacists with the computer systems their pharmacies use in order to bill insurance companies for their clients' medication? A survey was sent to 600 pharmacy managers throughout the West Coast of the United States. In all, 144 managers responded. Two questions concerned their degree of satisfaction and ease of use with the computer systems and with the level of training they had received. The response was structured according to a 10 point scale, with 1 meaning "dissatisfied", 5 meaning "moderately satisfied", and 10 meaning "completely satisfied".

    a. What do you think is the population for this study? There are some major flaws in the data collection for this experiment. What are they? These flaws impact the credibility of any information derived from them.

    b. The average response for the question about satisfaction with ease of use was $\bar{x} = 6.5$. Give a 95% confidence interval for the population mean. Suppose we know that $\sigma = 3$.

    c. For the question about satisfaction with training, the average response was $\bar{x} = 5$. If $\sigma = 3$, give a 98% confidence interval for the population mean.

    d. The distribution of responses for any of the questions in the survey is certainly not Normal since they take only integer values in the interval [1,10]. However, the use of the Normal distribution in calculating the confidence intervals is correct. Explain why.

12. Barry Bonds, arguably the best active left fielder in the game of baseball, had a torrid hitting start during the 1994 baseball season. After 50 games and 160 at bat, his batting average was 0.425. Suppose that in his previous years in the major leagues Bonds had averaged 0.315.

    a. Based on his lifetime average of 0.315, and 500 at bat during a full season, what is the highest batting average Bonds is expected to achieve in a full season? Use a confidence level of 95%.

    b. Based on his 1994 batting average after 160 at bat, what is the lowest batting average Bonds is expected to achieve assuming 500 at bat during a full season? Use a confidence level of 95%.

    c. Compare the answers from **a.** and **b.** above. What can you conclude about the potential of Bonds as a hitter?

    d. An avid baseball fan argues that Bond is the next most likely ball player to hit for a batting average of over 0.400 in a season. This feat was last accomplished in 1941 when Ted Williams hit 0.406. What would you say to this fan?

13. Suppose that $\bar{x} = 12.3$, $s = 5.3$ and $n = 50$.

    a. Find a 90% confidence interval for μ

    b. What is the confidence that μ is within the interval 12.3 ± 1.0?

    c. What sample size is needed to be 99% confident that a future sample $\bar{x}$ will be within 1 unit of the true μ?

14. The probability that a four is rolled on a four-sided tetrahedron is p. The tetrahedron is rolled 100 times. A four appears 28 times.

    a. Find a 90% confidence interval for p

    b. What is the confidence that p is within the interval 0.28 ± 0.09?

    c. What sample size is needed to be 99% confident that a future sample p' will be within 0.09 units of the true population proportion p?

15. A poll shows that 63 voters in a sample of 94 favor proposition A. Let X be the random variable that describes whether a voter prefers A. If $X = 1$ they prefer A. If $X = 0$ they do not. Assume $X \sim B(1, p)$.

    a. What is the estimate of p? (the proportion of voters who prefer A).

    b. Find the 90 percent confidence interval for p

    c. Find the 98 percent confidence interval for p

    d. How confident are we that p is within 0.05 of the estimate?

    e. How many voters must we poll if we wish to be 95% confident of being within 0.05 of the true proportion who prefer A?

Chapter 9

Testing Statistical Hypotheses and Inference as Decision

9.1 What is a statistical test?

Confidence intervals are one of the two most common types of statistical inference. We have seen that confidence intervals are most useful when we wish to estimate a population parameter. The second type of inference has a different purpose: *to assess the evidence provided by the sample data in favor of some belief or claim about the population.* The basis for statistical testing rests on asking what would happen if we take repeated samples from the population. In this sense, the Central Limit Theorem again plays a large role in these developments. However, keep in mind that just like with confidence intervals, we look at data from one sample and not from the entire sample distribution.

Example 1

Red wines from the great producing wine regions of the world are supposed to get better with age. Storage conditions are key to how well a wine ages.[1] Wine collectors and wholesalers regularly test the stock in their possession by having randomly selected experts rate, by tasting, the condition of the wine. For simplicity, a scale between –2 and 2 is used to indicate that the wine is deteriorating (negative) or the wine is healthy and aging well (positive). Here are the scores, for a recent tasting of a particular wine, by 25 random raters at the cellar of a large New York wholesaler: 2, –1, 1, 2, 2, 2, –2, 1, –1, 1, 1, –1, 0, 0, 2, 2, 2, –1, 1, 1, –2, 0, 1, –2, 1. Do the data present strong and convincing evidence that the wine is aging well?

Discussion

It will make sense to compute the average score and proceed from there. That is, if X = score, then $\bar{x} = \dfrac{(-2)\cdot 3 + (-1)\cdot 4 + 0\cdot 3 + 1\cdot 8 + 2\cdot 7}{25} = \dfrac{12}{25} = 0.48$. The average rating is positive, even though uncomfortably close to zero (i.e., zero meaning no improvement in the wine since it was originally stored). A statistical test asks: Does the sample average of 0.48 reflect a true no improvement?; or, Is it common to get an average score of 0.48 just by chance? These are two different questions. Whatever conclusion we draw from the data it is always regarding the corresponding population parameter. In this

---

[1] For example, a temperature between 55 and 70 degrees Fahrenheit is considered optimal.

case, the population parameter of interest is μ, where μ is the average rating that a very large number of expert tasters would give the wine. The 25 expert tasters are a random sample from the population of all such experts. Every statistical test has two hypotheses: the *null hypothesis* and the *alternative hypothesis*. The null hypothesis always states that there is no change or no effect in the population. If in reality, the null is true, the sample result is pure luck. In this example, the null hypothesis assumes that there is no change in the condition of the wine. We state this in terms of the **population parameter** as:

$$H_0: \mu = 0.$$

The symbol H_0 is pronounced to sound like "H not". The alternative hypothesis, written H_a, is almost always the opposite of the null hypothesis and reflects the effect we want to establish. In this case, since we are hoping that the wine is aging well, we want to establish an average rating larger than zero. Thus, we write:

$$H_a: \mu > 0.$$

We now reason as follows:

- Let's assume that the null hypothesis is the true state of things; that is, on average, there is no change in the condition of the wine.

- *Is the sample statistic, $\bar{x} = 0.48$, sufficiently large under the assumption of the null?* In other words, is 0.48 significantly different from zero in order to claim that the wine is aging well? If it is, then we have statistical evidence against the null and we will tend to favor the alternative.

To answer the above question in statistical terms, we appeal to our knowledge of the sampling distribution of sample means (i.e., our old friend – the CLT) under the assumption stated in the null hypothesis. That is, under H_0, $\bar{X} \sim N\left(0, \dfrac{\sigma^2}{25}\right)$ where σ is the standard deviation of the ratings for the population of all experts. Let's assume that from past experience and after keeping track of many such ratings, we know $\sigma = 1$. So, we may write, $\bar{X} \sim N\left(0, \dfrac{1}{25}\right)$. We can now establish if any sample value of $\bar{x}$ is small or large by locating it on the distribution of $\bar{X}$ and asking, How far is the obtained $\bar{x}$ from the center of its distribution (i.e., from zero)? The graph below illustrates this.

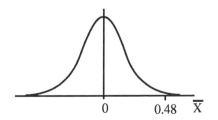

Distance from the mean is established in terms of the area in the tail of the distribution created by the sample statistic. That is, we wish to compute the area to the right of 0.48. In symbols, we want to find:[2]

$$P\left(\overline{X} > 0.48 \mid \mu_o = 0\right).$$

This is not a new problem, and we can easily dispose of it by writing it in terms of Z and using the standard normal table. That is,

$$P\left(\overline{X} > 0.48 \mid \mu_o = 0\right) = P\left(Z > \frac{0.48 - 0}{\frac{1}{5}}\right) = P(Z > 2.4) = 0.0082.$$

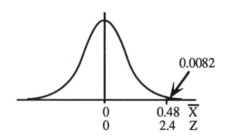

The above probability is called a *p-value* and it represents the probability of a result at least as far out as the result we obtained from our sample. The smaller this probability the more surprising the sample result and the stronger the evidence against the null hypothesis. Think of it this way: if the true mean of the distribution we are dealing with is 0 (as assumed by the null), how likely is it that a sample of size 25 will yield a mean of 0.48? Our answer, according to the above p-value is: not very likely (in fact, 82 in 10,000). So, we take the chance that this particular sample is not one of those 82's and we favor the alternative. Thus, the wholesaler will feel quite happy about the results of the tasting, concluding that the wine is aging as planned.

How small should a p-value be in order to claim that there is evidence against the null? There is no set rule. In the social sciences and related disciplines, the rule of thumb is 0.05. The authors prefer 0.10, but this is subjective and it really depends on the situation. For instance, if the hypothesis test involves the introduction of a new pharmaceutical drug to the market place, and this new drug is competing against a well established product, then we would probably require a very small p-value, probably 0.01 or perhaps even smaller, before favoring the alternative hypothesis. A test result with a small p-value, sufficiently small to cast serious doubt on the null hypothesis, is said to be **statistically significant**. This is the

---

[2] This is a conditional probability based on the assumption that the null is valid. The symbol μ_o is used to indicate the value of the population parameter used in the null. Likewise, the symbol μ_a will indicate the value of the population parameter as it pertains to the alternative hypothesis.

statisticians way of saying that pure chance or luck alone will not likely produce such result.

Here is a summary of the logic involved in any statistical test:

- Describe what is being tested in terms of a *population parameter* (for example: μ, p, σ, never $\bar{x}$, p', s).
- Write the null hypothesis representing the statement that there is no difference or effect on whatever we are testing. Thus, equality always belongs in the null.
- From the sample data, calculate the statistic corresponding to the parameter that is being tested and ask, How far is the value of this statistic from the value of the parameter stated in the null? To answer this question, determine the distribution of the random variable associated with the statistic, and compute the area in the tail of the distribution (either tail or both may be involved, depending on the situation and the way the alternative is set up).[3] If this area is small (i.e., small p-value) then we tend to favor the alternative over the null.
- Clearly state which hypothesis is being favored and write a conclusion in terms of the parameter being tested and within the context of the situation.

Surprisingly enough, the above outline applies to many different types of statistical hypotheses tests. It ignores some of the fine points (these will come later in the chapter), but it sets up a template from which we can formulate these types of problems. It will serve you well to make sure you understand what they say, especially in light of Example 1.

We now give an example of a two-sided hypothesis test following the above guidelines in very compact form.

Example 2

At a well known private university, the final exam for the Elementary Statistics course is written by the members of the Statistics Department, regardless of whether or not they are teaching a class during the current term. Those faculty members teaching the course are praised or reprimanded according to the average score on the final exam for their particular section of Statistics. The department believes that all sections of Elementary Statistics should score, on average, 70 on the final exam. It is known that the standard

---

[3] If only the right of left tail is involved we say the test is *one-sided*. If both tails are involved we say the test is *two-sided*.

deviation of scores on the final exam, σ, is 8. The 25 students who took the final exam in Professor Jenkins class averaged 68. Is this sufficient evidence to take action on Professor Jenkins?

Solution

- Formulate the null and alternative hypotheses:

  H_0: $\mu = 70$

  H_a: $\mu \neq 70$ (this is a two-sided test since there are consequences on both sides of the mean)

- Let X = scores on final exam and $\overline{X}$ = average score on final exam. Note that under H_0,

  $\overline{X} \sim N\left(70, \dfrac{64}{25}\right)$. We draw the graph of this distribution marking 68 and 72 on the $\overline{X}$

  scale (this is a two-sided situation). The p-value is the area in both tails. That is, we want

  the area to the left of 68 and to the right of 72.

Thus, the p-value is given by:

$$P\left(\overline{X} < 68 \text{ or } \overline{X} > 72 \mid \mu_o = 70\right) = P\left(\overline{X} < 68 \mid \mu_o = 70\right) + P\left(\overline{X} > 72 \mid \mu_o = 70\right) \Rightarrow$$

$$P\left(Z < \dfrac{68 - 70}{\frac{8}{5}}\right) + P\left(Z > \dfrac{72 - 70}{\frac{8}{5}}\right) = P(Z < -1.25) + P(Z > 1.25) = 2 \cdot 0.1056 = 0.2112.$$

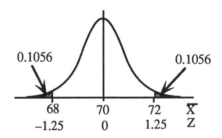

- A p-value of 0.2112 is considered large by almost any standard. That is, the area in the tails is not all that small. This tells us that 68 is not different from 70. Thus, we continue to favor the null hypothesis that the mean score for the students in Professor Jenkins class is not different from 70 and take no action against or in favor of the professor.

We close this section by working through an example of how to test a population proportion. In particular, we refer to problem 10, Chapter 8, regarding the 1976 election between Ford and Carter.

Example 3

In response to President Ford's question about whether or not the majority of voters favor Carter, a test of hypotheses is decided to be the best way to address the issue.

Solution

H_0: $p = 0.50$

H_a: $p > 0.50$ (one-sided. Indicates majority of voters in favor.)

Suppose 1500 voters were sampled and 765 said they favor Carter. That is, $p' = \dfrac{765}{1500} = 0.51$.

The random variable of interest and its distribution are given by: $P' \sim N\left(0.50, \dfrac{0.50 \cdot (1 - 0.50)}{1500}\right)$.

We compute the p-value. That is, we wish to compute the area under the Normal curve to the right of $p' = 0.51$. The graph below illustrates the entire situation.

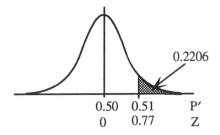

$$\text{p-value} = P(p' > 0.51 \mid p = 0.50) = P\left(Z > \dfrac{0.51 - 0.50}{\sqrt{\dfrac{0.50 \cdot (1 - 0.50)}{1500}}}\right) = P(Z > 0.7746).$$

From the standard normal table, rounding the z value to 0.77, we obtain,

$$\text{p-value} = P(Z > 0.77) = 0.2206.$$

With a p-value of 0.2206, there isn't sufficient evidence against the null hypothesis. We conclude that the percentage of voters who favor Carter does not appear to be larger than 50%.

9.2   Additional details and related terminology

Stating the null and alternative hypotheses

The most important thing to remember is that hypotheses always refer to some population and never to a particular outcome or statistic. Thus, *always state H_o and H_a in terms of population parameters*. In section **9.1** we tested hypotheses dealing with μ and p. We will test other parameters and related statements about populations in later chapters.

It is not always easy to decide whether H_a should be one-sided or two-sided. In Example **1**, the alternative is one-sided because we hope for the wine to age well (i.e., a positive average rating). In Example **2**, we wish to ascertain if there is a difference between the professor's class average on the final exam and the department's belief on what that average should be. Thus, we must consider both tails (left and right of 70).

Hypotheses must be formulated prior to looking at the data; otherwise, consciously or not, we will invariably formulate the hypotheses to fit the data. This is cheating. Statisticians do not use the word "cheating" as such, instead, the phrase "data mining" is most commonly accepted. In general, if there is no clear sense of direction (i.e., < or >), the safest way to proceed is to use a two-sided alternative.

The choice of hypotheses in Example **1**,

$$H_0: \mu = 0$$
$$H_a: \mu > 0$$

could have easily been rewritten as:

$$H_0: \mu \le 0$$
$$H_a: \mu > 0$$

without impacting the rest of the test procedure. The reason for this is that the effect the wine wholesaler was hoping for was to have a positive average rating. That is, using = or $\le$ in the null doesn't change the alternative. The latter set of hypotheses is mathematically impeccable. However, both sets of hypotheses are statistically equivalent.

All of that having been said, it might be easier to write a set of hypotheses by first writing the alternative hypothesis. Remember that, in general, H_a expresses whatever we hope to find evidence for. After H_a has been formulated, set H_0 as the statement that the hoped for effect does not exist. That is, H_0 represents the hypothesis of *no difference*.

Statistical significance and the p-value

Tests of significance use the information contained in the data in the form of a *test statistic*. In the three examples of section **9.1**, the test statistics were $\bar{x}$ and p'. These statistics estimated the value of the parameter that appeared in the hypotheses (i.e., μ and p). Since the random variables associated with both of these statistics (i.e., $\bar{X}$ and P') are distributed normally, we ended up computing a value of z in order to obtain the corresponding tail probability.[4] This tail probability is precisely the *p-value*.

The p-value is computed under the assumption that the null hypothesis is true. It is the probability that the sample or test statistic would take a value as large/small or larger/smaller than the one observed. If the p-value is small then there is very strong evidence against the null and we will be inclined to favor the alternative.

Sometimes it is customary to fix, in advance, the probability of the evidence against the null. That is, we compare the p-value to whatever pre-conceived probability we consider to be decisive. This pre-conceived probability is called the *significance level* of the test. We will denote it as α.[5] For instance, if we choose $\alpha = 0.05$ we are in fact requiring evidence against the null that will only occur 5% of the time *if* the null is true. In this sense, smaller values of α make it even more difficult to mount evidence against a true null. When comparing a p-value with a pre-conceived value of α, we adhere to the following rule:

if the p-value is as small or smaller than α, we claim that the data are statistically significant at level α.

Note that the word "significant" in the statistical sense means that it is not likely to happen by chance alone. Thus, when we claim that there is evidence to support the alternative, we are inferring that the observations are not likely to have occurred if the null would have been true. In fact, the opposite seems to be the case. That is, the observations are likely to have occurred if the alternative is true.

Example 4

Suppose we are testing the following hypotheses:

$$H_0: \mu = 10 \quad \text{vs.} \quad H_a: \mu > 10.$$

[4] This computed value of z is also often called a *test statistic*. In reality, it is the *standardized* value of the test statistic.

[5] We have used α in previous chapters to denote tail probabilities. This is the spirit in which we use it here as well. Think of the significance level of the test as a tail probability.

The sample data produce a p-value = 0.03 and the test is conducted using a pre-conceived $\alpha = 0.01$. What is the conclusion?

Solution

Since p-value > α (i.e., 0.03 > 0.01), we continue to favor the null hypothesis. That is, there isn't sufficient evidence to claim that the population mean is larger than 10.

Example 5

Same as Example **4.**, but let $\alpha = 0.05$.

Solution

Since p-value < α (i.e., 0.03 < 0.05), we tend not to favor the null hypothesis that the population mean is not larger than 10. Thus, we are inclined to believe that the population mean seems to exceed 10. [Note: this says nothing about what the "new" population mean might be!][6]

In Examples **4.** and **5.** above, how is it possible to favor the null and then favor the alternative for the same p-value? The answer lies on the pre-conceived α. Evidence in favor of the null says nothing as to the truth of the population parameter being tested. We are making statements based on sample observations and couched in probabilistic terms. All we are saying is that relative to a certain probability (the pre-conceived α), it is either likely or not likely to have obtained the observed data *if* the null hypothesis is true. Be aware that favoring a null *does not make the null true*. Likewise, favoring the alternative *doesn't make the alternative true*.

9.3 Testing hypotheses with fixed significance

If a hypotheses test is to be conducted strictly on the basis of a fixed, pre-conceived α, then there is little need to compute a p-value. This is far from ideal, but it expedites matters considerably.

The pre-conceived α defines a critical value (if the alternative is one-sided) or critical values (if the alternative is two-sided) so that if the test statistic falls in the interval beyond the critical value(s) the data

---

[6] All we know is that it is not 10 or less. In fact, it could be 11, 12.5, or any real number larger than 10.

are statistically significant at level α and we would favor the alternative.[7]

Examples **6, 7** and **8** below will reference the hypotheses test situations in Examples **1, 2** and **3** of section **9.1**.

Example 6

We refer to the situation described in Example **1**, with fixed significance $\alpha = 0.05$.

Solution

In Example 1, we tested: $H_0: \mu = 0$ vs. $H_a: \mu > 0$. This represents a one-sided test to the right of the hypothesized mean of 0. We set the area in the right tail to match the pre-set α of 0.05. The graph below illustrates what is going on.

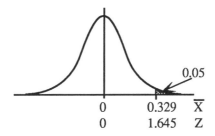

$$
\begin{array}{ccc}
0 & 0.329 & \overline{X} \\
0 & 1.645 & Z
\end{array}
$$

The critical value corresponding to an area to its right of 0.05 is found via the z-score formula. We will denote this value by $\overline{X}_c$. It is a value in the range of $\overline{X}$. Since $\overline{X} \sim N(0, \frac{1}{25})$ and $z(0.05) = 1.645$, we have:

$$1.645 = \frac{\overline{X}_c - 0}{\frac{1}{5}} \Rightarrow \overline{X}_c = 1.645 \cdot \frac{1}{5} + 0 \Rightarrow \overline{X}_c = 0.329.$$

We now compare the critical value obtained from the pre-set α to the test statistic from the data. Since $0.48 > 0.329$, the test statistic falls in the critical region. Thus, the conclusion is to favor the alternative that the wine is aging well.

---

[7] This interval defines the region where there is evidence against the null. This is called the critical region.

Example 7

For the situation of Example **2**, set $\alpha = 0.05$.

Solution

In Example 2, we tested: $H_0: \mu = 70$ vs. $H_a: \mu \neq 70$. This is a two-sided test. The pre-conceived area of 0.05 is split in two equal parts and we allocate 0.025 area to each, the left and right tails. Note that $z(0.025) = 1.96$ and $z(0.975) = -1.96$. We now find the left and right tail critical values in terms of $\overline{X}$ via the z-score formula. Recall that $\overline{X} \sim N(70, \frac{64}{25})$.

left critical value: $-1.96 = \dfrac{\overline{x}_{lc} - 70}{\frac{8}{5}} \Rightarrow \overline{x}_{lc} = -1.96 \cdot \frac{8}{5} + 70 \Rightarrow \overline{x}_{lc} = 66.864$.

right critical value: $1.96 = \dfrac{\overline{x}_{rc} - 70}{\frac{8}{5}} \Rightarrow \overline{x}_{rc} = 1.96 \cdot \frac{8}{5} + 70 \Rightarrow \overline{x}_{rc} = 73.136$.

Thus, since the test statistic, $\overline{x} = 68$, falls within the interval (66.864, 73.136), we favor the null hypothesis and no action is taken against or in favor of Professor Jenkins.

Note that setting up a two-sided hypotheses test at a pre-set significance level is equivalent to computing a confidence interval. If the observed test statistic lies in the computed interval then there is no evidence against the null. The graph below illustrates the entire situation.

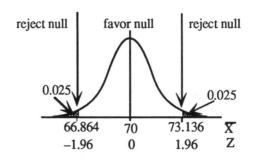

Example 8

Let pre-set $\alpha = 0.01$ for the situation of Example **3**.

Solution

The hypotheses are: $H_0: p = 0.50$ (or $p \leq 0.50$) vs. $H_a: p > 0.50$. This is a one-sided test to the right of the hypothesized $p = 0.50$. Set up the right tail area $= 0.01$. That is, $z(0.01) = 2.33$.

Note that $P' \sim N\left(0.50, \dfrac{0.50 \cdot (1 - 0.50)}{1500}\right)$. We compute the right tail critical value, p'_{rc}, using the z-score formula as follows:

$$2.33 = \frac{p'_{rc} - 0.5}{\sqrt{\dfrac{0.5 \cdot (1 - 0.5)}{1500}}} \Rightarrow p'_{rc} = 2.33 \cdot \sqrt{\frac{0.5 \cdot (1 - 0.5)}{1500}} + 0.5 = 0.5301.$$

Thus, since the test statistic does not fall in the critical region (i.e., $0.51 < 0.5301$), we conclude that there is no sufficient evidence to claim that the majority of the voters favor Carter. The graph below illustrates the situation.

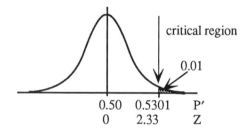

9.4   Inference as decision: Type I and Type II errors

We have seen that tests of significance assess the strength of the evidence against the null hypothesis. This evidence is measured by computing the p-value. The p-value is computed using the observed data under the assumption that the null is true. The role of the alternative hypothesis is to specify what outcomes mount evidence against the null hypothesis.

The introduction of a pre-set level of significance, α, points towards another way of thinking. We have been careful to point out that if the result of a hypothesis test is significant at level α, we would then tend to favor the alternative. A stronger way of saying this is: *reject H_0 in favor of H_a*. The change of view from favoring or not favoring the null hypothesis to rejecting the null hypothesis has serious consequences. For instance, many statisticians believe that *making decisions such as reject or favor better be left to the user.* After all, only the user, with his/her specialized problem and/or data, is in a position to judge the statistical evidence.

Perhaps the greatest drawback in making reject/favor decisions is the fact that decisions sometimes are wrong. That is, we may reject a null hypothesis when in fact the null is true. Likewise, we may favor a null hypothesis when the alternative is true. These are the two types of incorrect decisions. Of course, we may make a correct decision. That is, we may favor a true null or we may reject an invalid one. To differentiate among these errors and decisions we summarize all the possibilities in the table below.

Table1
Truth about the state of nature (population)

		H_0 is true	H_0 is false
Decision based on sample data	Reject H_0	Type I error $\alpha = P(I)$	Correct decision type B
	Favor H_0	Correct decision type A	Type II error $\beta = P(II)$

Armed with the above table, we can now judge the performance of a test by the probability of the Type I and Type II errors. That is, the goal is to carry out tests that would minimize both of these probabilities. As an added bonus, minimizing the error probabilities maximizes the probability of making a correct decision.

The Type I error probability

This is the probability of rejecting a true null hypothesis. We write:

Type I error probability = P(rejecting H_0 / H_0 is true).

Recall that we reject the null only if the test statistic falls in the critical region. The critical region is defined by the pre-set level of significance, α. Thus, it shouldn't come as a surprise that:

$$\alpha = \textbf{Type I error probability.}$$

If a hypothesis test is conducted without a pre-set significance level, then the p-value serves as a gauge on the magnitude of the Type I error probability. Think of the p-value as a *computed* α, instead of a pre-conceived one. This is the reason why small p-values cast suspicion on the null hypothesis.[8]

---

[8] A small p-value, meaning a small computed α, means that the chances of rejecting a valid null are small.

Example 9

A medical clinic claims that the mean systolic blood pressure for executives making over $250,000 a year is greater than the national mean of 128 millimeters of mercury (mm Hg). The study consisted of a random sample of 25 executives with mean blood pressure = 134. It is known that the standard deviation for the systolic blood pressure of adults in the United States is 15. Conduct a statistical test at the 5% level of significance.

Solution

$H_0: \mu = 128$ vs. $H_a: \mu > 128$ (one-sided to the right of the mean)

$\overline{X}$ = mean blood pressure $\Rightarrow \overline{X} \sim N\left(128, \dfrac{225}{25}\right)$. Pre-set $\alpha = 0.05 \Rightarrow z(0.05) = 1.645$. We now compute the z-score from the data and compare to the critical value of 1.645. Thus,

$$\text{test statistic} = z = \frac{134 - 128}{\sqrt{\dfrac{225}{25}}} = 2.$$

Since 2 > 1.645, there is evidence against the null at the 0.05 significance level.

Decision: reject H_0.

Conclusion: The data indicate that the mean systolic blood pressure of executives making over $250,000 a year exceeds the national mean of 128 mm Hg. The significance level of the test is 0.05.

Comments. Note that a decision and conclusion are now part of the test procedure. Also, note that computing the p-value was not necessary in order to make a decision. In retrospect, the p-value must be smaller than 0.05 (why?). Since we don't know how much smaller, though, we can't readily tell what would happen if the significance level were to be set smaller than 0.05. However, if a p-value is first computed, then it is easy to make decisions based on any level of significance. We compute the p-value in order to illustrate.

$$\text{p-value} = P\left(\overline{X} > 134 \mid \mu_0 = 128\right) = P(Z > 2) = 0.0228.$$

Thus, reject H_0 for any pre-conceived $\alpha > 0.0228$ and favor H_0 otherwise.

The Type II error probability and Power of a Test

A Type II error is made when favoring an invalid null hypothesis. It is the probability of believing the value of the parameter specified in the null when in reality the parameter takes a value specified in the alternative. This probability, which we will call β (pronounced "beta"), is computed for a particular alternative value of the parameter. The magnitude of this probability depends on the following three quantities: the specific alternative value of the parameter, the significance level of the test, and the sample size. The examples below will illustrate.

Example 10

Suppose an antique coin, from the treasures of the Atocha shipwreck, is produced. We wish to determine if this coin is fair.[9]

Discussion

A set of plausible hypotheses is:

$$H_0: p = 0.50 \text{ (coin is fair)}$$
$$H_a: p \neq 0.50 \text{ (coin is not fair. This is a two-sided test.)}$$

One way of conducting this test is to take the coin, flip it a set number of times, and count the number of heads/tails that come up. Let X = number of heads that come up. Suppose we agree to flip the coin n = 10 times. Note that, under the null, $X \sim B(10, 0.50)$. Now, prior to actually carrying out the 10 flips, we must decide on the number of heads we must observe in order to favor the null. Let's say that we agree on favoring the null if: $X = 3,4,5,6,7$. Such choice of region is subjective. Of course, you realize that by setting the above region we have also set the significance level of the test, α.[10] We need to find the value of α. From the Binomial table:

$$\alpha = P(\text{rejecting null} \mid \text{null is true}) = P(X = 0,1,2,8,9,10 \mid p = 0.50) = 0.1093.$$

Thus, we have set $\alpha = 0.1093$ and we agree this is a significance level we can tolerate. We now set up the computation of β as follows:

$$\beta = P(\text{favoring null} \mid \text{null is not valid}) = P(X = 3,4,5,6,7, \mid p \neq 0.50).$$

---

[9] The only reason for conducting such a test is because we suspect the coin is not fair.
[10] We have seen that α is subjective, albeit seldom larger than 0.10.

We realize that we must choose an alternate value of the parameter p in order to carry out the above computation . The alternative hypothesis says that p is not 0.50, but *it doesn't say* what p could or should be. It is up to you to decide what value p would take. This value could be agreed upon before conducting the experiment. Let's say we agree on p = 0.70. We use the Binomial table again, but note that we are now working with the distribution of X under the alternative hypothesis. That is, X ~ B(10, 0.70). Then,

$$\beta = P(X = 3,4,5,6,7 \mid p = 0.70) = 0.6156.$$

We think you would agree that conducting any hypotheses test when the probability of making a Type II error is as high as 0.6156 is detrimental to your statistical well being. We ask, how can we reduce β? One way is to try a different alternative value of p. Suppose we agree on p = 0.90 [i.e., X ~ B(10, 0.90)]. Then,

$$\beta = P(X = 3,4,5,6,7 \mid p = 0.90) = 0.059.$$

Aha! β has now been dramatically reduced. However, suppose we wish to reduce β and keep the alternative p = 0.70. What else can we do? We are now down to two choices. One such choice is to change the region where the null is favored. Suppose we agree on favoring the null if X = 4,5,6. This will certainly reduce β, but now we are faced with the problem of having a significance level higher than the previous 0.1093. That is,

$$\alpha = P[X = 0,1,2,3,7,8,9,10 \mid p = 0.50] = 0.3438 \quad \text{and} \quad \beta = P(X = 4,5,6 \mid p = 0.70) = 0.3398.$$

This tells us that increasing α reduces β and viceversa. It is not as hopeless as it seems. However, it does indicate that there are trade-offs to be made. For instance, one way to avoid this dilemma is to set up the hypotheses test so that only the Type I error is of any consequence.[11] We then control the magnitude of the Type I error by choosing a small significance level.

The other available course of action is to increase the sample size. For this example, that implies we will flip the coin more than 10 times. How does that reduce β? The reduction in β is due to the Law of Large Numbers. That is, the ratio of the number of heads to the number of total flips will approach the true value p of the coin, making it very unlikely to accept an hypothesis with an alternative value of p different from the true one.

---

[11] Here is one such example. H_0: victim at the site of an accident is alive vs H_a: victim at the site of an accident is dead. The consequences of committing a Type I error are drastic (i.e., victim is alive but is thought to be dead), while the consequences of committing a Type II error are trivial (i.e., victim is thought to be alive but in reality the victim is dead).

We illustrate the computation of β in the case of an hypothesis test about a population mean from an application in the field of acceptance sampling.

Example 11

The average strength of a thin cable is supposed to be 25 psi (pounds/square inch). The strength varies with standard deviation $\sigma = 1$ psi. When a lot of cables arrives, the buyer takes a random sample of 16 cables and tests them. The buyer rejects the lot if the mean strength for the sample is significantly different from 25 psi at the 5% significance level.

Discussion

An appropriate set of hypotheses is:

$$H_o: \mu = 25$$
$$H_a: \mu \neq 25 \text{ (two-sided)}$$

Since $\alpha = 0.05$, then $z(0.025) = 1.96$. We find the rejection region by calculating the left and right critical values for $\overline{X}$. We note that, under H_o, $\overline{X} \sim N\left(25, \frac{1}{16}\right)$. Then,

$$\text{left critical value: } -1.96 = \frac{\overline{x}_{lc} - 25}{\frac{1}{4}} \Rightarrow \overline{x}_{lc} = 24.51,$$

$$\text{right critical value: } 1.96 = \frac{\overline{x}_{rc} - 25}{\frac{1}{4}} \Rightarrow \overline{x}_{rc} = 25.49.$$

Thus, at the 5% significance level, we accept the lot if the sample of 16 cables yields a mean strength falling in the interval (24.51, 25.49). Suppose that the buyer and the manufacturer agree to reject the lot if the actual mean strength of the population of cables is 24.7 psi. That is, $\mu_a = 24.7$. Thus, a Type II error would be made if the lot is accepted when in fact the actual mean strength of the population of cables is 24.7. The graphs below illustrate this situation.

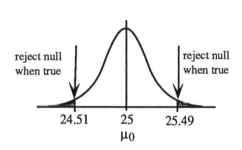
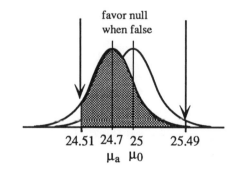

We now proceed to compute β under the assumption that $\mu_a = 24.7$. That is, $\overline{X} \sim N\left(24.7, \frac{1}{16}\right)$. Thus,

$$\beta = P(\text{Type II error}) = P\left(24.51 < \overline{X} < 25.49 \mid \mu_a = 24.7\right) = P\left(\frac{24.51 - 24.7}{\frac{1}{4}} < Z < \frac{25.49 - 24.7}{\frac{1}{4}}\right) \Rightarrow$$

$$\beta = P(-0.76 < Z < 3.16) = P(Z < 3.16) - P(Z < -0.76) = 0.9990 - 0.2236 = 0.7754.$$

This test will then accept approximately 78% of the lots when in fact the mean strength of the cables is 24.7 psi and will reject 5% of the lots when the mean strength is 25 psi.

Calculations of error probabilities are helpful in deciding when a particular hypotheses test is agreeable to the parties involved. In this sense, there are no absolutes. What may be agreeable to one party may not be agreeable to another. Allowing individuals to set their own error tolerances (i.e., α and β) is preferable to a blanket "reject H_0" type statement.

A high Type II error probability for a particular alternative value of the parameter says that the test is not sensitive enough to detect that alternative value.[12] In this light, calculating β is always useful even if a p-value approach, as opposed to a decision approach, is preferred.

The probability that a particular alternative value of the parameter will reject an invalid H_0, at a particular α level of significance, is called the **power** of the test against the alternative. The power of the test is the probability of making a correct decision Type B (refer to Table 1). That is,

power of a test = 1 − β.

To calculate the power of a test procedure, for a given α, and a given alternative, just compute β and subtract that value from 1. Statisticians favor tests with high power. As you have already noticed, this implies a low β. In practicality, tests with both, low α and β, are preferred in most cases.[13]

---

[12] It is very tedious to calculate β for a large set of values of the alternative. Computers are capable of simultaneuosly computing β for many alternative values of the parameter. This information is usually displayed in the form of a plot called an Operating Characteristic Curve (OCC).

[13] The mathematics has been worked out so as to find the necessary sample size in order to conduct a test for a pre-set α and β. In this sense, the experimenter chooses α and β ahead of time and then secures a sample of the indicated size n. This is beyond the scope of our discussion, but you should be aware of it.

Chapter 9

9.5 Practical significance vs. statistical significance

Statistical significance is what the user wishes to establish. It means that whatever effect was being sought has been found. When the null hypothesis of no difference can be rejected at the usual small α levels of 0.05 or 0.01, there is strong and convincing evidence against it. However, the effect detected might be very small, perhaps even meaningless. Detecting small effects may be theoretically pleasing but it might be insignificant in practice. After all, whenever very large sample sizes are used, *any* null hypothesis, at *any* level of significance will be rejected. Within this scenario, a decision to reject the null is not only meaningless but also futile.

The cure for placing too much credence in making decisions is to pay closer attention to the p-value. Looking at the data, before rushing through the actual hypotheses test itself, will always prove beneficial. How practically important is the effect we are seeking? Is the effect detectable without the need to carry out a hypotheses test? These are questions that must be answered before spending time and resources in conducting a full scale hypotheses test.

Here is an example of what we mean by practical significance.

Example 12

It is known that the average SAT score for high school seniors planning to attend college is 950 with $\sigma = 100$. Recent studies have shown that tutoring services, specializing in preparing the students for the SAT, cause an average increase on SAT scores of 10 points. Admissions personnel at all colleges will agree that an average increase of 10 points on the SAT has no impact on any one student being denied admission. However, this 10 point change can be statistically significant. To show how this can be, we will compute the p-value for each of the following situations for testing H_0: $\mu = 950$ vs. H_a: $\mu > 950$. Note that $\overline{X} \sim N\left(950, \frac{10000}{n}\right)$.

    a. The tutoring service reports that the mean SAT score for $n = 100$ students coached this year was 960.

    b. The tutoring service reports that the mean SAT score for $n = 1000$ students coached this year was 960.

Here is the p-value computation for each of the above situations:

a. p-value $= P\left(\overline{X} > 960 \mid \mu = 950\right) = P\left(Z > \dfrac{960 - 950}{\dfrac{100}{10}}\right) = P(Z > 1) = 0.1587.$

b. p-value $= P\left(\overline{X} > 960 \mid \mu = 950\right) = P\left(Z > \dfrac{960 - 950}{\dfrac{100}{\sqrt{1000}}}\right) = P(Z > 3.16) = 0.001.$

The 0.001 p-value obtained when n = 1000 is statistically significant; yet, it has no practical impact.

9.6 Summary

To test statistical hypotheses we need to formulate a null and an alternative hypotheses in terms of population parameters. In this chapter we have seen how to test a population mean and a population proportion. Later on, we will also test a population variance and also conduct similar tests about multiple parameters.

The distinction between the p-value approach and decision rules is subtle, yet, important. In a test of significance we focus on the null hypothesis and on the p-value. The p-value is computed using sample data. The goal is to measure the strength of the sample evidence against the null. If the p-value is considered small then we say that there is sufficient evidence against the null. Concluding that there is sufficient evidence against the null doesn't necessarily make the null false. Likewise, concluding that there is no sufficient evidence against the null doesn't make the null true.

If a significance level α is set in advance, then we make decisions about the null based on this significance level. If we think of the problem as a decision one, we now write decisions and conclusions stating whether or not we reject H_0. When making decisions, the focus shifts from p-value to the Type I and Type II error probabilities. We are forced to choose between the two hypotheses, H_0 or H_a, and cannot remain in neutral ground or make a case for "insufficient evidence".

On a historical note, testing hypotheses, as we know it today, has its roots at the University of California, Berkeley (UCB). The philosophical foundations were set by R. A. Fisher[14] but the mathematical formulation was worked out by Jerzy Neyman, at about the time of his arrival at UCB, circa 1940. Neyman developed an impressive body of mathematical theory. In a nutshell, this theory allows to find the test that has the smallest Type II error probability for a fixed significance level, α. As we have seen, such a goal is difficult to achieve in practical use; thus, the p-value approach prevails among statisticians.

---

[14] Fisher is widely acknowledged to be the father of modern statistics. His work on tests of significance was done in the 1920's and 30's at the Rothamsted Experimental Station in England.

Chapter 9 Problems

For problems **1-4**, state the null and alternative hypotheses in terms of the appropriate population parameter, μ or p.

1. We wish to test if the mean temperature during the summer months in the San Francisco Bay Area is less than 78 degrees Fahrenheit.

2. A study is conducted to check the claim that the proportion of homicides to other similar crimes in a certain city has declined since 1990. The proportion then was 0.12.

3. A certain type of bolt is assumed to have an average diameter of 2 cm.

4. The Highway Patrol is gathering data in order to test the claim that, on average, motorists travel at a speed exceeding 60 mph.

5. Suppose that the test of hypothesis for the situation in problem **4.** above yields a p-value = 0.051. What can be said about the average speed of motorists in relation to the speed limit?

6. If H_o: p = 0.40 and H_a: p > 0.40 and sample data gives $p' = 0.45$, is there sufficient evidence to favor the alternative? Explain.

7. If H_o: p = 0.40 and H_a: p > 0.40 and sample data gives $p' = 0.35$, is there sufficient evidence to favor the null? Explain.

8. A consumer protection group is interested in testing a brand of cereal because of the suspicion that, on average, the boxes contain less than the advertised mean of 18 ounces. A random sample of 9 boxes of cereal are weighed producing an average weight of 17.5 ounces. It is known that the standard deviation of the weight is 0.6 ounces.

    a. Set up the appropriate hypotheses and compute the p-value.
    b. Is there sufficient evidence against the null?

9. An incumbent city official was running for another term. She was interested in determining whether the percentage of registered Republicans in the state of California had stayed the same since the time of the last election. At that time, 44% of the registered voters in the state were Republicans. A recent poll claims that out of 500 randomly sample registered voters, 210 are Republicans.

    a. Set up the appropriate hypotheses and compute the p-value.
    b. Is there sufficient evidence in favor of the null?

10. The Survey of Student Attitudes for college students is a psychological test measuring the attitude toward college of adults living in the United States between the ages of 18 and 65. The range of scores in the survey is between 100 and 300, with higher scores meaning a better attitude. The mean score of United States adults is $\mu = 200$ and the standard deviation is $\sigma = 35$. A college professor suspects that older students have a much better attitude toward college than younger ones. The professor administers the survey to a random sample of 49 students 30 years of age or older. The result of the survey is an average score of 210.

    a. State the null and alternative hypotheses.

    b. Write the distribution of the random variable of interest under the assumption of the null.

    c. Find the critical value(s) if the test is conducted at the 5% significance level.

    d. Give the region (i.e., give the set of values for $\bar{x}$) where we will accept the null.

    e. According to the sample data, write a decision and conclusion.

    f. Compute the p-value. Is the p-value in accord with your answer to **e.**?

11. Refer to the situation of Example **2**, section **9.1**. Are there any major flaws in the data collection? What must be assumed about the students in Professor Jenkins' class?

12. Your friend, Joe Dweebs, is an avid sky diver. He just purchased a state of the art parachute that he can't wait to try. He is assuming that the new parachute will open. This is his null hypothesis.

    a. State the alternative hypothesis.

    b. State the consequences of making a Type I error.

    c. State the consequences of making a Type II error.

    d. If the parachute is defective and will not open, which of the following sets of α and β would Joe prefer? Explain.

        (i). $\alpha = 0.01$, $\beta = 0.50$ **(ii).** $\alpha = 0.50$, $\beta = 0.01$

    e. If the parachute will open, which of the following sets of α and β would Joe prefer? Explain.

        (i). $\alpha = 0.01$, $\beta = 0.50$ **(ii).** $\alpha = 0.50$, $\beta = 0.01$

13. In a certain country, a defendant is assumed guilty.

    a. Give the null and alternative hypotheses.

    b. State the consequences of making a Type I error.

    c. State the consequences of making a Type II error.

    d. Which set of α and β would you prefer if you are guilty?

        (i). $\alpha = 0.01$, $\beta = 0.5$ (ii). $\alpha = 0.50$, $\beta = 0.01$

    e. Which set of α and β would you prefer if you are innocent?

        (i). $\alpha = 0.01$, $\beta = 0.50$ (ii). $\alpha = 0.50$, $\beta = 0.01$

Answer (a)–(g) for problems **14–16**.

    (a) Give the distribution of the random variable under the assumption of the null.

    (b) Sketch and completely label an appropriate graph.

    (c) Give the critical value(s) corresponding to the significance level α.

    (d) Compute the test statistic and the p-value.

    (e) Give a decision and conclusion based on the pre-conceived α.

    (f) Give the confidence interval for the corresponding population parameter using a confidence level of $1 - \alpha$.

    (g) Compute β for the alternative value of the parameter.

14. Hypotheses: $H_0: \mu = 10$ vs. $H_a: \mu \neq 10$.
Assume $\sigma = 5$.
Data: $n = 25$; $\bar{x} = 12.3$.
Level of significance: $\alpha = 0.01$.
Alternative value of the parameter: $\mu_a = 12$.

15. Hypotheses: $H_0: \mu = 10$ vs. $H_a: \mu \neq 10$.
Assume $\sigma = 5$.
Data: $n = 25$; $\bar{x} = 12.3$.
Level of significance: $\alpha = 0.05$.
Alternative value of the parameter: $\mu_a = 12$.

16. Hypotheses: $H_0: p = 0.65$ vs. $H_a: p \neq 0.65$.
Data: $n = 100$; $x = 70$.
Level of significance: $\alpha = 0.05$.
Alternative value of the parameter: $p_a = 0.75$.

17. For the situation of problem **14.** above, compute β for the alternative $\mu_a = 14$. Explain why this value of β is considerably smaller than the one computed in part **(g)** of problem **14.** What does this mean?

18. It is believed that for a certain coin, P(heads) = p = 0.70. To test this hypothesis the following experiment is conducted:

> *flip the coin four times and if the number of heads is two or more, favor the hypothesis that*
> *P(heads) = p = 0.70.*

    a. Compute α. [Recall that p-value = computed α].

    b. If in reality, p = 0.50, compute β. (i.e., the value of the alternative is $p_a = 0.50$).

19. Computers have built–in random number generators that are supposed to produce random numbers that follow a uniform distribution in the interval (0,1). Recall from Chapter 5 that the mean and variance of a uniformly distributed random variable in the interval (a,b) are given by $\mu = \dfrac{a+b}{2}$ and $\sigma^2 = \dfrac{(b-a)^2}{12}$. Suppose you test the random number generator in your computer by generating a sample of 100 random numbers. The mean of the 100 numbers in the sample is $\overline{x} = 0.475$. We wish to test the hypotheses: H_0: $\mu = 0.50$ vs. H_a: $\mu \neq 0.50$.

    a. Calculate the test statistic.

    b. Is the result significant at the 10% level of significance?

    c. Is the result significant at the 5% level of significance?

20. An experiment on learning using pigeons counts the number of snacks a pigeon must be given before it is trained to respond to a certain stimulus. Past history indicates that the mean number of snacks is 25. A researcher thinks that placing the snack out of the reach of the pigeons prior to feeding it to the pigeons will cause the pigeons to respond to the stimulus quicker; thus, reducing the average number of snacks they must be fed. A random sample of 36 pigeons is taken and the experiment is conducted.

    a. Write an appropriate set of hypotheses for this situation.

    b. What are the consequences of making a Type I error?

    c. What are the consequences of making a Type II error?

21. Asked to explain the meaning of "statistically significant at the $\alpha = 0.01$ level", a student responds: "this means that the probablity that the null is true is 1% or less." Is this correct? Explain.

Chapter 10

The Student's–t Distribution

10.1 Testing hypotheses about μ when σ is not known.

In Chapter 9, each time we conducted a test about a population mean μ, it was assumed that the population standard deviation σ was known. This is unrealistic. In practice, s must be calculated from data. This calculated s then becomes an estimate for the unknown σ. In order to make inferences about the population mean under these conditions, the following assumptions are made about the data:

- *the data are a simple random sample of size n from the population,*

- *the underlying population has a Normal distribution with unknown mean μ and unknown standard deviation σ.*

The random variable of interest is still $\overline{X}$. By the Central Limit Theorem, $\overline{X} \sim N\left(\mu, \frac{\sigma^2}{n}\right)$. But, since we don't know σ, we can't use the Normal distribution. Instead, an approximation to the Normal must be used. This approximation is provided by the family of curves called the "student's t- distribution" (for short, we will refer to this distribution as the "t distribution"). Therefore, instead of writing $z = \dfrac{\overline{x} - \mu}{\frac{\sigma}{\sqrt{n}}}$, we write $t = \dfrac{\overline{x} - \mu}{\frac{s}{\sqrt{n}}}$ where the ratio $\dfrac{\overline{x} - \mu}{\frac{s}{\sqrt{n}}}$, called the t transformation equation, follows a t distribution with **degrees of freedom**[1] $= n - 1$. We write this as follows,

$$\frac{\overline{x} - \mu}{\frac{s}{\sqrt{n}}} \sim t_{n-1} \, .$$

The t statistic is very similar to the z statistic. It says how far $\overline{x}$ is from μ as measured in units of standard deviation. Furthermore, the family of t curves is also similar to the Normal distribution. The graph below shows the standard normal superimposed on a t_3 curve. Both curves are symmetrical about their mean of zero and are bell–shaped. However, the spread of the t distribution is larger than that of the standard normal. Note how the t distribution has longer tails and is less peaked than the standard normal.

---

[1] Think of the degrees of freedom, abbreviated df, as an index that tells us which t curve to use. For example, a t curve with df = 5 will be denoted by t_5.

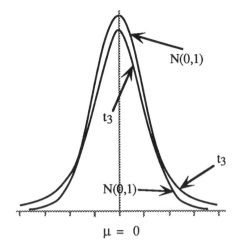

$\mu = 0$

As the degrees of freedom for the t distribution increase, the graph of t will approximate the standard normal. This makes sense , since as the degrees of freedom increase (i.e., sample size is "large") using s instead of σ causes no major disturbances since s estimates σ much more accurately.

Before proceeding to test hypotheses and consider confidence intervals, we must become acquainted with the t table of probabilities and critical values. The lay out for this table is as follows:

- Degrees of freedom on the far left column.[2]
- Areas in the right tail of the distribution are on the top row. They appear as subscripts to t. Because of symmetry about the mean of 0, these are also left tail areas.
- The body of the table contains right tail critical values. Again, because of symmetry, the opposite of these values are the left tail critical values.

The following examples will illustrate.

Example 1

Let $Y \sim t_{10}$. Find:

    a. $P(Y > 2.23)$ **b.** $P(Y < -1.37)$

    c. $t_{10,0.01}$ **d.** $P(-1.81 < Y < 2.76)$

    e. The 95th percentile of the Y distribution.

---

[2] Note that the very last row, indicating degrees of freedom beyond 29, consists of critical values similar to the standard normal.

Solution

a. To find P(Y > 2.23), enter the table at 10 degrees of freedom and find 2.23 along that particular row. The area to the right of 2.23 is the subscript of t appearing on the top row. Thus, P(Y > 2.23) = 0.025. The graph for this situation follows.

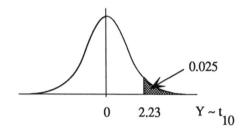

[Note: draw graphs for **b.,c.,d.,** and **e.** similar to the one above.]

b. Find 1.37 along the 10 degrees of freedom row. The question is to find the area in the left tail. By symmetry, the area to the left of –1.37 is the same as the area to the right of 1.37. Thus, P(Y < –1.37) = 0.10.

c. The notation $t_{10,0.01}$ refers to the critical value corresponding to a t distribution with 10 degrees of freedom and 0.01 area to its right. We notice that the 10 degrees of freedom row and the $t_{0.01}$ column intersect at the critical value 2.76. Thus, $t_{10,0.01}$ = 2.76.

d. P(–1.81 < Y < 2.76) = P(Y < 2.76) – P(Y < –1.81) = (1 – 0.01) – 0.05 = 0.99 – 0.05 = 0.94.

e. We want the value of Y, call it y, such that P(Y < y) = 0.95. The table gives 1.81. That is, P(Y < 1.81) = 0.95.

Example 2

For each of the probability questions below, use the t table to verify the answers. Draw graphs.

1. $P\left(t_5 > 2.02\right) = 0.05$

2. $P\left(t_5 < 2.02\right) = 1 - 0.05 = 0.95$

3. $P\left(t_{12} < 3.05\right) = 1 - 0.005 = 0.995$

4. $P\left(t_{57} < 2.04\right) = P(Z < 2.04) = 0.9793$. (You need to use the Z table for this one).

The one sample t test for a population mean

To carry out a test of hypotheses about a population mean when σ is not known, we just replace σ with s so that the standard deviation of $\overline{X}$ is $s/\sqrt{n}$ instead of $\sigma/\sqrt{n}$. The procedure is identical to those of Chapter 9 with the only exception being that we now work with the t distribution instead of the standard normal.

Example 3

Soft drink manufacturers test new recipes in order to rate their sweetness content. Nine randomly selected expert tasters rated a new recipe on a scale from 1 to 5 where 5 stands for "great tasting" and 1 stands for "poor tasting". An average rating larger than 3 is needed in order for the recipe to undergo further review. The ratings from the 9 experts are: 1, 2.5, 2, 3, 3.5, 3, 4.5, 4, 5. Do the data present sufficient evidence to justify submitting the recipe for further review?

Solution and discussion

We formulate the set of hypotheses:

H_0: $\mu = 3$ vs. H_a: $\mu > 3$ (one-sided on the right)

From the sample data, we use a calculator to compute $\overline{x} = 3.167$ and s = 1.25. The random variable of interest is $\overline{X}$. Under the null, $\overline{X} \sim N\left(3, \frac{\sigma^2}{9}\right)$. However, since σ is not known, we must use s. Thus, the t distribution with $n - 1 = 9 - 1 = 8$ degrees of freedom applies. We set up the p-value computation as follows:

$$\text{p-value} = P\left(\overline{X} > 3.167 \mid \mu_o = 3\right).$$

We now use the t transformation equation to obtain the computed test statistic:

$$\text{p-value} = P\left(\overline{X} > 3.167 \mid \mu_o = 3\right) = P\left(t > \frac{3.167 - 3}{1.25/3}\right) = P(t > 0.401).$$

We graph this situation before evaluating this last probability.

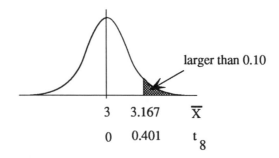

larger than 0.10

3   3.167 $\overline{X}$

0   0.401 t_8

In order to evaluate the required probability, we enter the t table at 8 degrees of freedom. The closest value to 0.401 we can find is 1.40. We note that the area to the right of 1.40 is 0.10. Thus, the area to the right of 0.401 must be larger than 0.10.[3] Therefore, with a p-value exceeding 0.10, the data favors the null hypothesis. Thus, there isn't sufficient evidence to justify submitting the new recipe for further evaluation.

10.2 Confidence intervals about μ when σ is not known.

The confidence interval for μ when σ is not known is similar in form to the confidence interval about μ when σ is known. The basic form is:

$$\overline{x} \pm \text{error bound,}$$

where the expression for the error bound incorporates a value of t, from the corresponding t distribution, and s replaces σ. That is, instead of $EB = z\left(\frac{\alpha}{2}\right) \cdot \frac{\sigma}{\sqrt{n}}$, we write:[4]

$$EB = t_{df,\alpha/2} \cdot \frac{s}{\sqrt{n}}.$$

Example 4

A recent study of calcium levels in a random sample of 25 six months old infants being breast fed gave a mean calcium level of 6.9 mg. with a standard deviation of 1 mg. Give a 95% confidence interval for the mean calcium level for the population of 6 months old infants that are breast fed.

---

[3] Using a computer, $P(t_8 > 0.401) = 0.3495$.

[4] The notation $t_{df,\alpha/2}$ denotes the critical value for a t distribution with df = degrees of freedom and $\alpha/2 =$ area to the right. This is similar to the meaning of the $z(\alpha/2)$ notation from previous chapters.

Solution

The confidence interval about the population mean is given by:

$$\bar{x} \pm EB \quad \text{where} \quad EB = t_{df,\alpha/2} \cdot \frac{s}{\sqrt{n}}.$$

Since $n = 25$, then $df = 25 - 1 = 24$. Also, 95% confidence means $\alpha/2 = 0.025$. From the t table, $t_{24, 0.025} = 2.06$. Thus,

$$EB = 2.06 \cdot \frac{1}{\sqrt{25}} = 0.412.$$

Thus, the 95% confidence interval about μ is:

$$6.9 \pm 0.412 \quad \text{or} \quad \mu \quad \text{lies in the interval} \quad (6.488, 7.312).$$

Example 5

Verify that $n = 13$ is the smallest sample size necessary in order to be 90% confident that $\bar{x}$ is within 1 unit of μ. Assume the sample standard deviation $= s = 2$.

Solution

Since $n = 13$ then $df = 12$ and from the t-table, with $\alpha/2 = 0.05$, $t_{12,0.05} = 1.78$. From the EB equation, we write:

$$EB = t_{12, 0.05} \cdot \frac{s}{\sqrt{n}} = 1.78 \cdot \frac{2}{\sqrt{13}} = 0.9874 < 1.$$

Note that if we pick a sample size smaller than 13, then $EB > 1$. For example, if $n = 12$, then

$$EB = t_{11, 0.05} \cdot \frac{s}{\sqrt{n}} = 1.80 \cdot \frac{2}{\sqrt{12}} = 1.0392 > 1.$$

Thus, for a sample size of 13, or larger, we are 90% confident that the sample mean will lie within 1 unit away from the population mean. Likewise, for sample sizes less than 13, the error bound is always larger than 1.

Example 6

If a sample of size 16 is taken, and s = 4, how confident are we that the sample mean is within 1.75 units of the population mean μ?

Solution

The problem asks for the confidence level; thus, we use the EB formula to first solve for α. We proceed as follows,

$$EB = t_{15,\ \alpha/2} \cdot \frac{s}{\sqrt{n}} \quad \Rightarrow \quad 1.75 = t_{15,\ \alpha/2} \cdot \frac{4}{\sqrt{16}}\ ; \quad \text{thus,}$$

$$t_{15,\ \alpha/2} = 1.75 \cdot \frac{4}{4} = 1.75.$$

Entering the t table at 15 degrees of freedom, we note that the area to the right of the critical value of 1.75 is 0.05. That is,

$$\frac{\alpha}{2} = 0.05 \quad \Rightarrow \quad \alpha = 0.10.$$

Therefore, confidence level = $1 - \alpha = 1 - 0.10 = 0.90$. Thus, we are 90% confident that the population mean lies within 1.75 units of the sample mean.

10.3 General comments about using the t distribution

Testing statistical hypotheses and computing confidence intervals using the t distribution give statistically correct results only if the underlying population follows a Normal distribution. Real data are rarely exactly normally distributed. This says that the usefulness of the t distribution depends on how strongly the data are affected by lack of normality. In practical applications, lack of normality is manifested in terms of extreme data values. That is, non-normality is primarily caused by data values that fall well into the tails of the distribution, causing some sort of skewness on the graph. Fortunately, the t distribution is quite resistant to the presence of extreme values. In fact, a sample size of around 15 is usually sufficient for producing acceptable results. Here are some guidelines for using the t distribution.

- Make sure the data comes from a simple random sample. In almost all cases (except for very small sample sizes), this is a considerably more important feature than the assumption that the underlying population distribution is Normal.

- For any sample size less than 15, make sure the data are very close to being normally distributed. If not, it is preferable not to use t.[5]

- If the sample size is at least 15 but less than 30, then the t distribution can be confidently used as long as there are no extreme values that produce a marked skewness.

- For sample sizes at least 30, even the presence of extreme values will have very little effect on the accuracy of the results.

---

[5]In real applications, whenever this situation arises, statisticians use a totally different methodology called *non-parametric statistics*. This is beyond the scope of this book.

Chapter 10

Chapter 10 Problems

1. Find the indicated probability. Sketch a graph and shade the appropriate region.

   a. $P(t_{18} < 2.10)$

   b. $P(t_{18} > 2.10)$

   c. $P(t_{18} > -2.10)$

   d. $P(t_7 > -3.50)$

   e. $P(t_{56} > -2.41)$

   f. $P(t_{103} < -0.96)$

   g. $P(1.37 < t_{10} < 3.17)$

   h. $P(-1.37 < t_{10} < 3.17)$

2. Find the indicated critical value. Sketch a graph and shade the appropriate region.

   a. $t_{15, \, 0.05}$

   b. $t_{5, \, 0.975}$

   c. $t_{12, \, 0.99}$

   d. $t_{16, \, 0.95}$

   e. $t_{8, \, 0.01}$

   f. $t_{67, \, 0.995}$

3. Find the value of t_{df}. (hint: t_{df} is a critical value). Sketch a graph and shade the appropriate region.

   a. $P(t > t_8) = 0.05$

   b. $P(t < t_{12}) = 0.995$

   c. $P(t < t_9) = 0.05$

   d. $P(-t_{20} < t < t_{20}) = 0.95$

4. The t statistic for testing H_0: $\mu = 5$ vs. H_a: $\mu < 5$, based on a random sample of size 10, has the value $t = -2.35$.

   a. What are the degrees of freedom for this statistic?

   b. Between what two probabilities from the t table does the p-value lie?

5. Suppose it is required that the mean operating life of size "D" batteries be 22 hours. If a random sample of 9 batteries has a mean operating life of 20 hours and a standard deviation of 3.1 hours, can we conclude that the mean operating life of "D" batteries is not 22 hours?

   a. Write the null and alternative hypotheses.

   b. Give the distribution of the appropriate random variable and give the distribution used in performing the hypothesis test.

   c. Find the critical value(s) for a pre-set $\alpha = 0.05$. Sketch an appropriate graph.

   d. For $\alpha = 0.05$, make a decision and give a conclusion.

6. The administration at your college announces that, on average, commuting students live farther than 30 miles from campus. The announcement came as somewhat of a surprise and took place at a press conference where it was important to make the point that the college attracts students who live "far" from campus. A student advocacy group takes a random sample of 9 commuting students and records how far, in miles, they live from campus: 19, 22, 25, 28, 30, 35, 40, 46, 50.

    a. Write the null and alternative hypotheses.

    b. Give the distribution of the appropriate random variable and give the distribution used in performing the hypothesis test.

    c. Find the critical value(s) for a pre-set $\alpha = 0.10$. Sketch an appropriate graph.

    d. For $\alpha = 0.10$, make a decision and give a conclusion.

    e. Based on this evidence, did the administration make a misleading claim at the press conference regarding the average commute distance for students? Explain.

7. Refer to Example 3 for this chapter. Write the data for the ratings in decimal form: 1.0, 2.5, 2.0, 3.0, 3.5, 3.0, 4.5, 4.0, 5.0.

    a. Construct a stem-leaf diagram where the stem is the units digit and the leaf is the tenth digit.

    b. Is the distribution of the ratings sufficiently symmetrical and without extreme values in order to claim that the test results are accurate? Explain.

8. A random sample of 25 elementary statistics students shows an average of 72 on the first midterm with a standard deviation of 10. Find the 95% confidence interval for the population mean of first midterm scores.

9. A certain printing press is known to turn out an average of 45 copies per minute. An adjustment is made to the machine in an attempt to increase its output. In 9 randomly selected test runs it turns out an average of 47 copies per minute with a sample standard deviation of 2.

    a. Write the null and alternative hypotheses.

    b. Give the distribution of the appropriate random variable and give the distribution used in performing the hypothesis test.

    c. Find the critical value(s) for a pre-set $\alpha = 0.01$. Sketch an appropriate graph.

    d. For $\alpha = 0.01$, can it be claimed that the adjustment was successful? Explain.

10. Advances in plant genetics have made possible the creation of genetically engineered food products. The first of these products to reach the market is a tomato produced by Calgene Inc, based in Davis, California. Besides having a longer shelf life, the genetically engineered tomato plants are also expected to yield, on average, more tomatoes. An average difference of 5 or more tomatoes per plant when comparing the genetically engineered tomato plants to the traditionally grown ones is considered to be significant. A sample of 25 genetically engineered tomato plants is taken and $s = 10$.

    a. If we test the hypotheses H_0: $\mu = 20$ vs. H_a: $\mu > 20$, and from the sample of 25 plants $\bar{x} = 24$, do we reject the null? Explain.

    b. For the hypotheses of **a.** above, what is the approximate power of the test if the alternative mean $\mu_a = 26$? **Note:** recall that power $= 1 - \beta$ and compute β in a manner similar to that of Chapter 9 with s replacing σ.

    c. Find α for this situation.

11. The data set consisting of the ages at the time of their inauguration for the US Presidents has mean $\approx$ 54.5 and standard deviation $\approx$ 5.

    a. Why is it that it will not make sense to use the t distribution (or for that matter, any other distribution), to give a 95% confidence interval for the mean age of the Presidents at the time of their inauguration? Explain.

    b. What must be assumed in order to justify giving such confidence interval? What will be the meaning of the confidence interval?

12.   **a.** Repeat Example **5** to verify that $n = 18$ is the smallest sample size necessary if confidence level $= 95\%$.

    b. Carry out the computations to show that when $n = 16$, EB > 1. Use a 95% confidence level.

13. A blood test is given to a random sample of 36 male patients to estimate their average level of hemoglobin. The mean hemoglobin level for the 36 patients is $\bar{x} = 4.5$ millions with standard deviation $= s = 1$ million. How confident are we that the true average hemoglobin level for the population of male patients similar to those in the sample will be within 0.25 million of the sample mean of 4.5 millions?

For problems **14** to **18**, include the following:

    a.   null and alternative hypotheses

    b.   distribution of the appropriate random variable: $\overline{X}$ or P' or $t = \dfrac{\overline{x} - \mu}{s/\sqrt{n}}$

    c.   sketch and label an appropriate graph

    d.   critical values for the given α

    e.   p-value

    f.   conclusion

14.   A student group claims that, on average, students travel for at least 25 minutes in order to reach college each day. The college admissions office obtained a random sample of 25 one-way travel times from students. The sample had a mean of 19.4 minutes and a standard deviation of 9.65 minutes. Let $\alpha = 0.01$.

15.   On a popular self-image test the mean score for public assistance recipients is 65 and the standard deviation is 5. A random sample of 64 public assistance recipients in Emerson County are given the test. They achieved a mean score of 60. You wish to test if the Emerson scores differ from the average. Let $\alpha = 0.05$.

16.   Homes in a nearby college town have a mean value of \$158,950. It is assumed that homes in the vicinity of the college have a higher value. To test this theory, a random sample of 16 homes are chosen from the college area. Their mean valuation is \$162,460 and the sample standard deviation is \$5,400. Let $\alpha = 0.1$.

17.   A politician believes that she will receive at least 60% of the vote in an upcoming election. The results of a properly designed random sample of 300 voters showed that 155 of those sampled will vote for her. Let $\alpha = 0.05$.

18.   The full-time student body of a college is composed of 50% males. Does a random sample of students (305 males, 230 females) from an introductory chemistry course show sufficient evidence to reject the hypothesis that the proportion of male and female students who take this course is the same as that of the whole student body? Let $\alpha = 0.05$.

Chapter 11

Testing Means and Proportions about Two Populations

11.1 Comparing Two Populations

Often, we are interested in a comparison of two populations: whether cigarette smokers have a shorter life expectancy than nonsmokers; whether children who watch television frequently are more violent than children who seldom watch television; whether people who take large dosages of vitamin C have fewer colds than those who don't. Educators often compare the performance of students who have been taught in different ways; engineers compare the reliability of different chip designs; economists compare the rate of return of different investments. By extending the methods of Chapters 9 and 10 we can easily tackle the above situations.

In this chapter we will study ways of carrying out procedures to test hypotheses for three different designs arising from situations similar to those presented above. The three procedures are:

- *matched pair samples (also known as dependent means)*

- *two independent population means (small and large sample sizes)*

- *two independent population proportions*

11.2 Matched Pair Samples

The matched pair design is a way to compare two treatments while using a one sample test procedure (i.e., like in Chapter 10). In a matched pair design, the subjects are matched in pairs and each treatment is given to one subject in each pair. The parameter of interest is the mean difference in the response to the two treatments within the matched pairs of randomly selected subjects.

Statisticians favor single sample comparisons because they tend to eliminate many of the sources of sampling error. However, matching subjects in pairs in such a way that one subject mirrors the other (like identical twins) is difficult to accomplish. Let's illustrate. Consider medical researchers who are interested in determining if a certain cholesterol-reducing drug reduces the risk of a heart attack. Many factors figure on heart attacks: gender, age, smoking habits, blood pressure, and others. Because of these factors, the results of such an experiment will vary substantially. One way to control for these factors is to choose subjects who are of the same gender and age, have similar blood pressure readings, and have similar smoking habits. This is precisely what is done. Matching pairs with similar medical histories and lifestyles, albeit difficult to do, is the only way we can be reasonably assured that the experimental results are only attributable to the treatment and not to extraneous factors or variables we cannot possibly control.

However, another way of thinking about matched pairs is to use the same subject twice. That is, instead of applying the treatment once to the matched subjects, we now apply the treatment twice to the same subject. The parameter of interest is still the mean difference in the treatment response. For the time being, this rules out a number of interesting experiments[1], but it expedites matters and it makes life easier. These designs are also known as *before-after* comparisons. The example below will illustrate.

Example 1

Twelve overweight persons, randomly chosen from the population, are invited to join an exercise and diet program. Of interest is the mean weight loss after three months in the program. The weight, in pounds, for each person is recorded at the start of the program and also at the end of the three months period. The following data are recorded:

Weight at start	160	220	300	145	195	182	250	135	210	280	160	200
Weight at end	155	205	290	140	198	187	240	132	200	272	165	200

The research question is: on average, is the weight loss significant?

Solution

We set up the statistical hypotheses: H_0: $\mu_d = 0$ vs. H_a: $\mu_d > 0$. Note that d = weight at start – weight at end. The logic here is that if there was any weight loss after three months, then the persons are lighter than at the start and the set of d's should be positive. We form the set of d's:

$$d = \{5, 15, 10, 5, -3, -5, 10, 3, 10, 8, -5, 0\}.$$

Using a calculator, $\overline{d} = 4.417$ and $s_d = 6.557$. In effect, we have turned a set of 24 observations (the total number of weight measurements before and after) into a single data set of 12 observations. The random variable of interest is $\overline{D}$. Its distribution is $N\left(\mu_d, \dfrac{\sigma_d^2}{n}\right)$. However, since σ is not known, we use the t distribution with df = n – 1 = 12 – 1 = 11. We now compute the p -value:

$$\text{p-value} = P\left(\overline{D} > 4.417 \mid \mu_d = 0\right) = P\left(t > \frac{4.417 - 0}{6.557/\sqrt{12}}\right) = P(t > 2.33).$$

---

[1] For instance, if two different dosages of a drug are being tested, it is impossible to use the same person for both dosages. Later in the chapter we will see how we can accomplish this.

Entering the t table at 11 degrees of freedom, we see that this probability is slightly less than 0.025. The graph below shows the entire situation.

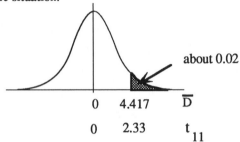

Thus, with such a small p-value, we tend to favor the alternative and conclude that on average, it appears that the diet and exercise program will cause people to lose weight.

Note that for a pre-set significance smaller than about 0.02, the null will still be favored. Thus, if someone wishes to make a decision using $\alpha = 0.01$, the decision will be to favor the null and conclude that the average weight loss is not significantly different from 0.

11.3 Two Sample Problems

Comparing two populations or two treatments is one of the most common occurrences in statistical practice. These situations are called *two-sample* problems. Two-sample problems can arise from a randomized comparative experiment that randomly divides subjects into two groups and applies a different treatment to each group. Comparing random samples separately chosen from the same population is also a two-sample problem. Unlike the matched pairs design, there is no matching of the subjects in the samples. Inference procedures for the two-sample problem differ from those for matched pairs. In this section we will study how to compare two means and two proportions.

Comparing two population means

When two populations are being studied, a comparison of the mean response in the two populations is the most common goal of inference. We make the following assumptions:

- *two random samples from two distinct populations are taken. The samples are independent. That is, one sample has no influence on the other. The same variable is measured for both samples.*

- *both populations are approximately normally distributed. The means and the standard deviations are not known.*

Let's call the random variable we measure X_1 in the first population and X_2 in the second. We assume that their distributions are approximately Normal. Random samples of size n_1 and n_2 are taken from each population. The mean and variance are computed for each sample. We turn our attention to the sample mean and, in particular, to the sampling distribution of the random variables $\overline{X}_1$ and $\overline{X}_2$. From the Central Limit Theorem, we know:

$$\overline{X}_1 \sim N\left(\mu_1, \frac{\sigma_1^2}{n_1}\right) \quad \text{and} \quad \overline{X}_2 \sim N\left(\mu_2, \frac{\sigma_2^2}{n_2}\right).$$

The set of hypotheses of interest for the two–sample problem is of the form:

$$H_0: \mu_1 - \mu_2 = 0 \quad \text{vs.} \quad H_a: \mu_1 - \mu_2 \overset{<}{\underset{>}{\neq}} 0,$$

where the quantity $\mu_1 - \mu_2$ makes us consider the sampling distribution of the corresponding difference of the random variables $\overline{X}_1$ and $\overline{X}_2$. That is,

$$\overline{X}_1 - \overline{X}_2 \sim N\left(\mu_1 - \mu_2, \frac{\sigma_1^2}{n_1} + \frac{\sigma_2^2}{n_2}\right).$$

The only surprising thing about the sampling distribution of $\overline{X}_1 - \overline{X}_2$ is that the variances add. That is, when we add or subtract independent random variables, the resulting variance is the sum of the individual variances. However, since the population variances are not known and must be estimated from the data via s_1^2 and s_2^2, we can't use the Normal distribution when working inference problems about two samples. Instead, we will use the t distribution. We will define two different statistics, call the *two-sample* t *statistics*. Their exact distribution is not known, but they approximately follow a t distribution. Here are the two cases we will consider.[2]

---

[2] The two cases presented here depend on the population variances being equal or on the magnitude of the combined sample sizes. In practice, there are ways of testing for the equality of two population variances, but it is not recommended to do so in order to decide which case applies. This has to do with causing a drastic decrease in the power of the test procedure. Instead, sophisticated computer software uses a recently developed algorithm to compute the degrees of freedom from all of the data and bypass having two different cases. The results are superior to ours, but for our purposes, they are not worth the effort. See, for example, David Moore: *The Basic Practice of Statistics*, Freeman, 1995, page 450.

Case 1: $\sigma_1^2 \neq \sigma_2^2$ or $n_1 + n_2 > 30$.

$$\text{Test statistic} = t = \frac{\bar{x}_1 - \bar{x}_2 - (\mu_1 - \mu_2)}{\sqrt{\dfrac{s_1^2}{n_1} + \dfrac{s_2^2}{n_2}}} \sim t_{df}$$

where $df = $ minimum between $(n_1 - 1)$ and $(n_2 - 1)$.

Case 2: $\sigma_1^2 = \sigma_2^2$ or $n_1 + n_2 \leq 30$.

$$\text{Test statistic} = t = \frac{\bar{x}_1 - \bar{x}_2 - (\mu_1 - \mu_2)}{s_p \cdot \sqrt{\dfrac{1}{n_1} + \dfrac{1}{n_2}}} \sim t_{df}$$

where $df = n_1 + n_2 - 2$ and $s_p = \sqrt{\dfrac{(n_1 - 1) \cdot s_1^2 + (n_2 - 1) \cdot s_2^2}{n_1 + n_2 - 2}}$.

The s_p term is called a "pooled" standard deviation. It is just the square root of the weighted average of the combined variances. The pooled degrees of freedom is the sum of $n_1 - 1$ and $n_2 - 1$; that is, $df = n_1 + n_2 - 2$.

Example 2

An experiment was conducted to compare the mean absorption rate, in mg. per hour, for two drugs in specimens of similar muscle tissue. The sample results are as follows:

	n	average	standard deviation
Drug 1	30	7.9	0.41
Drug 2	20	8.5	0.32

Solution

We first formulate a set of hypotheses:

$$H_0: \mu_1 - \mu_2 = 0 \quad \text{vs.} \quad H_a: \mu_1 - \mu_2 \neq 0.$$

The distribution of the random variable of interest is $\overline{X}_1 - \overline{X}_2 \sim N\left(0, \dfrac{\sigma_1^2}{30} + \dfrac{\sigma_2^2}{20}\right)$. Since the population variances are unknown we use the t distribution with df = 19. Note we are using Case 1 since the combined sample size exceeds 30. In order to obtain the p-value, we first compute the test statistic:

$$\text{test statistic} = \frac{\overline{x}_1 - \overline{x}_2 - (\mu_1 - \mu_2)}{\sqrt{\dfrac{s_1^2}{n_1} + \dfrac{s_2^2}{n_2}}} = \frac{7.9 - 8.5 - 0}{\sqrt{\dfrac{0.41^2}{30} + \dfrac{0.32^2}{20}}} = -5.794;$$

thus, p-value $= P(t < -5.794 \text{ or } t > 5.794) \approx 0$.

The graph below contains all the information.

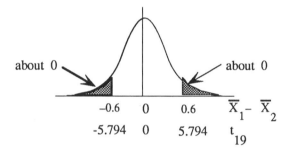

Since the p-value is very near 0, we reject the null and conclude that there is a difference in the mean absorption rate of the two drugs.

Example 3

The average reaction time to a certain dosage of a medication is suspected to be faster for females than males between the ages of 30 and 50. A random sample of 9 males and 16 females yields the following data:

	n	average reaction time	variance
Males	9	3 hours	1.00
Females	16	2.5 hours	0.64

Solution

For expediency, let males = group 1 and females = group 2. The set of hypotheses is:

Ho: $\mu_1 - \mu_2 = 0$ vs.   Ha: $\mu_1 - \mu_2 > 0$ (group 2 takes less time).

Chapter 11

The distribution of the random variable of interest is $\overline{X}_1 - \overline{X}_2 \sim N\left(0, \dfrac{\sigma_1^2}{9} + \dfrac{\sigma_2^2}{16}\right)$. Since the population variances are unknown we use the t distribution with df = 23. Note we are using Case 2 since the combined sample size does not exceed 30. In order to obtain the p-value, we first compute the test statistic:

$$\text{test statistic} = \frac{\overline{x}_1 - \overline{x}_2 - \left(\mu_1 - \mu_2\right)}{s_p \cdot \sqrt{\dfrac{1}{n_1} + \dfrac{1}{n_2}}} = \frac{3 - 2.5 - 0}{s_p \cdot \sqrt{\dfrac{1}{9} + \dfrac{1}{16}}} = \frac{0.5}{0.8748 \cdot \sqrt{\dfrac{1}{9} + \dfrac{1}{16}}} = 1.372;$$

thus, p-value = P(t > 1.372).

Entering the t table at df = 23, we note that P(t > 1.372) falls between 0.05 and 0.10. Therefore, the evidence tends to cast some doubt on the null hypothesis and we may be inclined to believe that the reaction time for the medication, on average, is faster in females than in males. Using a computer, the exact p-value is 0.0917. Thus, for a pre-set significance larger than 0.0917, the decision is to reject the null. The graph below contains the pertinent information.

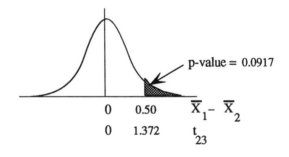

Comparing two population proportions

Sometimes we wish to compare the proportion of successes in two groups. The two groups are assumed independent. For clarity, we will call them Group 1 and Group 2. The set of hypotheses of interest is of the form:

$$H_0: p_1 - p_2 = 0 \quad \text{vs.} \quad H_a: p_1 - p_2 \overset{<}{\underset{>}{\neq}} 0.$$

The logic for this test follows the development of the two-sample mean test. As usual, we must first recognize the random variable of interest and its sampling distribution. To accomplish this, we begin by considering the sampling distribution of the random variables P_1' and P_2'. We developed this distribution in section 2 of Chapter 8. That is, *if X_1 = number of successes in group 1 and X_2 = number of successes in group 2, then $X_1 \sim B(n_1, p_1)$ and $X_2 \sim B(n_2, p_2)$. For sufficiently large n_1 and n_2,[3] we can approximate these Binomial distributions by the Normal. That is, $X_1 \sim N[n_1 p_1, n_1 p_1 (1 - p_1)]$; $X_2 \sim N[n_2 p_2, n_2 p_2 (1 - p_2)]$. Since $P_1' = \dfrac{X_1}{n_1}$ and $P_2' = \dfrac{X_2}{n_2}$, we then write:*

$$P_1' \sim N\left(p_1, \frac{p_1 \cdot (1 - p_1)}{n_1}\right) \quad and \quad P_2' \sim N\left(p_2, \frac{p_2 \cdot (1 - p_2)}{n_2}\right)$$

Finally,

$$P_1' - P_2' \sim N\left(p_1 - p_2, \frac{p_1 \cdot (1 - p_1)}{n_1} + \frac{p_2 \cdot (1 - p_2)}{n_2}\right).$$

This last distribution is the one we will use. Contrary to the two-sample mean tests, we will not use the t distribution. If the conditions specified in footnote 3 below are met, the Normal approximation is quite accurate. Thus,

$$\text{test statistic} = z = \frac{p_1' - p_2' - (p_1 - p_2)}{\sqrt{\dfrac{p_1 \cdot (1 - p_1)}{n_1} + \dfrac{p_2 \cdot (1 - p_2)}{n_2}}}.$$

One problem with the above test statistic is that neither p_1 nor p_2 are known. However, from the null, it is assumed that $p_1 - p_2 = 0$. This implies that $p_1 = p_2$. Assuming that this is the case, we call the unknown proportion p_c. That is, $p_1 = p_2 = p_c$. We may estimate p_c by combining the data from both groups as follows:

$$p_c = \frac{x_1 + x_2}{n_1 + n_2}.$$

After a bit of algebraic manipulations and setting $p_1 - p_2 = 0$, the above test statistic may be rewritten in the form,

$$\text{test statistic} = z = \frac{p_1' - p_2' - 0}{\sqrt{p_c \cdot (1 - p_c) \cdot \left(\dfrac{1}{n_1} + \dfrac{1}{n_2}\right)}} \sim N(0,1).$$

---

[3] The necessary conditions to make this claim are: $n_1 p_1$, $n_2 p_2$, $n_1(1 - p_1)$, $n_2(1 - p_2) \geq 5$.

Example 4

An Affirmative Action group at your school wishes to dispel the belief that the number of men taking courses in the life sciences is smaller than the number of women. It was decided that only students with sophomore standing would be sampled. Two random samples, one for males and one for females, were taken. The sample data are given in the table below.

	n	X
Females	100	52
Males	50	23

Do the data present sufficient evidence to dispel the belief? Test at the 0.05 significance level.

Solution

Let F denote the female group and M denote the male group. The null and alternative hypotheses are:

$$H_o: \; p_F - p_M = 0 \quad \text{vs.} \quad H_a: \; p_F - p_M > 0 \, .$$

Let X_F = number of females taking life science courses and X_M = number of males taking life science courses. The estimates for the proportion of females and males taking science courses are:

$$p_F' = \frac{x_F}{n_F} = \frac{52}{100} = 0.52 \quad \text{and} \quad p_M' = \frac{x_M}{n_M} = \frac{23}{50} = 0.46.$$

The combined proportion is: $\quad p_c = \frac{x_F + x_M}{n_F + n_M} = \frac{52 + 23}{100 + 50} = 0.50; \; \text{thus} \; 1 - p_c = 0.50.$

From these data, the test statistic is given by:

$$\text{test statistic} = z = \frac{p_F' - p_M' - 0}{\sqrt{p_c \cdot (1 - p_c) \cdot \left(\frac{1}{n_F} + \frac{1}{n_M}\right)}} = \frac{0.52 - 0.46}{\sqrt{0.50 \cdot 0.50 \cdot \left(\frac{1}{100} + \frac{1}{50}\right)}} \approx 0.69.$$

Using the standard normal table, p-value = $P(Z > 0.69) = 0.2451$. Such a high p-value tends to favor the null hypothesis that there is no difference in the proportion of females or males taking life science courses. Thus, for $\alpha = 0.05$, we favor the null and conclude that there is no difference between the number of sophomore men and women taking life science courses.

11.4 Confidence Intervals for Matched Pairs, Two-Sample Means and Two Proportions.

Confidence interval computations for the procedures covered in this chapter follow the same format as confidence intervals from previous chapters. The one thing to keep in mind is the pertinent random variable and its appropriate distribution. We will give the formulas for each of these procedures, with actual computations appearing in the problem set.

Matched Pairs

Let d = set of differences. Random variable and distribution: $\overline{D} \sim N\left(\mu_d, \dfrac{\sigma_d^2}{n}\right)$. However, since σ_d^2 is not known, we use the t distribution with $df = n - 1$.

The $100 \cdot (1 - \alpha)\%$ confidence interval is of the form: $\overline{d} \pm EB$ where $EB = t_{df, \alpha/2} \cdot \dfrac{s_d}{\sqrt{n}}$.

Two-Sample Means

- *Case 1:* $\sigma_1^2 \neq \sigma_2^2$ or $n_1 + n_2 > 30$.

   Random variable and distribution: $\overline{X}_1 - \overline{X}_2 \sim N\left(\mu_1 - \mu_2, \dfrac{\sigma_1^2}{n_1} + \dfrac{\sigma_2^2}{n_2}\right)$. However, since the population variances are not known, we use the t distribution with df = minimum between $n_1 - 1$ and $n_2 - 1$.

   The $100 \cdot (1 - \alpha)\%$ confidence interval is of the form:

   $$\left(\overline{x}_1 - \overline{x}_2\right) \pm EB \text{ where } EB = t_{df, \alpha/2} \cdot \sqrt{\dfrac{s_1^2}{n_1} + \dfrac{s_2^2}{n_2}}.$$

- *Case 2:* $\sigma_1^2 = \sigma_2^2$ or $n_1 + n_2 \leq 30$.

   Random variable and distribution: $\overline{X}_1 - \overline{X}_2 \sim N\left(\mu_1 - \mu_2, \dfrac{\sigma_1^2}{n_1} + \dfrac{\sigma_2^2}{n_2}\right)$. However, since the population variances are not known, we use the t distribution with $df = n_1 + n_2 - 2$.

   The $100 \cdot (1 - \alpha)\%$ confidence interval is of the form:

$$\left(\bar{x}_1 - \bar{x}_2\right) \pm EB \quad \text{where} \quad EB = t_{df,\alpha/2} \bullet s_p \bullet \sqrt{\frac{1}{n_1} + \frac{1}{n_2}} \quad .$$

$$\left[\text{Note: recall that} \quad s_p = \sqrt{\frac{\left(n_1 - 1\right) \bullet s_1^2 + \left(n_2 - 1\right) \bullet s_2^2}{n_1 + n_2 - 2}}\right].$$

Two Proportions

Random variable and distribution:

$$P_1' - P_2' \sim N\!\left(p_1 - p_2, \ \frac{p_1 \bullet \left(1 - p_1\right)}{n_1} + \frac{p_2 \bullet \left(1 - p_2\right)}{n_2}\right) \quad \text{or}$$

$$P_1' - P_2' \sim N\!\left(p_1 - p_2, \ p_c \bullet \left(1 - p_c\right) \bullet \frac{1}{n_1} + \frac{1}{n_2}\right), \quad \text{where} \quad p_c = \frac{x_1 + x_2}{n_1 + n_2} \ .$$

The $100 \bullet (1 - \alpha)\%$ confidence interval is of the form:

$$\left(p_1' - p_2'\right) \pm EB \quad \text{where} \quad EB = z\!\left(\frac{\alpha}{2}\right) \bullet \sqrt{p_c \bullet \left(1 - p_c\right) \bullet \left(\frac{1}{n_1} + \frac{1}{n_2}\right)}.$$

Chapter 11 Problems

For problems **1–7**, identify the statistical procedure that fits the situation best. Choose from the following list:

- matched pairs
- two-sample means
- two proportions

1. Deciding if one section of elementary statistics performs better than another on the final exam.

2. Measuring mean improvement for a set of individuals by administering a pre-test and a post-test.

3. Determining if the mean IQ of group A is greater than the mean IQ of group B.

4. Deciding if the number of voters, among all registered constituency, favors candidate A over candidate B.

5. Determining the superiority of tire manufacturer A over tire manufacturer B.

6. Deciding the superiority of one of two methods of teaching speed reading.

7. Measuring the average drop in time for a one mile run after 12 weeks of training.

8. Large banks constantly gather data from their customers in an attempt to improve services. Recently, a large bank wanted to know if offering a credit card without the customary annual fee would increase the amount charged on the credit card by customers who the previous year charged in excess of $3,000. The bank mails a promotional letter to a random sample of 400 credit card customers. It then compares the amount they charge this year to the amount they charged last year. For the sample of 400 customers, the average increase = $300 with a standard deviation = $200.

   a. Is there a significant difference, at the 1% level, that the mean amount charged increases under the no annual fee offer? State H_0 and H_a and carry out a full hypothesis test.

b. The distribution of the amount charged is skewed right. However, extreme values are avoided because credit cards have a credit limit that is carefully enforced by the bank. Is the use of the t distribution justified in this case, even though the underlying population is not normally distributed? Explain.

c. An advocacy group claims that the data for the experiment are confounded. They point out that customers on the promotional list would have charged more this year than last even without the no annual fee. The group explains that the economy is quite prosperous and that interest rates are lower this year. How would you conduct the experiment in order to avoid confounding the no annual fee feature with the drop in interest rates?

9. A supplier of roof materials is interested in testing whether there is a difference in roof life between homes in the Northeast and in the Southwest regions of the United States. A random sample of twelve homes from each region is selected. The roofs on these homes exhibit similar characteristics (age, materials, workmanship). The following data are collected.

	Northeast	Southwest
Mean life	14.7 years	16.9 years
Variance	9	8

a. State an appropriate null and alternative hypotheses.

b. Compute the test statistic. To ease the computations, we give both standard deviation terms. You must choose the correct one.[4] (You may also wish to verify our computations).

$$\sqrt{\frac{s_{NE}^2}{n_{NE}} + \frac{s_{SW}^2}{n_{SW}}} = 1.1902; \qquad s_p \cdot \sqrt{\frac{1}{n_{NE}} + \frac{1}{n_{SW}}} = 1.1902.$$

c. What are the degrees of freedom for the t distribution?

d. Make a decision and give a conclusion for a pre-set significance of 0.05.

---

[4] Even though in this case both standard deviation terms are numerically the same, choosing the correct form will determine the correct degrees of freedom.

10. A political pollster wishes to determine voter opinion on an upcoming election. In particular, it is desired to determine if the voters' opinion is the same in two neighboring districts. The following data are obtained from a random sample of 100 voters in each district.

District A: 70 voters in favor
District B: 78 voters in favor

a. State an appropriate null and alternative hypotheses.

b. Give the distribution of the random variable of interest.

c. Compute the test statistic and the p-value.

d. Is the voters opinion the same in the two neighboring districts? Explain.

11. For the situation of problem **8**, compute the 95% confidence interval for the mean increase.

12. Two groups of university students were compared with respect to their computer science aptitude. Group 1 was composed of students who had taken at least one computer science course in high school, and Group 2 was composed of students who had never taken such a course. Both groups were given a standardized computer science aptitude test. We wish to determine if Group 1 students show an increased aptitude. The sample data are given in the table below.

	n	Mean score	Standard deviation
Group 1	125	15.5	2.7
Group 2	115	14.3	3.0

To ease the computations, we give both standard deviation terms. You must choose the correct one.

$$\sqrt{\frac{s_1^2}{n_1} + \frac{s_2^2}{n_2}} = 0.369568; \qquad s_p \cdot \sqrt{\frac{1}{n_1} + \frac{1}{n_2}} = 0.367949.$$

a. State the null and alternative hypotheses.

b. Compute the test statistic and the p-value.

c. Make a decision and give a conclusion for a pre-set α of 0.01.

13. If a random sample of 12 homes south of Center Street in Provo, NY, have a mean selling price of $50,000 with a variance of $2,400 and a random sample of 10 homes north of Center Street have a mean selling price of $52,000 with a variance of $4,800, can it be concluded that the mean price of the homes north of Center Street is greater than the mean price of homes south of Center Street? Test at the $\alpha = 0.025$ significance level. The standard deviation terms are provided below.

$$\sqrt{\frac{s_{north}^2}{n_{north}} + \frac{s_{south}^2}{n_{south}}} = 26.0768; \qquad s_p \cdot \sqrt{\frac{1}{n_{north}} + \frac{1}{n_{south}}} = 25.2587.$$

14. In a survey taken to help understand personality, 22 out of 71 persons under the age of 18 expressed a fear of meeting people while 23 of 91 persons at least 18 years of age expressed the same fear. Is there a significant difference in the true proportions of people who fear meeting people between the two age groups? Test using $\alpha = 0.03$.

For each of problems **15–17**:

a. Write the null hypothesis

b. Find the distribution of the appropriate random variable

c. Find the critical value(s) for the given α

d. Sketch and label an appropriate graph. Mark critical value(s) and shade the reject null region

e. Calculate the p-value for any test that involves the standard normal

f. Write a conclusion

g. Find the $100 \cdot (1 - \alpha)\%$ confidence interval for $\mu_A - \mu_B$

15. H_a: $\mu_A \neq \mu_B$ for $\alpha = 0.01$.

	n	$\overline{X}$	s
Group A	12	100.2	6.8
Group B	15	101.9	7.6

$$\sqrt{\frac{s_A^2}{n_A} + \frac{s_B^2}{n_B}} = 2.7756$$

$$s_p \cdot \sqrt{\frac{1}{n_A} + \frac{1}{n_B}} = 2.81135$$

16. H_a: $\mu_A < \mu_B$ for $\alpha = 0.025$.

	n	$\overline{X}$	s
Group A	12	84.5	4
Group B	15	85.9	5

$$\sqrt{\frac{s_A^2}{n_A} + \frac{s_B^2}{n_B}} = 1.73205$$

$$s_p \cdot \sqrt{\frac{1}{n_A} + \frac{1}{n_B}} = 1.77651$$

17. H_a: $\mu_A > \mu_B$ for $\alpha = 0.025$.

	n	$\overline{X}$	s
Group A	26	133.2	4.1
Group B	35	122.8	7.2

$$\sqrt{\frac{s_A^2}{n_A} + \frac{s_B^2}{n_B}} = 1.4587$$

$$s_p \cdot \sqrt{\frac{1}{n_A} + \frac{1}{n_B}} = 1.5748$$

18. A memory improvement program is tested with 12 randomly chosen individuals. Each individual is tested before the program is administered and again at the conclusion of the program. We want to know if the program is successful. The table below gives a partial list of the results with the pertinent statistics in the last two rows.

	After	Before	d = After – Before
	18	19	–1
	24	23	1
	21	18	3
	...	...	...
Mean	20.417	19.833	0.5837
Variance	10.992	9.061	1.9015

a. Perform a matched pairs test with $\alpha = 0.10$. Write a conclusion.

b. Perform a two-sample mean test with $\alpha = 0.10$. Write a conclusion.

Note: $\sqrt{\dfrac{s_A^2}{n_A} + \dfrac{s_B^2}{n_B}} = s_p \cdot \sqrt{\dfrac{1}{n_A} + \dfrac{1}{n_B}} = 1.2927$.

c. Explain any contradictions between parts **a.** and **b.**

Chapter 12

The Chi-Square Distribution and its Applications

12.1 Testing a Single Population Variance

So far, our hypotheses tests have been concerned with averages and proportions. There are many situations where the variance, instead of an average or a proportion, is of major concern. This is most frequently encountered in industrial settings where averages are easier to control than variation.

The general framework from which we test a single variance is as follows. The set of hypotheses of interest is:

$$H_0: \sigma^2 = \text{some number} \quad \text{vs.} \quad H_a: \sigma^2 \underset{>}{\overset{<}{\neq}} \text{some number.}$$

The random variable of interest is the sample variance, s^2. The data from which the sample variance is calculated is assumed to come from a population that is normally distributed. That is, $X \sim N(\mu, \sigma^2)$. Just as in the case of the t distribution, if this assumption is violated, then the hypothesis test is not reliable. Even though the data used to calculate s^2 is assumed to follow a Normal distribution, s^2 itself does not follow a Normal distribution. In fact, it took quite a while before statisticians were able to determine the exact distribution of the sample variance.[1] The key result involves the ratio of the sample variance and the assumed value, according to the null hypothesis, of the unknown population variance. That is,

$$\frac{(n-1) \cdot s^2}{\sigma^2} \quad \textit{follows a Chi-Square distribution with } (n-1) \textit{ degrees of freedom.}$$

In other words,

$$\text{test statistic} = \chi^2 = \frac{(n-1) \cdot s^2}{\sigma^2} \sim \chi^2_{n-1} \, .$$

The family of Chi-Square curves is skewed right with μ = degrees of freedom = $n-1$. The above ratio is always non-negative; thus, the smallest value χ^2 can ever take is zero. As the degrees of freedom increase (i.e., more data), the curve tends to be symmetrical about its center and resembles a Normal distribution; however, most of the applications involving the Chi-Square distribution rarely have large sample sizes. The following graph illustrates the above points.

---

[1] K. Pearson, circa 1900, was the first statistician to construct a chi-squared test of a hypothesis.

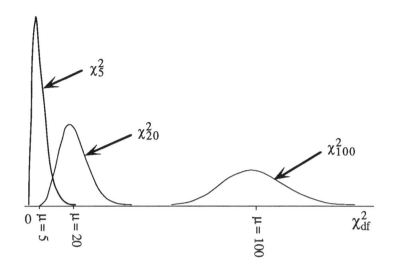

The lay out for the Chi-Square table is similar to that of the t distribution with the exception that the lack of symmetry necessitates the inclusion of left and right tail critical values. The following example illustrates how to use the table in order to read probabilities and critical values.

Example 1

Let $Y \sim \chi^2_{10}$. Find:

a. $P(Y > 18.31)$

b. k so that $P(Y < k) = 0.99$

c. $P(Y < 3.94)$

d. k so that $P(Y > k) = 0.99$

e. α if $\chi^2_{10,\alpha} = 0.025$

f. $P\left(Y > \chi^2_{10,0.005}\right)$

Discussion and Solutions

a. In order to find $P(Y > 18.31)$, locate the critical value 18.31 along the row with 10 degrees of freedom. The area to the right of 18.31 is given at the top of that column. The answer is 0.05. The graph below illustrates the situation.

Chapter 12

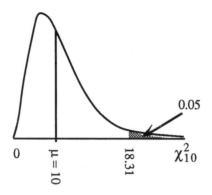

[Note: as you read through **b.**, **c.**, **d.**, **e.**, **f.**, draw sketches like the one above.]

b. $P(Y < k) = 0.99$ implies k is a critical value so that the area below it is 0.99. We note that the intersection of the row with 10 degrees of freedom and the column with 0.01 at the top is 23.21. Thus, $k = 23.21$ since $P(Y < 23.21) = 1 - P(Y > 23.21) = 1 - 0.01 = 0.99$.

c. Note that $P(Y > 3.94) = 0.95$; thus, $P(Y < 3.94) = 1 - P(Y > 3.94) = 1 - 0.95 = 0.05$.

d. $k = 2.56$.

e. The notation $\chi^2_{10,\alpha}$ stands for a critical value of the Chi-Square distribution with 10 degrees of freedom such that the area to the right is α; thus, $\alpha = 0.025$.

f. The answer to the probability question is clearly 0.005. Note that $\chi^2_{10,0.005} = 25.19$.

Note that the Chi-Square table is not complete. That is, the table doesn't give probabilities or critical values for all possible situations. Computers, and some calculators, have the capability to carry out the necessary computations in order to have access to the complete probability distribution. Thus, in testing hypotheses involving the Chi-Square distribution, it may not be possible to obtain a precise p-value. However, just like with the t distribution, we can always use the Chi–Square table to find the necessary bounds in order to make decisions and reach conclusions.

The next example illustrates how to use the Chi-Square distribution to test a single population variance.

Example 2

A bottling process produces, on average, bottles containing 12 ounces of a certain cola. The bottling company prices the bottles as if they, in fact, contain 12 ounces. Small deviations from the average of 12 ounces hardly matter. That is, differences such as 11.8 ounces or 12.2 ounces are hardly noticeable. However, if large deviations from the mean of 12 ounces suddenly occur, the bottling company runs into trouble on two counts. First, if bottles are shipped containing considerably less soda than 12 ounces, consumers will complain that they are being short changed. On the other hand, if the amount of soda significantly exceeds 12 ounces, the bottling company is, in effect, distributing "free" soda. The point being that it is critical to keep a close watch on the **variance** of the bottling process. In most bottling processes, a standard deviation not to exceed 0.5 ounces is acceptable. Suppose that the variance of a production line is being tested. Twenty five randomly selected bottles are obtained and their contents weighed. The sample variance for the 25 bottles in the sample is 0.36. Is there sufficient evidence to claim that the bottling process is out of control? Test at the 0.05 significance level.

Solution

The set of hypotheses is: H_0: $\sigma^2 = 0.25$ vs. H_a: $\sigma^2 > 0.25$. Note that this is equivalent to testing: H_0: $\sigma = 0.5$ vs. H_a: $\sigma > 0.5$. We compute the test statistic,

$$\chi^2 = \frac{(n-1) \cdot s^2}{\sigma^2} = \frac{(25-1) \cdot 0.36}{(0.5)^2} = 34.56.$$

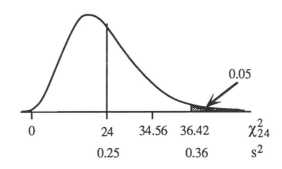

From the Chi-square table with df = 24, we note that the critical value for $\alpha = 0.05$ is 36.42. Since 34.56 < 36.42, it is clear that the p-value exceeds 0.05. That is, $P(\chi^2 > 34.56) > 0.05$. Thus, the decision is to continue to favor the null and conclude that the standard deviation does not exceed 0.5 ounces; thus, the bottling process is "not out of control". Notice that changing the significance level to $\alpha = 0.10$ will cause us to conclude that there is evidence against the null; thus, the bottling process would then be considered to be "out of control".

12.2 Confidence Interval about a Single Population Variance

The form of the confidence interval for σ^2 is no longer of the type $\sigma^2 \pm$ margin of error, since the Chi–Square distribution is not symmetrical. Instead, the end points of the confidence interval must be individually computed using left and right tail critical values for the appropriate Chi-Square distribution. This change in the computation of the confidence interval does not change its prior interpretation.

However, there are other problems. In particular, it must be made clear that the normality assumption underlying the distribution of the population we are sampling from plays havoc with the reliability of the confidence interval about a single population variance. The key difficulty is that while the standard deviation is a very useful measure of spread for normal/symmetric distributions, it is not nearly as useful for other distributions in general. In fact, because non–symmetric distributions have unequally spread tails, no single numerical measure can reasonably describe their spread. This is precisely the case with the s^2 random variable. The meaning of all this is to be very, very cautious when carrying out inference procedures about variances (i.e., testing hypotheses, calculating confidence intervals). More so than with any other procedures studied in elementary statistics, inferences about variances involving real applications should be done under the supervision of expert advice.

Example 3

We refer to the situation of Example 2. above, where $n = 25$ and $s^2 = 0.36$. We wish to construct a 95% confidence interval about the population variance, σ^2.

Solution and Discussion

For a given α level, we can find left and right critical values for the corresponding Chi-Square distribution according to the following graph:

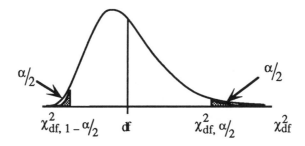

where,

$$left \; tail \; critical \; value = \chi^2_{df, \, 1- \alpha/2} \quad and \quad right \; tail \; critical \; value = \chi^2_{df, \, \alpha/2}.$$

For $n = 25$ and $\alpha = 0.05$ (use the Chi-square table to verify):

$$\text{left tail critical value} = \chi^2_{24,0.975} = 12.40 \quad \text{and right tail critical value} = \chi^2_{24,0.025} = 39.36.$$

We have already seen that $\dfrac{(n-1) \cdot s^2}{\sigma^2}$ = value of Chi-square. If we set value of Chi-square equal to the left tail and right tail critical values, we can compute the end points of the confidence interval about σ^2. That is,

$$\text{left endpoint of confidence interval: } \frac{(n-1) \cdot s^2}{\text{right tail critical value}} = \frac{24 \cdot 0.36}{39.36} = 0.2195.$$

$$\text{right endpoint of confidence interval: } \frac{(n-1) \cdot s^2}{\text{left tail critical value}} = \frac{24 \cdot 0.36}{12.40} = 0.6968.$$

These calculations are reflected in the following graph.

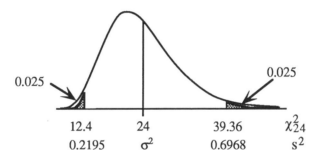

Thus, the 95% confidence interval for the population variance, σ^2, is (0.2195, 0.6968).   The corresponding 95% confidence interval for the population standard deviation, σ, is (0.4685, 0.8347) (i.e., just take the square root of the endpoints for the σ^2 interval).

12.3 Other Applications of the Chi-Square Distribution

At different places throughout the book, we have warned the reader against using statistical procedures when distributional assumptions about the underlying population cannot be reasonably verified. *Goodness-of-fit* procedures, based on the Chi-Square distribution, give us an opportunity to test statistical hypotheses about the distribution of data.

In addition, all hypotheses test situations we have previously encountered have involved numerical values of population parameters. The Chi-Square distribution allows us to compare categorical variables via the the formulation of categorical hypotheses. Included in these hypotheses will be methods to handle *Contingency Tables* and multiple comparisons.

Goodness-of-fit

Suppose we have a data set obtained through random sampling. We wish to determine if the underlying population (i.e., the population the data came from) follows a particular distribution. There are different ways of doing this. For instance, if the data set is sufficiently small, a stem-leaf diagram might be all that is necessary in conducting a preliminary investigation about the nature of the data. If the data set is large in size, other plots might be more appropriate. For instance, we have seen that histograms could be useful, even though they are extremely sensitive to the class interval width.[2]

Goodness-of-fit tests use numerical methods, instead of graphical ones, in order to test statistical hypotheses about the distribution of a data set. The logic of such tests is as follows.

- State a set of hypotheses based on the distribution being tested. Appropriate parameters must be specified. For instance, it is not sufficient to state an hypothesis to include any normal distribution. Instead, specific values of μ and σ must be explicitly stated.

- The heart of the procedure is to compare the observed data with what is called the "expected" data. The expected data comes from theoretical considerations. It represents what is supposed to have happened if the observed data came from the distribution specified in the null. This comparison is made in terms of squared deviations standardized by the expected frequency.

- The sum of the standardized squared deviations follows a Chi-Square distribution with the appropriate degrees of freedom. We can now either compute a p-value or compare the obtained sum to the appropriate critical value from the Chi-Square table.

The above logic describes the necessary steps in carrying out any Goodness-of-fit tests. We realize that some of the details have been left out. The following example will fully illustrate the procedure while at the same time providing pertinent details.

---

[2] There are other plots available for determining if a data set fits a particular distribution. For instance, plots made on "probability paper" are used to check for how close the data fits a particular normal distribution. These procedures are beyond the scope of our discussion.

Example 4

Dice manufacturers constantly run tests in order to ensure that the dice being produced are fair. Suppose we choose one die at random from a production line. We wish to determine if the die is fair.

Solution and discussion

Intuitively, we would immediately think of rolling the die a given number of times, tally out the outcomes, and then compare the observations to some standard about the fairness of a die. The set of hypotheses of interest would then be:

$$H_o: \text{the die is fair} \quad \text{vs.} \quad H_a: \text{the die is not fair.}$$

Note that we have stated a set of qualitative hypotheses (as opposed to quantitative hypotheses). Also, note that a statement like "the die is fair" includes the need for multiple comparisons. That is, in order to carry out such test, we must compare the outcomes related to all six possible categories (i.e., one category per face of the die).

Prior to carrying out the actual test, we must decide how many times the die will be rolled. This is not a trivial decision. The number of times the die is rolled has an impact on the outcome of the procedure.[3] Suppose we decide to roll the die 42 times. The observed data are recorded in the table below.

Face on die	Observed Frequency
1	4
2	8
3	7
4	11
5	4
6	8

The random variable of interest for this experiment is X = number on face of die. Under the null, the distribution of X is Uniform in the interval $[1,6]$.[4] Thus, from a theoretical viewpoint, we would

---

[3] We will see this later on in the discussion; however, it is closely connected to the power of the test, the sensitivity of the test procedure and the non-symmetrical nature of the Chi-Square distribution.

[4] We realize that X is discrete. We also realize that in Chapter 5 the uniform distribution was used to model a continuous random variable. The discrete uniform behaves like its continuous counterpart with the one exception that its range is the set of integers in [a,b].

expect each of the faces on the die to appear exactly seven times (i.e., 42/6). We expand the above table by including the Expected Frequency column.

Face on die	Observed Frequency	Expected Frequency
1	4	7
2	8	7
3	7	7
4	11	7
5	4	7
6	8	7

We must now compare the observed frequencies to the expected ones. We do this by computing the quantity:

$$\frac{\left(\text{Observed Frequency} - \text{Expected Frequency}\right)^2}{\text{Expected Frequency}}$$

for each face on the die. For expediency, we will denote the above by $\dfrac{(O - E)^2}{E}$. We now have the completed table.

Face on die	Observed Frequency	Expected Frequency	$\dfrac{(O - E)^2}{E}$
1	3	7	16/7
2	8	7	1/7
3	7	7	0/7
4	12	7	25/7
5	4	7	9/7
6	8	7	1/7

The quantity $\displaystyle\sum_{\text{all } X} \frac{(O - E)^2}{E}$ follows a Chi-Square distribution with degrees of freedom = number of categories – 1. That is, $\displaystyle\sum_{\text{all } X} \frac{(O - E)^2}{E} \sim \chi_5^2$. We note that the sum of the $\dfrac{(O - E)^2}{E}$ column is $52/7 \approx 7.43$. Entering the Chi-Square table at 5 degrees of freedom, we note that a critical value of 7.43 will have an area to its right in excess of 0.10. The graph below depicts this situation.

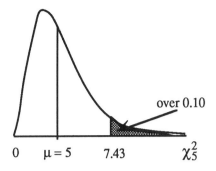

Thus, p-value = $P(\chi^2 > 7.43) > 0.10$. Therefore, the evidence is in favor of the null. This means that there isn't sufficient evidence to claim that the die is not fair.

Example 5

As in Example **4**, but we now roll the die 420 times. For comparison purposes, we assume that the observed frequencies are in proportion with those of Example **4**. The completed table is given below.

Face on die	Observed Frequency	Expected Frequency	$\dfrac{(O - E)^2}{E}$
1	30	70	1600/70
2	80	70	100/70
3	70	70	0/70
4	120	70	2500/70
5	40	70	900/70
6	80	70	100/70

The sum of the $\dfrac{(O - E)^2}{E}$ column is 74.29. A look at the Chi-Square table with 5 degrees of freedom shows that the area to the right of 74.29 is considerably smaller than 0.005. The picture below depicts the situation.

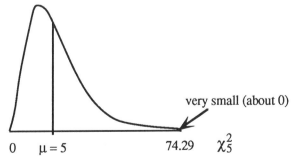

Thus, with p-value smaller than 0.005, there is sufficient evidence to reject the null and favor the belief that the die is biased.

Chapter 12

What causes the rejection of the null hypothesis in Example **5** even though the outcomes were in the same proportion as in Example **4**? The answer lies in the power of the test. That is, deviations from the expectation when the experiment is conducted a small number of times are not nearly as fatal as when the experiment is conducted a large number of times. Realize that this follows from the Law of Large Numbers.

Example 6

In the game of baseball, one of the most important statistics is a pitcher's ERA.[5] We are interested in determining if the ERA distribution for Tom Seaver's pitching career follows a normal distribution. Tom Seaver's pitching career in the major leagues spanned a period of 20 years (1967–1986). The ERA data are from: *The Baseball Encyclopedia; MacMillan, 1990.*

Year	Team	ERA	Year	Team	ERA
1967	New York Mets	2.76	1968	New York Mets	2.20
1969	New York Mets	2.21	1970	New York Mets	2.81
1971	New York Mets	1.76	1972	New York Mets	2.92
1973	New York Mets	2.08	1974	New York Mets	3.20
1975	New York Mets	2.38	1976	New York Mets	2.59
1977	New York Mets and Cincinnati Reds	2.58	1978	Cincinnati Reds	2.87
1979	Cincinnati Reds	3.14	1980	Cincinnati Reds	3.64
1981	Cincinnati Reds	2.55	1982	Cincinnati Reds	5.50
1983	New York Mets	3.55	1984	Chicago White Sox	3.95
1985	Chicago White Sox	3.17	1986	Chicago White Sox and Boston Red Sox	4.03

Solution and discussion

In formulating the set of hypotheses, we must specify the parameters of the Normal distribution we are testing. Since this is all of the data (i.e., Seaver is not coming out of retirement to pitch again), we compute μ and σ^2. Using a calculator, we obtain: $\mu = 2.9945$ and $\sigma^2 = 0.6855$. Thus,

H_0: data came from $N(2.9945, 0.6855)$ vs. H_a: data did not come from $N(2.9945, 0.6855)$.

---

[5] ERA stands for Earned Run Average. It is a measure of how efficient a pitcher is in terms of allowing the opposition to score runs per nine innings pitched. Low ERA's (typically 3.00 or lower) are indicative of superior pitching performances.

In order to compute the Chi-Square statistic, we must build a table similar to the one in Example **5**. It is tempting to consider each of the twenty seasons as a category, but this will result in diluting the available data. Instead, we group the data in an attempt to reduce the number of categories. How many categories to pick is subjective. From past experience using the Normal distribution, we have seen that if the data are symmetrical, any number of categories between 6 and 14 is adequate. We choose 8 categories by setting the interval width at 0.40 and starting at 1.8.[6] Note that the last category serves a dual purpose. It includes any value above 4.2 while not allowing the extreme value of 5.5 to unduly influence the Chi-Squrare statistic. Here are the group data.

Class interval	Observed Frequency
below 1.8	1
1.8 to 2.2	2
2.2 to 2.6	5
2.6 to 3.0	4
3.0 to 3.4	3
3.4 to 3.8	2
3.8 to 4.2	2
above 4.2	1

The Expected Frequency column is constructed by computing the probability of an observation falling in each category and multiplying this probability by 20. This is laborious, since we must use the z transformation repeatedly and read the probabilities from the standard normal table. We used a computer to complete our table. We demonstrate the computations for the first two categories:

$$P(X < 1.8) = P\left(Z < \frac{1.8 - 2.9945}{\sqrt{0.6855}}\right) = P(Z < -1.443) = 0.0745;$$

$$P(1.8 < X < 2.2) = P\left(\frac{1.8 - 2.9945}{\sqrt{0.6855}} < Z < \frac{2.2 - 2.9945}{\sqrt{0.6855}}\right) = P(-1.443 < Z < -0.96) = 0.0941.$$

Thus, the Expected Frequency for the first two categories are: $20 \cdot 0.0745 = 1.49$ and $20 \cdot 0.0941 = 1.88$. The completed table follows.

---

[6] 0.40 is roughly half of one standard deviation. This choice is arbitrary but useful. As a rule of thumb, it will bring out any symmetrical tendencies present in the data.

Chapter 12

Class interval	Observed Frequency	Expected Frequency[7]	$\frac{(O - E)^2}{E}$
below 1.8	1	1.49	0.1611
1.8 to 2.2	2	1.88	0.0077
2.2 to 2.6	5	3.56	0.5825
2.6 to 3.0	4	3.72	0.0211
3.0 to 3.4	3	3.70	0.1324
3.4 to 3.8	2	2.94	0.3005
3.8 to 4.2	2	1.85	0.0122
above 4.2	1	0.86	0.0228

The sum of the $\frac{(O - E)^2}{E}$ column is about 1.24. This is the Chi-Square statistic. Entering the Chi-Square table at 7 degrees of freedom, we see that the area to the right of 1.24 is 0.99. That is, p-value = $P(\chi^2 > 1.24) = 0.99$. This is overwhelming evidence in favor of the null.

Goodness-of-fit tests are always one-sided on the right. In other words, evidence against the null hypothesis occurs if the computed value of the Chi-Square statistic (i.e., the sum of the $\frac{(O - E)^2}{E}$ column) falls in the right tail of the distribution. Values of the Chi-Square statistic falling in the left tail of the distribution (i.e., close to 0) are an indication that the observed and expected frequencies are very close to each other; thus, a "good fit" is imminent.

For a Goodness-of-fit test to be reliable, the number of data values falling in each of the established categories should exceed 1. In fact, if 1 or less values occur in more than 20% of the established categories the test is meaningless. This is true for both, the observed and the expected frequencies. Ideally, each category should contain at least 5 data values in order for the test to have sufficient power. In the Seaver example, two categories have values of 1 or less. This is barely within the indicated guideline of 20% of the established categories (i.e., 20% of 8 = 1.6). Only one category contains five or more data values. Thus, we know that in this example, the power is less than optimal.[8]

---

[7] The last entry in this column, 0.86, was obtained by subtracting the sum of the prior expectations from 20.

[8] See, for example, *Goodness-of-fit techniques*, D'Agostino and Stephens, Marcel Dekker, New York, 1986, pages 63-95.

Suppose we wish to compare the proportion of successes in more than two treatment groups. We need a new statistical test. We begin by presenting the data in a new format: *a two-way table.* One immediate advantage is that two-way tables have more uses than comparing proportions of successes in several groups. They can also be used to describe how categorical variables relate to each other.[9] The clincher is that the same statistical procedure is applicable to both situations.

The ability to carry out multiple comparisons with one single test are many. For instance, if we wish to test the null hypothesis: $p_1 = p_2 = p_3$ using the method for two-sample proportions, we would have to conduct three different tests. That is, we would have to run a separate test for each of the following null hypotheses: $p_1 = p_2$; $p_2 = p_3$; $p_1 = p_3$. One major weakness of this approach is that we will end up with three different p-values. None of the three p-values tells us how likely it is that three sample proportions are spread apart as far as these may be. It may be that $p_1 = 0.10$ and $p_3 = 0.45$ are significantly different if we look at just group 1 and group 3, but not significantly different if we know that they are the smallest and largest proportions in three groups. In fact, as the number of groups increases, we expect the gap between the smallest and largest sample proportion to get larger. If this is not clear, think of the shortest and tallest person in larger and larger groups of people. As the number of people in the groups increases, the gap between the shortest and the tallest person increases as well.

Methods involving multiple comparisons belong in more advanced statistical courses. At this point, we are definitely beyond the scope of elementary statistics. Without being patronizing, we tell you up front that you should definitely feel a certain sense of pride about getting this far.

Statistical procedures for handling multiple comparisons usually consist of two stages:

1. An overall test to determine if there is sufficient evidence against the null hypothesis of no difference.

2. If there is sufficient evidence against the null, then a more detailed analysis is necessary before it can be determined which groups or parameters differ and how large the difference(s) is(are).

The overall test is straightforward (as we will see in the examples below). The follow up analysis, if needed, is a lot more complex and detailed. We will look only at the overall test and leave the other details to future courses in your statistical development.

---

[9] The problem of comparing multiple treatment means pertains to a different statistical methodology and will be addressed in the next chapter.

Example 7

A Gallup poll (*Newsweek*, April 1984, page 21) asked 260 males and 263 female students whether male or female students are more assertive in class. The results were arranged in a two-way table (this is a *3 by 2* table: 3 rows, 2 columns) as follows:

	Males	Females	Totals
Men are	80	61	141
Females are	104	112	216
No difference	76	90	166
Totals	260	263	523

We wish to test the hypotheses that the answer given is the same regardless on whether the student is a male or female.

Solution and discussion

The question is to determine if there is any relationship between the gender factor and the assertiveness response. We may rephrase the question and simply ask, "is the response independent of gender?". The null hypothesis, stated qualitatively, will be that there is no difference on the given response due to gender. That is:

H_0: response is independent of gender

while the corresponding alternative hypothesis is:

H_a: response depends on gender.

Similar to the Goodness-of-fit tests procedure, we must compare the observed data in the above table with the expected data under the assumption of the null hypothesis. That is, we must obtain a set of *expected frequencies*, these will be the frequencies we would expect if H_0 were true.

The above table has *six cells* of interest. The column and row totals are also called the *marginals*. The cell counts are also called the *elements*. For the above table, the *table total* is 523. The formula to obtain the expected frequency for each of the six cells is:

(1)
$$\text{expected frequency} = \frac{\text{row total} \cdot \text{column total}}{\text{table total}}.$$

To understand why the above formula works, think in terms of proportions. Let's find the expected frequency for the cell composed of the "Men are" row and the "Males" column. The proportion of Males among all 523 subjects is:

$$\frac{\text{total of Males column}}{\text{table total}} = \frac{260}{523} = 0.4971.$$

Think of this last number as p_m, the overall proportion of males. If H_0 is true, we expect (except for random variation), the same proportion of males answering "Men are". So, the expected number of males among the 141 persons who answer "Men are" is:

$$n \cdot p_m = 141 \cdot 0.4971 = 70.1.$$

Note that we obtain the same result if we instead use formula (1) above. That is,

$$\text{expected frequency} = \frac{141 \cdot 260}{523} = 70.1.$$

Again, the computations could be laborious and are better relegated to a computer or an appropriate calculator. We use our computer to obtain the remaining expected frequencies. The table below shows the expected frequencies in parenthesis and in italics (rounded off to 1 decimal).

	Males	Females	Totals
Men are	80 *(70.1)*	61 *(70.9)*	141
Females are	104 *(107.3)*	112 *(108.6)*	216
No difference	76 *(82.5)*	90 *(83.5)*	166
Totals	260	263	523

There is more! We now need to compute the Chi-Square statistic. It is the sum, over all six cells, of the familiar quantity $\dfrac{(O - E)^2}{E}$. That is,

$$\text{Chi-Square statistic} = \frac{(80 - 70.1)^2}{70.1} + \frac{(61 - 70.9)^2}{70.9} + ... + \frac{(90 - 83.5)^2}{83.5} = 4.02.$$

The degrees of freedom for the corresponding Chi-Square distribution is given by:

$$df = (\textit{number of rows} - 1) \cdot (\textit{number of columns} - 1)$$
$$= (3 - 1) \cdot (2 - 1) = 2.$$

Thus, to find the p-value, enter the Chi-Square table at 2 degrees of freedom and find the closest value to

4.02. This value is 4.61. The area to the right of 4.61 is 0.10; thus, the area to the right of 4.02 must be larger than 0.10. In fact, from our computer,

$$\text{p-value} = P(\text{Chi-Square} > 4.02) = 0.134.$$

Regardless of whether or not you are able to obtain the exact p-value, the evidence favors the null hypothesis of independence in the response due to gender.

The reliability of using the Chi-Square distribution when testing hypotheses in a Contingency Table format also hinges on the cell count. Just like with the Goodness-of-fit procedure, a cell count of at least 5 is recommended, no cells can have a zero count, and no more than 20% of the cells can have counts of 1. These guidelines are stricter if a 2 by 2 Contingency Table is being analyzed: all four cells must have counts of 5 or greater.

Chapter 12 Problems

1. Assume that $X \sim \chi^2_{df, \alpha}$. Find:

   a. $\chi^2_{20, \, 0.01}$

   b. $\chi^2_{20, \, 0.95}$

   c. $P\left(X < \chi^2_{7, \, 0.005}\right)$

   d. $P\left(X > \chi^2_{15, \, 0.005}\right)$

2. Assume that $X \sim \chi^2_{df, \alpha}$.

   a. If $P\left(X > \chi^2_{15}\right) = 0.01$, find χ^2_{15}

   b. If $P\left(X < \chi^2_{12}\right) = 0.01$, find χ^2_{12}

   c. If $P\left(X < \chi^2_{21}\right) = 0.1$, find χ^2_{21}

   d. If $P\left(X < \chi^2_{16}\right) = 0.99$, find χ^2_{16}

3. The makers of a car muffler claim that the life of the muffler has a standard deviation of 0.8 of a year. A random sample of 16 mufflers showed a standard deviation of 1.1 years. At the 5% level of significance, does the data indicate that the variation exceeds the claim?

4. Suppose that a random sample of n items is taken with sample variance $s^2 = 0.0384$. We wish to test the following hypotheses at $\alpha = 0.05$:

$$H_0: \; \sigma = 0.1225 \quad vs \quad H_a: \; \sigma > 0.1225$$

   a. Test the above if the sample size is 25.

   b. Test the above if the sample size is 7.

5. Construct the 95% confidence interval about σ^2 for the situation of **4a.** and **4b.** above.

6. A random sample of size 10 produced a variance of 14. Is this sufficient to reject the null hypothesis that $\sigma^2 = 6$ when tested using a 0.05 level of significance? Using a 0.01 level of significance?

7. A company wishes to determine if 5 sales people have equal sales records. The individual sales records over a specific time period are given in the chart below.

a. State the null and alternative hypotheses.

b. Complete the chart below.

Actual sales   110   130   70   90   100

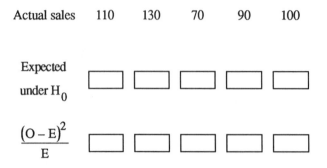

Expected under H_0

$$\frac{(O-E)^2}{E}$$

c. Test H_0 at the 0.01 level of significance.

8. A local university studied student performance in a course required for its Liberal Arts degree. One issue of interest is the relationship between time spent in activities not related to school (i.e., work, parenting, etc.) and whether a student earned a C or better in the course. Here are the data for the 120 students who answered the question.

	Hours per week not related to school		
	< 5	**5 to 20**	**> 20**
C or better	12	70	2
D or F or W	8	23	5

a. This is a two-way Contingency Table. How many rows? How many columns?

b. Give the row and column marginals.

c. Find the proportion of successful students (C or better) in each of the three time slots for activities not related to school. What kind of relationship between hours per week not related to school and succeeding in the course do these proportions appear to indicate?

d. State the null hypothesis for this situation.

e. Find the expected frequency for each of the six cells.

f. Compute the Chi-Square statistic and test using $\alpha = 0.05$.

g. Does the fact that one cell has a count of only 2 have a bearing on the reliability of the test procedure? Explain.

9. In the sport of thoroughbred horse racing, the horses designated to run in a given race are randomly assigned to a post position. Post positions are the slots at the starting gate in which the horses are placed. A typical starting gate has 12 slots. It is rare when more than 12 horses are entered in a race. For instance, the number 1 post position is next to the rail and the number 12 post position is farthest from the rail. Horse handicappers (i.e., horse players) keep detail records of the number of winners for each post position for each type of race in the hope of detecting "biases" that would give them a betting advantage. Here are the records for Bay Meadows Race Track (Bay Meadows is in San Mateo, California) for 90 randomly selected sprint races of the 1994 fall meet.[10] Test the null hypothesis: "winning is independent of post position" at the 0.05 significance level.

Post Position	Number of Winners	Races using this Post Position
1	13	90
2	9	90
3	15	90
4	8	90
5	12	90
6	8	90
7	10	75
8	7	60
9	3	30
10	1	25
11	2	20
12	2	15

10. A large study of child care used samples from the Current Population Survey over a period of several years. The sample data can be safely considered to form a random sample of child-care workers. The Current Population Survey has three classes of child-care workers: private households, non-households, and preschool teacher. Here are the data on the number of blacks among women workers in these three classes.[11]

	Black	Total
Household	172	2455
Non-household	167	1191
Preschool teacher	86	659

a. Give the percent of black workers for each class of child-care.

---

[10] A sprint race is any race at a distance of less than 1 mile. Races at a mile or longer are called "routes".

[11] David Blau, "The child care labor market", *Journal of Human Resources*, volume 27, 1992, pages 9-39.

b. Rearrange the data into a two-way table of class of worker by race (black or other).

c. State the null and alternative hypotheses for the two-way table situation.

d. Can we safely use the Chi-Square distribution? Explain.

e. The Chi-Square statistic for the two-way table is 53.19. What are the degrees of freedom for this situation?

f. Use the Chi-Square table to approximate the p-value and give a conclusion.

11. The following data represent a random sample of 1000 observations from a Poisson distribution with mean $= \mu = 1$. We wish to test if the data could have been produced by a Binomial with n = 100 and p = 0.01. Test at the 0.05 significance level.

X	0	1	2	3	4	5	6
Observed Frequency	361	370	184	65	16	3	1

Note: Here is the PDF, up to X = 6, for the Binomial distribution with n = 100 and p = 0.01.

X	0	1	2	3	4	5	6
P(X = x)	0.3660	0.3697	0.1849	0.0610	0.0149	0.0029	0.0005

12. A student group claims that, on average, students travel for at least 25 minutes in order to reach college each day. The college admissions office obtained a random sample of 25 one-way travel times from students. The sample had a mean of 19.4 minutes and a standard deviation of 9.65 minutes.

a. Find the 90% confidence interval for μ and σ.

b. We wish to determine the sample size needed to estimate μ within 1.5 minutes with 90% confidence. We are concerned with 9.65 as the estimte of σ. Use the confidence interval of part **a.** to determine a 90% confidence interval for μ using a conservative estimate for σ.

Chapter 13

The F Distribution and its Applications

13.1 Testing Two Population Variances

The two most descriptive characteristics of a distribution are its center and spread. In a Normal distribution, we measure center and spread by the mean and standard deviation. We have alluded to the fact that for non-symmetric distributions there is no single measure of spread that can account for the skewness of the data, especially in light of the fact that such skewness causes unequally spread tails.

There are methods for inference about the standard deviations of normal populations. The most common procedure is called the *F test* for comparing the spread of two normal populations. The key assumption is that we have two random samples from two normal populations. That is, we have a random sample of size n_1 from $N(\mu_1, \sigma_1^2)$ and another random sample of size n_2 from $N(\mu_2, \sigma_2^2)$. Both, the population means and population variances, are unknown. The set of hypotheses of interest is:

$$H_0: \sigma_1^2 = \sigma_2^2 \quad \text{or} \quad \sigma_1 = \sigma_2 \, ,$$

$$H_a: \sigma_1^2 \overset{<}{\underset{>}{\neq}} \sigma_2^2 \quad \text{or} \quad \sigma_1 \overset{<}{\underset{>}{\neq}} \sigma_2 \, .$$

The F statistic consists of the ratio of the corresponding sample variances. This follows from the fact that the F distribution is the ratio of two Chi-Squares. We recall from Chapter 12 that to test a single variance the Chi-Square distribution is used. In terms of two independent Chi-Squares, the F ratio is defined as follows:

$$\text{for population 1:} \quad \frac{(n_1 - 1) \cdot s_1^2}{\sigma_1^2} \sim \chi^2_{n_1 - 1}$$

$$\text{for population 2:} \quad \frac{(n_2 - 1) \cdot s_2^2}{\sigma_2^2} \sim \chi^2_{n_2 - 1}$$

thus,

$$(1) \qquad \text{F statistic} = \frac{\dfrac{(n_1 - 1) \cdot s_1^2}{\sigma_1^2}}{\dfrac{(n_2 - 1) \cdot s_2^2}{\sigma_2^2}} \; .$$

However, from the null, it is assumed that $\sigma_1^2 = \sigma_2^2$. Thus, we may express equation (1) in the form:

$$(2) \qquad \text{F statistic} = \frac{s_1^2}{s_2^2} \sim F_{n_1 - 1, \, n_2 - 1} \; .$$

That is, the ratio $\dfrac{s_1^2}{s_2^2}$ is distributed F with $n_1 - 1$ and $n_2 - 1$ degrees of freedom.

The F distributions are a family of distributions with two parameters: degrees of freedom for the numerator and degrees of freedom for the denominator. The degrees of freedom for the numerator are always first. Interchanging the degrees of freedom changes the distribution. That is, the distribution denoted by $F_{5,8}$ is different from $F_{8,5}$. The F distributions are not symmetric but are skewed right. This follows on the footsteps of the associated Chi-Square (i.e., also right skewed). The figure below shows the basic shape. Because variances are always non-negative quantities, the F ratio is always non-negative; thus, values of F are always zero or larger. The peak of the F distribution is always near 1. When the two populations have the same variance, we expect the two sample variances to be close in magnitude, so that F takes a value close to 1. Values of F far from 1, in either direction, are evidence against the null hypothesis of equal variances.

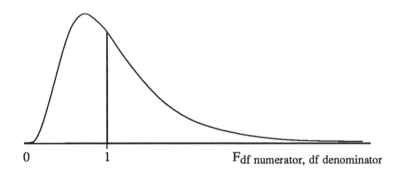

Tables of critical values for the F distribution are quite extensive because we need a separate table for every pair of degrees of freedom. The F tables in the back of the book give critical values for the following right tail probabilities: 0.01, 0.025, 0.05, and 0.10. For example, the right tail critical values for the $F_{5,8}$ distribution are:

right tail probability	0.01	0.025	0.05	0.10
critical value	6.63	4.82	3.69	2.73

The extreme skewness of the F distribution causes new complications. In particular, it is somewhat cumbersome to obtain left tail critical values. Of course, there is software that does away with this inconvenience. Yet, with a bit of care, it is possible to compute left tail critical values from right tail ones. Also, if we arrange the null hypothesis in such a way that the larger sample variance is always in the numerator we will never have to deal with the left tail. The following examples will illustrate these points.

Example 1

Let $X \sim F_{10,6}$. Find the following:

    a. $P(X > 4.06)$ **b.** If $P(X > k) = 0.025$, find k.

    c. $F_{10,6,0.01}$ **d.** If $P(X < k) = 0.05$, find k.

Solution and discussion

    a. Since $P(X > 4.06)$ is a right tail probability, we go through the F tables in order to locate the critical value 4.06 corresponding to 10 degrees of freedom for the numerator and 6 degrees of freedom for the denominator. The corresponding right tail probability is 0.05. Thus, $P(X > 4.06) = 0.05$. The picture below depicts the situation.

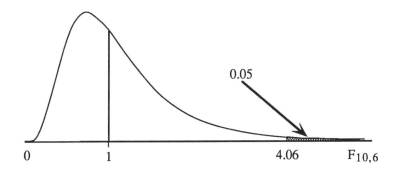

         Chapter 13

[Note: draw similar pictures for **b.** and **c.**]

b. Look in the 0.025 F table and locate the critical value corresponding to 10 degrees of freedom for the numerator and 6 degrees of freedom for the denominator. The critical value is 5.46. Thus, $P(X > k) = 0.025$ implies $k = 5.46$.

c. The notation $F_{10,6,\,0.01}$ denotes the right tail critical value corresponding to 10 degrees of freedom for the numerator and 6 degrees of freedom for the denominator such that the right tail probability is 0.01. To find the critical value, look in the 0.01 F table and find 7.87. That is, $F_{10,6,\,0.01} = 7.87$.

d. This is a left tail situation. That is, we must find the critical value, k, such that the area to its left is 0.05. To do this, we use the corresponding right tail critical value and reverse the degrees of freedom. The procedure is as follows:

1. Find the right tail critical value of the F distribution with degrees of freedom reversed. That is, find the right tail critical value corresponding to a right tail probability of 0.05 coming from the $F_{6,10}$ distribution. Note that this number is 3.22.

2. Compute the reciprocal of 3.22. That is,

$$F_{10,6,0.95} = \frac{1}{F_{6,10,0.05}} = \frac{1}{3.22} \approx 0.311 = k.$$

The picture for this situation is given below.

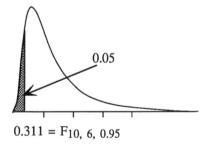

$0.311 = F_{10,\,6,\,0.95}$

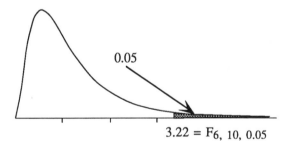

$3.22 = F_{6,\,10,\,0.05}$

<u>**Example 2**</u>

It has been noted that calcium changes the variability of blood pressure in black men. Two independent random samples of 9 and 10 black men are chosen. The sample with 9 men receives a placebo and the sample with 10 men is given the calcium. The sample standard deviations are: for the sample with 9 men, s = 8.95; for the sample with 10 men, s = 6.011.

Solution

The set of hypotheses is:

$$H_0: \sigma_1 = \sigma_2 \quad \text{vs.} \quad H_a: \sigma_1 \neq \sigma_2 \text{ (two-tailed situation) .}$$

In order to force the F statistic to fall in the right tail of the F distribution, we choose population 1 to coincide with the larger of the two standard deviations. That is, we choose population 1 to be the group with 9 men. The test statistic is:

$$\text{F statistic} = \frac{s_1^2}{s_2^2} = \frac{8.95^2}{6.011^2} = 2.217.$$

The F distribution of interest is $F_{8,9}$. From the F tables, we see that the right critical value closest to 2.217 is 2.47. The area to the right of 2.47 is 0.10; thus, since this is a two-tailed test, the p-value exceeds 0.20. That is, $2 \cdot P(F > 2.217) > 0.20$ (from our computer, $2 \cdot P(F > 2.217) = 0.2572$). Thus, the result is not significant. This means that the data favors the null hypothesis that the standard deviations for the two populations are not different.

However, things are not quite what they appear to be. The above conclusion is only valid *if* the underlying populations were normal. However, the original data (not shown here) for the group of 10 men show marked deviations from normality. Thus, we can't be all that sure about the conclusion. The lesson to be learned is to be extremely careful when making inferences using the F distribution. There must be ample evidence of normality before any procedure dealing with spread can be fully trusted.

13.2 Comparing Several Means: The One Way Analysis of Variance

In Chapter 11 we studied two-sample test procedures using the t distribution to test hypotheses about means from two independent populations. We need a method for comparing multiple means. Suppose there are three independent groups or populations. Of interest is the hypotheses:

$$H_0: \mu_1 = \mu_2 = \mu_3 \quad \text{vs.} \quad H_a: \text{not all of } \mu_1, \mu_2, \mu_3 \text{ are equal.}$$

It is conceivable to think of comparing these three population means by using the two-sample t test several times. That is, we could test:

$H_0: \mu_1 = \mu_2$, in order to look for differences between the mean of groups 1 and 2, or

$H_0: \mu_2 = \mu_3$, in order to look for differences between the mean of groups 2 and 3, or

$H_0: \mu_1 = \mu_3$, in order to look for differences between the mean of groups 1 and 3.

We have already seen that the weakness of doing three separate test is that we get three p-values, one for each test. That doesn't tell us how likely it is that three sample means are spread apart as far as these might be.

The problem of how to do multiple comparisons at once belongs in advanced statistics courses. Statistical methods for dealing with multiple comparisons consist of two stages:

1 . An overall test to see if there is sufficient evidence of any differences among the parameters,

2 . A detailed follow-up analysis to decide which of the parameters differ and to actually estimate by how much they differ.

The overall test is a lot easier than the follow-up analysis. In this section we present an overall test for comparing several population means at once. This is called the **Analysis of Variance**, abbreviated *ANOVA*.

The F test for the Analysis of Variance

The general hypotheses for an Analysis of Variance test comparing several means from k independent populations is of the form:

$$H_0: \mu_1 = \mu_2 = ... = \mu_k \quad \text{vs.} \quad H_a: \text{not all } \mu_1, \mu_2, ..., \mu_k \text{ are equal.}$$

The alternative hypothesis is no longer one–sided or two–sided. It is, in fact, many–sided. It is many-sided because, for example, the hypotheses includes the case where $\mu_1 = \mu_2$ but perhaps μ_3 is different. The ANOVA F test, generally carried out by computers, assesses the evidence for some difference among the population means. In practicality, we expect the F test to be significant. That is, researchers do not embark on such time consuming task unless they believe, prior to collecting the data, that some effect is to be found. The follow-up analysis, when done by expert professionals, is the most useful part of an ANOVA study. It will tell us which means differ and by how much, with high confidence (usually 95%) that the results are correct.

We will rely on a preliminary exploratory analysis of the data in order to detect sufficiently large differences in the means that might be of practical interest. Only then we will proceed to conduct a more formal overall ANOVA procedure.

The preliminary exploratory analysis consists of side-by-side stem-leaf plots. This is possible only when the raw data are available. The purpose for the stem-leaf plots is to ascertain that the distribution is symmetrical and that there are no extreme values. In addition, the stem-leaf plots should allow us to quickly compare the mean for each group. If there are no large differences in the means, then there is no reason to proceed with a more detailed analysis.

The main idea for comparing means is this: what matters is not how far apart the sample means are but how far apart they are *relative to the variability present in the data*. Small differences among sample means could be significant if the sample sizes are large. Large differences in sample means could be insignificant if the sample sizes are small. The basic idea is to detect sample means that are apart relative to the variation among the individual observations in the same group.

The numerical methodology for ANOVA is based on testing whether several populations have the same mean by comparing how far apart the sample means are with how much variation there is within the group data. In a sense it is odd that we will conduct a test for multiple means by considering the ratio of two variances. The reason for this is that information about the sample means is extracted by comparing two kinds of variations. This takes the form:

(3) $$\text{ANOVA F statistic} = \frac{\text{variation among sample means}}{\text{variation among observations within the same sample}}.$$

Again, since all ANOVA calculations are almost always done with software, the ideas are a lot more important than the computational details. We have already seen that the F statistic can only take values that are zero or larger. The above ratio is zero only if the variation among the sample means is zero. If this happens, then there is overwhelming evidence in favor of the null hypothesis and we declare that the population means are all equal. However, randomness creates variation among the sample means even when the population means are equal. In fact, when the null hypothesis is true, we expect the ANOVA F statistic to take values around 1. As the sample means get farther apart, the ANOVA F statistic gets larger. Large values of the ANOVA F statistic are evidence against the null that all population means are equal. Although we have already seen that the alternative hypothesis is many-sided, the ANOVA F test is one sided on the right because evidence against the null occurs only if the ANOVA F statistic produces a large value. To determine how large is large, we must compare this F statistic with specific critical values of the corresponding F distribution. In order to do this, we need to define the degrees of freedom for the numerator and denominator:

df for numerator = number of treatment groups – 1,

df for denominator = number of total observations for all groups - number of treatment groups.

Like all inference procedures, ANOVA is valid only in certain circumstances. Here are the key assumptions:

- **We take independent simple random samples, one from each of k populations. The sample sizes may or may not be the same.**

- **The jth population has a Normal distribution with unknown mean μ_j.**

- **All of the k populations have the same unknown variance σ^2.**

Because in reality, no population follows exactly a Normal distribution, the usefulness of inference procedures that assume normality depends on how sensitive the procedures are to departures from normality. Fortunately, procedures for comparing means are not all that sensitive to normality departures. The reason for this is that means tend to follow a Normal distribution (remember the Central Limit Theorem). ANOVA becomes safer as the sample sizes get larger. Extreme values in the data will cause trouble, especially if the sample sizes are fairly small. If there are no extreme values in the data for each group, samples as small as 4 or 5 per group are safe to use. [1]

The assumption of all the k populations having the same unknown variance σ^2 is quite difficult to check. The ANOVA procedure is not all that sensitive to violations of this assumption, especially when the sample sizes are the same for all groups and no sample size is smaller than 4 or 5. When doing ANOVA try to design the experiment in such a way that all groups have the same sample size. In order to actually check the equal variance assumption, we give the following rule of thumb:

the equal variance assumption is not violated in ANOVA if, among all groups, the largest sample variance is no more than four times as large as the smallest sample variance.

---

[1] Don't confuse the ANOVA F with the F statistic of the previous section which compares two variances or standard deviations. The latter is much more sensitive to extreme values in the data than the former.

Example 3

Three versions of a T–cell collecting device are being tested to check the efficiency of different manufacturing materials related to the coating on the surface of the device. T-cells are associated with the immune system. Current therapies attempt to remove damaged T-cells, treat them, and return them to the patient. T-cells are removed by taking blood samples. In about 3 cc.'s of blood, millions of T-cells are generally found. Five patients for each T-cell collecting device are randomly chosen and 3 cc.'s of blood are collected from each one. One cc. of blood is used for each of the devices for each of the patients. The data, in millions, represents the number of T-cells collected for each patient for each of the devices.

Treatment Groups

	Device 1	Device 2	Device 3
Patient 1	8	7	5
Patient 2	10	12	9
Patient 3	7	6	10
Patient 4	12	14	11
Patient 5	9	8	7

We wish to determine if the average number of cells collected by the three devices is the same.

Solution and discussion

Before doing any computations, we do a side-by-side stem leaf plot for the data.

Device 1		Device 2		Device 3	
Stem	Leaf	Stem	Leaf	Stem	Leaf
0	7 8 9	0	6 7 8	0	5
1	0 2	1	2 4	0	7 9
				1	0 1

No extreme values are detected. Normality is not really a concern. Besides, it is impossible to check for it with only 5 samples for each group. We proceed to check the assumption of equality of variances using the rule of thumb given above. We use a calculator to compute the sample variance for each of the three treatment groups:

$$\text{sample variance for Device 1} = s_1^2 = 3.7$$
$$\text{sample variance for Device 2} = s_2^2 = 11.8$$
$$\text{sample variance for Device 3} = s_3^2 = 5.8$$

The ratio of the largest variance to the smallest variance is $\frac{11.8}{3.7} \approx 3.189 < 4$; thus, the equality of variance assumption is not violated.

We proceed with the ANOVA F test. The set of hypotheses of interest is:

$$H_0: \mu_1 = \mu_2 = \mu_3 \quad \text{vs.} \quad H_a: \text{not all of } \mu_1, \mu_2, \mu_3 \text{ are equal.}$$

In order to compute the variation among the sample means, we first need to compute the sample means for each of the devices:

$$\text{sample mean for Device 1} = \overline{x}_1 = 9.2$$
$$\text{sample mean for Device 2} = \overline{x}_2 = 9.4$$
$$\text{sample mean for Device 3} = \overline{x}_3 = 8.4$$

We now compute the variance of the three sample means. This is the numerator of equation (3):

$$\text{variation among sample means} = \frac{n_1 \cdot (\overline{x}_1 - GM)^2 + n_2 \cdot (\overline{x}_2 - GM)^2 + n_3 \cdot (\overline{x}_3 - GM)^2}{3-1}$$

where n_k = sample size for group k, and GM = grand mean = mean of all 15 observations = 9. Thus,

$$\text{variation among sample means} = \frac{5 \cdot (9.2 - 9)^2 + 5 \cdot (9.4 - 9)^2 + 5 \cdot (8.4 - 9)^2}{2} = 1.40.$$

The denominator of equation (3), the variation among observations within the same sample, is the weighted average of the three sample variances. Since, in this case, the sample sizes are equal, this is just the arithmetic average of the sample variances.[2] That is,

$$\text{variation among observations in the same sample} = \frac{s_1^2 + s_2^2 + s_3^2}{3} = \frac{3.7 + 11.8 + 5.8}{3} = 7.1.$$

Thus,

$$\text{ANOVA F statistic} = \frac{\text{variation among sample means}}{\text{variation among observations within the same sample}} = \frac{1.4}{7.1} \approx 0.20.$$

---

[2] If the sample sizes were not the same, the formula to compute the weighted average of the sample variances is: $\dfrac{(n_1 - 1) \cdot s_1^2 + (n_2 - 1) \cdot s_2^2 + \ldots + (n_k - 1) \cdot s_k^2}{n_1 + n_2 + \ldots + n_k - k}$.

We compare the 0.20 ANOVA F statistic with the corresponding critical value from the corresponding F distribution. The degrees of freedom are:

df for numerator = number of treatment groups – 1 = 3 – 1 = 2,

df for denominator = number of total observations – number of treatment groups = 15 – 3 = 12.

From the F tables, we note that the closest critical value of $F_{2,12}$ to 0.20 is 2.81. The area to the right of 2.81 is 0.10. Thus, the area to the right of 0.20 is much bigger than 0.10. In fact, since 0.20 is relatively close to 0, we suspect that the area to its right is well in excess of 0.50. This is overwhelming evidence in favor of the null hypothesis that the three devices, on average, collect the same number of T-cells.

Some computer packages that perform ANOVA procedures display the result of the computations in a slightly different format to the one presented above. We will avoid such format but will show it here in case you ever encounter it. We use the numerical results from Example 3 to illustrate.

Analysis of Variance Table

Source	df	SS	MS	F	p-value
Treatment	2	2.80	1.40	0.20	0.8236
Error	12	85.20	7.10		
Total	14	88.00			

Some comments about this table are in order. Under *Source*, Treatment refers to the variation due to each Treatment Group, Error refers to the variation within each of the treatment groups, and Total refers to the variation among all of the data. The *df*, degrees of freedom, column is self explanatory. *SS* means Sum of Squares. The SS, by itself, doesn't give any useful information. Note that SS/df = MS. MS stands for Mean Square. The *MS* column matches the numerator and denominator of equation (3). The one real advantage is that the p-value is given. As we suspected, $P(F_{2,12} > 0.20) = 0.8236$, well in excess of 0.50.

Chapter 13 Problems

1. Assume that $X \sim F_{dfn, dfd}$. Find:

    a. $F_{10, 15, 0.01}$ **b.** $F_{10, 15, 0.95}$

    c. $P\left(X < F_{10, 15, 0.01}\right)$ **d.** $P\left(X > F_{10, 15, 0.01}\right)$

2. Assume that $X \sim F_{dfn, dfd}$.

    a. If $P\left(X > F_{8, 20}\right) = 0.05$, find $F_{8, 20}$.   **b.** If $P\left(X < F_{8, 20}\right) = 0.9$, find $F_{8, 20}$.

    c. If $P\left(X > F_{15, 12}\right) = 0.05$, find $F_{15, 12}$.   **d.** If $P\left(X < F_{12,25}\right) = 0.99$, find $F_{12, 25}$.

3. A group of 32 monkeys was randomly divided into two groups of 16 monkeys each. Two types of lesions were produced. The experimenter then observed each animal after surgery and rated the amount of aggression each animal displayed. He theorized that the two groups would differ primarily in variability. The data is summarized in the table below:

	Lesion 1	Lesion 2
$\overline{X}$	95.3	94.8
s^2	13.7	6.13
n	16	16

Do the groups differ in variability? Test at the 0.02 level of significance.

4. A new computer component is under consideration. The cost of the new part is lower than the old. It will be purchased if the standard deviation of the new part is not greater than the standard deviation of the old part. The following data is collected.

	Old part	New part
s	0.345	0.481
n	26	13

Is the variability of the new part greater than the old? Test at the 0.025 level of significance.

5. Four typists are tested to determine their typing speed (measured in words per minute). Each of the four is given 6 tests. The results are as follows:

	Typist A	Typist B	Typist C	Typist D
$\overline{X}$	100	99.08	98.08	97.75
s^2	3.091	1.556	2.992	5.659

The quantities below are computed from the above data:

variance among group means = 6.237

variation among observations within the same sample = 3.325

a. Give the null and alternative hypotheses.

b. Give the degrees of freedom for the F distribution.

c. Is the assumption of equality of variances for the four treatment groups violated? Explain.

d. Calculate the ANOVA F statistic.

e. What is your conclusion at the 1% level of significance?

6. Five randomly chosen manufacturing machines are tested to determine if, on average, their outputs are different. Eleven samples are taken from each machine. The results are as follows:

	Machine 1	Machine 2	Machine 3	Machine 4	Machine 5
$\overline{X}$	99.5	99.725	99.475	97.45	97.25
s^2	6.9744	6.9224	4.0506	4.5103	5.5251

The variance among the group means = 16.374.

a. Give the null and alternative hypotheses.

b. Give the degrees of freedom for the F distribution.

c. Is the assumption of equality of variances for the five treatment groups violated? Explain.

d. Calculate the ANOVA F statistic.

e. What is your conclusion at the 5% level of significance?

Chapter 13

7. How much corn per acre should be planted in order to obtain the highest yield? In 1962 (*Agronomy Journal, volume 54, pages 235-238*) the results of such a study were reported. Farmers have always known that if few plants are planted there will be a low yield. However, if too many plants are planted they will compete for nutrients and moisture and the yield will also fall. For the experiment, five similar one acre plots of land were used. All five plots were treated the same in terms of fertilizer, watering, etc. Here are the data (slightly modified to make the computations easier).

Plants per acre	Yield (bushels per acre)
12,000	150, 113, 118, 142
16,000	166, 120, 135, 149
20,000	165, 130, 139, 149
24,000	134, 138, 156
28,000	119, 150, 125

a. Make five side-by-side stem-leaf plots of yield for each number of plants per acre. Use a two digit stem. What do the data appear to show about the influence of plants per acre on yield?

b. Find the mean yield for each planting rate. Do these means appear to validate your response to a. above?

c. State the null and alternative hypotheses for this situation. Do this first in words and then in symbols.

d. Give the degrees of freedom for the F distribution.

e. The ANOVA F statistic is 0.65 with p-value = 0.64. What is your conclusion?

f. The observed differences among the mean yields in the sample were fairly large. Why are they not statistically significant? Explain.

8. The table below represents a computer output (with two entries left blank) for an ANOVA situation.

Source	df	SS	MS	F	p-value
Treatment	3	30	10	?	0.075
Error	?	140	4		
Total	38	170			

a. Use appropriate symbols to write the null hypothesis.

b. Give the degrees of freedom for the F distribution and find the ANOVA F statistic.

c. What is the conclusion at the 0.05 level of significance?

Chapter 14

Bivariate Data: Correlation and Regression

14.1 Comparing Two Variable Data

Most statistical studies involve more than one variable. It comes as no surprise that most of the real interesting problems in statistics are multivariate. That is, statisticians seek to assess the nature of the relationship among several variables. Of keen interest is the situation when some of the variables cause changes in others.

Bivariate data consists of two variables. This is the easiest of all multivariate cases; however, the ideas and concepts developed for the two variables problem extend to three or more variables. Multivariate methods are quite advanced and are best relegated to future courses in statistics. In the bivariate case, statisticians are most interested in identifying a *response variable* and an *explanatory* or *control variable*. A *response variable* measures the outcome of some experiment. An *explanatory variable* attempts to explain the observed outcomes.

Example 1

It is known that alcohol consumption causes a drop in body temperature. To determine the exact nature of this relationship, experimenters give several different amounts of alcohol to mice and then measure the change in each mouse's body temperature after 30 minutes. The *explanatory variable* is amount of alcohol and the *response variable* is the drop in body temperature.

In the literature and in other textbooks, you will often find explanatory variables called *independent* variables and response variables called *dependent* variables. We have used the terms independent and dependent previously and in a different context. We will stick with *explanatory* or *control* and *response*. However, the idea behind the independent–dependent convention is that the response variable *depends* on the explanatory variable.

It is possible to have bivariate data where one or both of the variables are categorical. Ideally, the data will be quantitative. Quantitative data lends itself to numerical analysis. Methods incorporating categorical variables are beyond the scope of our discussion.

Example 2

For a long time, the most common treatment for breast cancer was removal of the affected breast. Recent research findings have now shown that it is more effective, and less psychologically taxing, to remove the tumor and nearby lymph nodes, followed by radiation treatment. The research was done over a long period of time, with randomly chosen patients, comparing both treatments. The patients were closely watched to see how long they lived following surgery.

The explanatory variable for the above study is the type of treatment. This is categorical. The response variable is time, measured in some convenient unit (i.e., months, years). This is quantitative.

In the remainder of this chapter we will use only quantitative variables and we will study the graphical and numerical methods associated with them.

14.2 Scatterplots, Outliers, and Influential Points

Scatterplots

The most effective way to display the relationship between two quantitative variables is a scatterplot. The horizontal axis of a scatterplot is called the "x-axis" and the vertical axis is called the "y-axis". By convention, we always plot the explanatory variable on the x-axis. The response variable is plotted on the y-axis. We typically gather the data in the form (x,y). This is consistent with the notation used for indicating the location of points in two-dimensional space.

Example 3

For a certain mathematics course, we wish to study the relationship between the score on the second exam of the academic term and the score on the final exam. A random sample of 10 students was chosen.

Student	1	2	3	4	5	6	7	8	9	10
Second exam	75	60	55	65	85	95	98	52	48	70
Final exam	72	65	58	60	80	88	92	50	45	70

The explanatory variable is the score on the second exam. The response variable is the score on the final exam. Here is the scatterplot of the data.

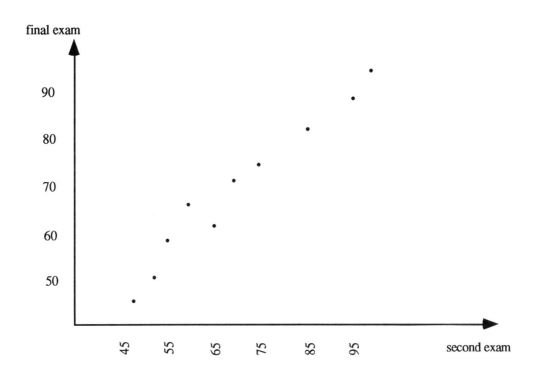

To interpret a scatterplot, we look at three things: *direction, form,* and *strength*. The above scatterplot clearly shows that the *direction* of the relationship is positive.[1] That is, as the score in the second exam increases, so does the score on the final exam. The *form* is that of something close to a straight line. The *strength* of the relationship is very strong. That is, the points are strongly displayed in a linear pattern, with very little scatter.

Strong linear relationships, like the one exhibited in Example **3**, make accurate predictions of the response variable possible. This is an important point that will be discussed later in the chapter.

Not all relationships are linear in form and not all relationships have a clear direction. Relationships could have curvilinear forms. Sometimes the data are so scattered that there is no clear direction. In such cases, predictions are meaningless and there is neither a positive nor a negative association.

---

[1] Two variables are *positively associated* when an increase/decrease in one causes an increase/decrease in the other. Likewise, they are *negatively associated*, if an increase/decrease in one causes a decrease/increase in the other.

Outliers

An *outlier* in any scatterplot of data is any observation that falls outside the overall pattern of the graph.[2] In the bivariate data case, observations that might be classified as outliers are readily spotted. An observation may be an outlier due to extraneous values of either, the response or explanatory variable.

Example 4

Suppose in Example **3**, the 10th student data are: second exam = 70, final exam = 45. The scatterplot for this situation is given below.

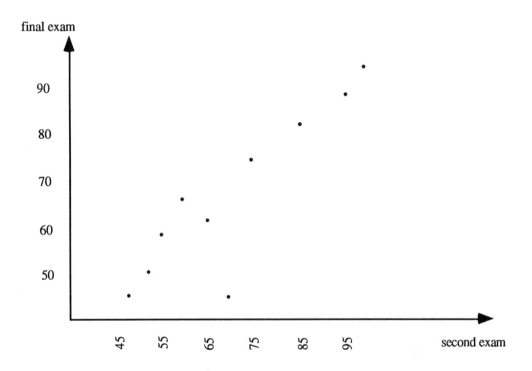

It is quite clear that the data point (70,45) falls outside the strong linear direction of the rest of the data. We classify the point (70,45) as an outlier. What do we do with outliers? It is not easy to make decisions about how to handle outliers. The first thing that should be done is to make sure that no errors have been made in recording the data. For instance, if the data are being gathered by reading an instrument, we must take steps to be sure that the instrument was functioning properly at the time the data were gathered. An experimenter should do everything possible to seek plausible explanations for the appearance

---

[2] This is a graphical description of an oulier. Later in the chapter, we will recast this definition in quantitative terms.

of outliers. For instance, in the case of the 10th student, it might be wise to ask questions such as: was there something terribly wrong (i.e., illness, other extreme circumstances) with the student the day of the final exam? If after looking for an explanation the experimenter considers the point to have occurred due to extreme circumstances, it might be prudent to exclude the point from further analysis.

Influential Points

An observation is classified as *influential* if removing it would markedly change the form, direction, or strength of the scatterplot. Points that are outliers in the x direction are often influential points.

Influential points are often times much more difficult to detect than outliers. Be aware that influential points can dramatically change the interpretation of the data.

Example 5

Suppose the bivariate data are as follows: (10,20); (15,25); (20, 40); (30, 45); (60, 50). The scatterplot follows.

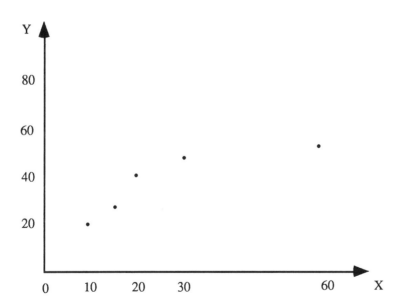

The four points that are clustered together anchor the direction of the straight line pattern for the data. The point (60,50) is influential. To see this note that a slight change in either the x or y scale changes the direction of the line. The graph below shows the dramatic switch in direction if the point is changed, for instance, to (60, 90).

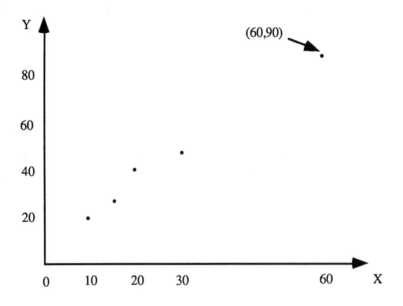

14.3   Correlation

Linear relations between two variables are important because of their simplicity. Intuitively, we say that a linear direction is strong if the points lie close to a straight line. Likewise, we say that a linear direction is weak if the points are scattered about a line. Judging the strength of a linear relationship by eye is tricky. The visual perception can easily be manipulated by changing the scale in the x or y direction or by changing the size of the scatterplot itself. Thus, a numerical measure of linear strength and direction is needed. This is precisely what *correlation* provides.

The correlation measures the strength and direction of the linear relationship between two quantitative variables. The symbol used for the correlation of the sample data is *r*. The symbol for the correlation of the unknown population is ρ (pronounced "rho").

The computational formula for the sample correlation between two variables x and y is given by

(1) $$r = \frac{1}{n-1} \sum_{\text{all } i} \left(\frac{x_i - \bar{x}}{s_x} \right) \left(\frac{y_i - \bar{y}}{s_y} \right), \quad \text{where}$$

n = number of data points; x_i and y_i are the values for the explanatory and response variable for each of the points; and s_x and s_y are the standard deviation of the set of x_i's and y_i's respectively.

In practice, the correlation is done by computer or by calculator (once the data are entered in an appropriate format). Notice that formula (1) uses the standardized data in the x and y direction. It essentially averages the product of the standardized observations. In calculating the correlation it makes no difference which variable is labeled x and which is labeled y.

Here are some useful facts about r.

- The value of r always falls between –1 and 1, inclusive. Values of r close to zero indicate a very weak linear relationship. The extreme values –1 or 1 occur only in the case where all of the points lie along a straight line.

- Positive values of r indicate a positive association between x and y. Likewise, negative values of r indicate a negative association between x and y.

- Changing the units of measurement in x or y does not change the value of r. This is because r is computed using standardized values. The correlation itself is a unitless measure.

- The correlation r measures only the strength of the **linear** relationship between x and y. It does not say anything about curvilinear relationships.

- As you can guess by paying close attention to formula (1), r is heavily affected by outliers or other extreme points. In that sense, it behaves like the mean or standard deviation. Pay close attention to r when outliers appear in the scatterplot.

- The correlation does not measure any cause and effect between x and y. *Determining cause and effect is up to the experimenter.* It is possible, and this is often the case, that two variables could be strongly linearly correlated and have nothing to do with each other.[3]

- In order to assess if the correlation is significant, use the table of critical values for the correlation in back of the book. Note that the degrees of freedom are given by n – 2. The critical values are positive or negative. For example, if from data, r = 0.85 or r = – 0.85 and n = 7, we see that r is significant at alpha levels of 0.10, 0.05, 0.025, and 0.01. Note that r is not significant at an alpha level of 0.005 since 0.85 < 0.874 or the equivalent, –0.85 > –0.874.

---

[3] A few years ago, the New York Times noted that a raise of 5% in teacher's annual salaries was immediately followed by an increase in the rate of alcohol consumption. A scatterplot of the data showed a very strong linear relationship. However, it would be ill conceived to conclude that raising teacher's salaries would cause an increase in alcohol consumption.

The example below shows how the correlation measures different linear associations.

Example 6

$r = 0.90$ $\qquad\qquad\qquad$ $r = -0.95$

close to $r = 0$ $\qquad\qquad\qquad$ $r = 1$

14.4 Least–Squares Regression

Correlation measures the strength of the linear relationship between two variables. If a scatterplot shows a strong linear relationship, and this is further verified by computing a significant r, we would like to summarize the overall pattern by obtaining the equation of the line that best fits the data. Not any line drawn through the scatterplot classifies as the "best line". *Least–squares regression* is the method used to find this best line.

A *regression* line is a straight line that describes how a response variable y changes as an explanatory variable x changes. The main use of a regression line is to predict the value of y for a given value of x. The major difference between correlation and regression is that regression requires that we have a response variable and an explanatory variable.

Given a scatterplot, it is quite clear that no line will pass through all the points (unless, of course, all the points lie exactly on a straight line). The next best thing is a line that will pass close to all the points in the vertical direction. That is, we wish to minimize prediction errors. These are errors in the y variable. In fact, we will assume that the x variable is measured without error. We define an error as the difference between the observed value of y and the predicted value of y. That is, for a given data point,

(2) $$\text{error} = \text{observed } y - \text{predicted } y.$$

The graph below illustrates this idea. For a given point, say (x_1, y_1) there is a corresponding point on the line, call it $(x_1, \hat{y}_1)$. Note that the x_1 value is the same for both points but the vertical distance is not. The $\hat{y}$ symbol is pronounced "y hat". It stands for the *predicted value of y* for a corresponding x. Points denoted by $(x, \hat{y})$ always fall on the regression line.

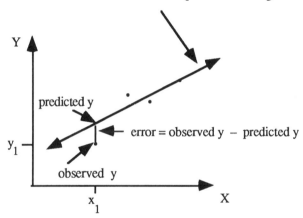

best line or least squares line or regression line

The least–squares line makes the sum of the squared errors minimum. That is, the computation of the line is predicated by the condition:

(3)   minimize: $$\text{Sum of Squared Errors} = \text{SSE} = \sum_{\text{all points}} (y - \hat{y})^2.$$

The regression line is of the form $\hat{y} = b_1 x + b_0$, where b_1 stands for the slope and b_0 stands for the y-intercept. The computation of b_1 and b_0 are as follows:[4]

---

[4] The slope, b_1, is computed by minimizing equation (3). To do this, knowledge of the Differential Calculus is neccesary. However, this doesn't preclude using the result given in equation (4).

$$(4) \qquad\qquad \text{slope} = b_1 = r\frac{s_y}{s_x},$$

$$(5) \qquad\qquad \text{y-intercept} = b_o = \overline{y} - b_1\overline{x}.$$

Note that equation (5) implies that the regression line passes through the point $(\overline{x}, \overline{y})$. This makes sense since, in minimizing the total error, the best line "balances" the data.

We now apply the above equations to the data given in Example **3**, section **14.2**.

Example 7

We first calculate the correlation r. Instead of using equation (1), we use a calculator to obtain r = 0.981 (we will round all decimals to three decimal places). Since n = 10 (i.e., there are 10 students), degrees of freedom = 10 – 2 = 8. We look in the correlation table to note that the computed correlation of 0.981 is significant for any of the significance levels shown. This confirms the strong linear relationship indicated by the scatterplot. We now use equations (4) and (5) to obtain the regression equation, but first we use a calculator to compute the following quantities from the data (verify):[5]

$$\overline{x} = 70.3; \quad \overline{y} = 68; \quad s_x = 17.689; \quad s_y = 15.513.$$

From equation (4), $b_1 = 0.981 \cdot \dfrac{15.513}{17.689} = 0.86$, and from equation (5), $b_0 = 68 - 0.86 \cdot 70.3 = 7.542$; thus, the equation for the regression line is:

$$\hat{y} = 0.86 \cdot x + 7.542.$$

The equation of the regression line makes predictions easy. To find a predicted y for a given value of x, we simply substitute the value of x into the regression equation. To predict what a student who obtained a score of 69 on the second exam might get on the final, substitute x = 69:

$$\hat{y} = 0.86 \cdot 69 + 7.542 = 66.022.$$

To plot the regression line on the scatterplot, use the regression equation to find $\hat{y}$ for two values of x, one near each end of the range of values of x in the data. Locate these two points on the scatterplot and join them with a straight line.

---

[5] Recall that x = explanatory variable = score on second exam; y = response variable = score on final exam.

14.5 Details about Least-Squares Regression Lines

Coefficient of Determination

How do we assess the accuracy of the regression line when making predictions? There are different ways of answering this question. We start by noting the following connection between correlation and regression:

the square of the correlation, r^2, is called the *coefficient of determination*. It is the fraction of the variation in y explained by the least squares line.

The idea is that when there is a significant linear relationship, some of the variation in y is accounted for by the fact that as x changes it pulls y along with it. Looking at the scatterplot for the data in Example **3**, section **14.2**, we note that as x increases y is pulled up along with it. However, there is a bit of variation still left in y. This appears in the way the points are scatter about the regression line. The least squares line explains only the way y varies with x. The variation of the data points about the regression line remains unexplained. Thus, the square of the correlation measures the variation we expect as x moves and $\hat{y}$ moves along the regression line. We can express this as a ratio:

$$r^2 = \frac{\text{variation in } \hat{y} \text{ as x moves along line}}{\text{total variation in observed values of y}}.$$

Whenever you deal with a regression problem, give r^2 as a measure of how successful the regression is in explaining the variation in the response variable. Note that when the correlation is perfect (i.e., r = ±1), then r^2 = 1. As you would expect, this means that 100% of the variation in y is completely explained by the line.

What is an acceptable value of r^2? There is no clear cut answer. In the social sciences, a coefficient of determination as small as 0.25 (i.e., 25% of the variation in y is accounted for) is sometimes considered a huge success. In the behavioral sciences, especially when modelling human behavior, small values of r^2 are also considered adequate. In fields where experimental error could cause a major disaster, values of r^2 close to 1 are the only acceptable ones.

Extrapolation and Extraneous Variables

In Example **7**, we note that $r^2 = (0.981)^2 = 0.962$. This means that over 96% of the variation on final exam scores is explained by the score on the second exam. You may conclude that students need not bother taking the final exam for the particular course where the data came from, since, with uncanny accuracy, we can predict the final exam score based on the score for the second exam. Well, things are not that simple. For instance, in order to apply the regression equation obtained in Example **7** to a different set of data, we must make sure that the data for the second exam score is in the same range as the one used in computing the regression line. There are no guarantees that a future set of students will obtain scores on the second exam corresponding to the ones used in constructing the regression line. *Extrapolation* is the use of a regression line to make predictions outside the range of values of the explanatory variable x that you used to obtain the line. These predictions are often misleading and cannot be trusted.

Often, the relationship between two variables is strongly influenced by other variables. In the bivariate case, these other variables are not being taken into account. More advanced statistical methods incorporate the handling of multiple variables. The point to remember is that sometimes the relationship between two variables is heavily influenced by other variables that we are not measuring or perhaps not even considering. We call these variables *extraneous*. For instance, in Example **7**, it may very well be that the class for which the data were collected was a morning class. Morning classes are usually considered "prime time". Students like morning classes for a variety of reasons. Any effect due to the "morning class" variable is not accounted for in computing the regression line. If we try to use this regression line in predicting final exam scores for an evening class, we are allowing an extraneous variable to influence the outcome. In this case, one such extraneous variable is "time of day".

14.6 The Regression Model: Confidence Intervals and Inference

Whenever a scatterplot indicates a strong linear relationship between two variables, we may compute the correlation to verify the strength of the apparent linear relationship and, if appropriate, proceed to fit the least-squares regression line. With this line we can predict values of y for given values of x. We are now interested in doing hypotheses tests and in obtaining confidence intervals.

The slope b_1 and y-intercept b_o of the regression line are *statistics*. That is, they are computed using sample data and would be different if we were to use a different sample of data from the same population. To do inference, we must think of b_1 and b_o as values in the range of their corresponding random variables and we must also know which population parameters they estimate. The parameters appear in what we call a *model*. Here are the assumptions that describe the *regression model*.

- We have n observations of the form (x,y) where x is the explanatory variable and y is the response variable.

- For any fixed value of x, the response y varies according to a Normal distribution. Repeated responses of y are independent of each other.

- The mean response of the Normal distribution of y for a fixed value of x takes the linear form:

$$\mu_{y\,|\,x} = \beta_1 x + \beta_0,$$ where β_1 and β_0 are unknown population parameters.

- The unknown standard deviation of y about the line, $\sigma_{\hat{y}}$, is the same for all values of x.

The key feature of this model is that the straight line relationship between x and y takes the form of an "average". The true regression line (i.e., the one that pertains to the entire population under study), says that the mean response μ_y moves along a straight line as x changes. In this sense, $\hat{y}$, the predicted y for a given value of x, is interpreted as an average. The values of y we observe in the sample data vary about their means according to a Normal distribution. The graph below illustrates these ideas.

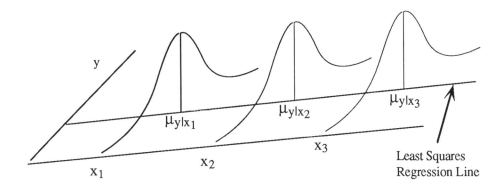

The first step in inference is to estimate the unknown parameters β_1, β_0 and $\sigma_{\hat{y}}$. Equations (4) and (5) above show how to compute b_1 and b_0. These are the estimates of β_1 and β_0. The remaining parameter to be estimated is $\sigma_{\hat{y}}$, which describes the variability of the response variable y about the true regression line. The least-squares regression line estimates the true regression line. Thus, the error[6] estimates how much y varies about the true line. There are n errors, one for each data point. We use equation (3) to compute the estimate of $\sigma_{\hat{y}}$. We will denote this estimate by $s_{\hat{y}}$:

$$(6) \qquad s_{\hat{y}} = \sqrt{\frac{SSE}{n-2}} = \sqrt{\frac{\sum_{all\ data}(y - \hat{y})^2}{n-2}}.$$

In fact, interpret $s_{\hat{y}}$ as the standard deviation of the predicted value of y for a given value of x. The reason we divide by $n - 2$, instead of the more familiar $n - 1$, is that the regression model requires **two**

---

[6] This error is also called *residual*. Recall that an error or residual is the vertical deviation of each data point from the least-squares regression line.

parameters to be estimated from the data (i.e., the slope and the y-intercept). Calculating $s_{\hat{y}}$ is messy. You must find $\hat{y}$ for each value of x, then the error associated with each $\hat{y}$, and then use equation (6) to finally obtain $s_{\hat{y}}$. In practice, nobody does this by hand. Computers do this quite adequately. All that having been said, here is an example, done by hand, to make sure we all understand how $s_{\hat{y}}$ is obtained and what it actually means.

Using the data from Example **3**, section **14.2**, we have already computed the regression line to be $\hat{y} = 0.86 \cdot x + 7.542$. We then have,[7]

x	y	$\hat{y}$	$y - \hat{y}$	$(y - \hat{y})^2$
75	72	72.042	−0.042	0.00176
60	65	59.142	5.858	34.3162
55	58	54.842	3.158	9.973
65	60	63.442	−3.442	11.8474
85	80	80.642	−0.642	0.4122
95	88	89.242	−1.242	1.5426
98	92	91.822	0.178	0.0317
52	50	52.262	−2.262	5.1166
48	45	48.822	−3.822	14.6077
70	70	67.742	<u>2.258</u>	<u>5.0986</u>
		Totals =	0.0	82.9478

Using equation (6),

$$s_{\hat{y}} = \sqrt{\frac{SSE}{n-2}} = \sqrt{\frac{\sum\limits_{all\ data} (y - \hat{y})^2}{n-2}} = \sqrt{\frac{82.9478}{8}} = 3.22.$$

The rule of thumb interpretation of this result is as follows: for a given value of x, we expect, on average, the value of $\hat{y}$ to be off from its actual value by about ±3.22.

We may also use $s_{\hat{y}}$ to quantitatively define an outlier (see section **14.2**):

a data point is considered an outlier if the absolute value of $y - \hat{y}$ exceeds $2 \cdot s_{\hat{y}}$.

From the above table, we see that none of the $y - \hat{y}$, in absolute value, exceeds $2 \cdot 3.22 = 6.44$; thus, there are no outliers.

---

[7] Note that the sum of the errors column, $y - \hat{y}$, is 0. This confirms the fact that the least-squares regression line balances the data.

Confidence Interval for $\hat{y}$

For a given value of x, $\hat{y}$ is interpreted as the mean response. What this really means is that if we observe many responses corresponding to the same x value, the average of those responses will be $\hat{y}$. However, since we typically observe a single value of y from a single value of x, we know we are predicting y with error. We use the t distribution with n – 2 degrees of freedom in order to obtain an expression for the error bound.[8] That is, the $100 \cdot (1 - \alpha)\%$ confidence interval for $\hat{y}$ for a given value of x, say x', is:

$$\hat{y} \pm \text{error bound} = \hat{y} \pm t_{n-2, \alpha/2} \cdot \textit{standard deviation term}$$

(7)   where *standard deviation term* $= s_{\hat{y}} \cdot \sqrt{\dfrac{1}{n} + \dfrac{(x' - \bar{x})^2}{\sum\limits_{\text{all } x} (x - \bar{x})^2}}$.

Example 8

For the data of Example **3**, section **14.2**, we wish to find the 95% confidence interval for the mean response when x = 72.

Solution and discussion

The regression line is $\hat{y} = 0.86 \cdot x + 7.542$. The predicted value of y when x = 72 is:

$$\hat{y} = 0.86 \cdot 72 + 7.542 = 69.462.$$

This means that if we observe many students who obtain a second midterm score of 72, we predict their average score on the final exam to be 69.462. We proceed to compute the standard deviation term,

from the data, verify[9] that $\sum\limits_{\text{all } x} (x - \bar{x})^2 = 2816.106$ and $(x' - \bar{x})^2 = 2.89$. Also, from above, $s_{\hat{y}} = 3.22$. Using equation (7),

---

[8] The reason for using the t distribution is that we are dealing with a sample mean with unknown population variance.

[9] Recall that $s_x = \sqrt{\dfrac{\sum\limits_{\text{all } x} (x - \bar{x})^2}{n - 1}}$; thus, $\sum\limits_{\text{all } x} (x - \bar{x})^2 = s_x^2 \cdot (n - 1)$.

$$\text{standard deviation term} = 3.22 \cdot \sqrt{\frac{1}{10} + \frac{2.89}{2816.106}} = 1.023.$$

Therefore, the error bound is:

$$t_{8,0.05} \cdot \text{standard deviation term} = 2.31 \cdot 1.023 = 2.363.$$

Finally, the 95% confidence interval for the mean response when $x = 72$ is:

$$\hat{y} \pm \text{error bound} = 69.642 \pm 2.363.$$

This means that, on average, and with 95% confidence, we expect students who score 72 on the second exam to obtain a score on the final exam in the interval $(67.279, 72.005)$.

Note that predicting values of the response variable for a given value of the explanatory variable is most accurate when the values of x are close to $\overline{x}$. That is, the result of equation (7) is minimum when $x' = \overline{x}$. Likewise, as x' is far from $\overline{x}$, the result of equation (7) gets larger and larger, resulting in a much larger error bound term. This is why attempting to make predictions beyond the range of the values of the explanatory variable is inaccurate.

Inference about the slope of the regression line

The slope of the regression line is generally considered to be the most important parameter in regression problems. Just like the slope of any other line, it is interpreted as the rate of change in the response variable per unit change in the explanatory variable. The slope of the true regression line is estimated by the slope of the regression line computed from the sample data. This is done using equation (4). Each new batch of sample data yields a different estimate for the slope of the true regression line. Thus, we treat the slope of the regression line as if it were a random variable. The earlier assumption about the normality of the response variable y for a given value of x results on the distribution of the slope random variable being also Normal. The mean of this distribution is β_1, with estimated standard deviation given by

$$(8) \qquad \text{estimated standard deviation for slope of regression line} = s_{b_1} = \frac{s_{\hat{y}}}{\sqrt{\displaystyle\sum_{\text{all } x} (x - \overline{x})^2}}.$$

In making inferences about the slope of the true regression line the set of hypotheses of interest is:

$$H_0: \beta_1 = 0 \quad \text{vs.} \quad H_a: \beta_1 \neq 0.$$

That is, we are interested in the case when the regression line is not a horizontal line (i.e., slope 0). If the data favors the null, then there is no evidence that the data exhibit a linear relationship. If we reject the null then we are claiming that the slope of the regression line is different from zero and we conclude that the data exhibit a significant linear relationship.

By far, the best way to carry out this hypothesis test is to compute the confidence interval for β_1. If zero is included in the confidence interval we then favor the null; otherwise, the null is rejected in favor of the alternative. We again use the t distribution with $n - 2$ degrees of freedom. The form of the $100 \cdot (1 - \alpha)\%$ confidence interval about β_1 is:

$$(9) \qquad b_1 \pm t_{n-2,\,\alpha/2} \cdot s_{b_1}, \text{ where } s_{b_1} \text{ is obtained using equation (8).}$$

Example 9

Test the set of hypotheses: $H_0: \beta_1 = 0 \quad \text{vs.} \quad H_a: \beta_1 \neq 0$ for the slope of the true regression line for the data of Example 3, section **14.2**. Use $\alpha = 0.05$.

Solution

We have already seen that $b_1 = 0.86$ and $s_{\hat{y}} = 3.22$. Also, from Example **8**, $\sum\limits_{\text{all } x} (x - \overline{x})^2 = 2816.106$. Thus, from equation (8),

$$s_{b_1} = \frac{3.22}{\sqrt{2816.106}} = 0.061.$$

Since $t_{8,\,0.025} = 2.31$, equation (9) gives the 95% confidence interval for β_1:

$$0.86 \pm 2.31 \cdot 0.061.$$

That is, we are 95% confident that the slope of the true regression line will fall in the interval (0.719, 1.001). Since this interval does not include zero, we conclude that there is sufficient evidence to reject the null hypothesis that $\beta_1 = 0$. Thus, the slope of the regression line is significant.

14.7 Checking Assumptions in Regression

Least-squares regression lines may be computed for any set of (x,y) data when both variables are quantitative. If the scatterplot doesn't show a strong linear direction, the fitted line is almost always useless since predictions will be extremely inaccurate. However, it is still the line that fits the data best in the least-squares sense (i.e., it is the line that minimizes the sum of squared errors).

To use inference about regression, however, the data must satisfy the regression model assumptions listed in section **14.6**. Before proceeding to carry out any of the inference procedures covered in this chapter, these assumptions must be carefully checked.

1. The true relationship between x and y is linear.

It is impossible to observe the *true* regression line. Look at the scatterplot to check for an overall linear pattern. Obtain the correlation and check for significance at an appropriate significance level.

2. The standard deviation of the response about the true line is constant throughout the range of values of x.

Look at the scatterplot again. Pay attention to the scatter of the data points about the regression line. This should be about the same over the entire range of x values. A common occurrence is for the scatter of points about the line to increase as the response variable gets larger. If this is the case, inference can't be safely used since it is a clear indication that the standard deviation is changing with x. Thus, there is no fixed $\sigma_{\hat{y}}$ to be estimated.

3. The response variable is normally distributed about the true regression line.

Again, we can't observe the true regression line, but we can compute the equation for the least-squares regression line and then obtain the residuals for each of the data points. Residuals show the variation of the response about the fitted line. These residuals should follow a Normal distribution. Usually a stem-leaf plot of the residuals is sufficient to check for any undue skewness or other signs of non-normality. Like other procedures using the t distribution, inference for regression is not very sensitive to departures from normality, especially when the number of observations is adequate (about 20 or so data points). There are a number of more elaborate methods to test for normality of residuals. We are sure you will encounter them as you continue your pursue of statistical endeavors.

We agree that the assumptions for regression inference are tedious. However, it is not all that difficult to check for gross violations. It is still possible to carry out inferences for regression even when violations of these assumptions occur. When that happens, though, expert advice is warranted.

Chapter 14 Problems

For problems **1 - 4,** determine the explanatory and response variables.

1. A consumer advocate group wishes to determine if sausages that are high in calories are also high in sodium content.

2. A study wishes to predict height as a function of shoe size.

3. A headache relief pill is being tested. Of interest is the number of pills taken and the time it takes for the headache to disappear.

4. An agricultural study is undertaken in order to determine the effect on yield based on different quantities of fertilizer.

5. The following statistics are for a random sample of 20 observations about an experiment to determine the relationship between wheat yield and amount of fertilizer. Wheat yield is measured in bushels per acre and fertilizer is measured in hundreds of pounds per acre.

$$\hat{y} = 0.25x + 2.5; \quad r = 0.85; \quad SSE = 1200.$$

a. Is the correlation significant? Use a significance level of 0.05.

b. What is the response variable?

c. If a farmer adds 200 lbs. of fertilizer per acre, by how much is the yield expected to increase?

d. What yield can be expected if 200 lbs. of fertilizer per acre are applied?

e. What is the slope of the regression line?

f. Find the coefficient of determination and explain its meaning within the context of this problem.

g. Find the standard deviation of $\hat{y}$.

6. An economist is conducting research about the savings habits of American families. A random sample of ten families yields the following (all quantities are in thousands):

X = annual income	Y = annual savings
16	1.2
22	2.2
18	2.0
12	1.3
12	0.8
34	3.0
21	0.6
50	4.0
48	4.0
28	2.0

The following statistics are computed:

$$s_x = 13.844; \quad s_y = 1.222; \quad \bar{x} = 26.1; \quad \bar{y} = 2.11; \quad r = 0.924; \quad SSE = 1.976;$$

$$\sum_{\text{all } x} (x - \bar{x})^2 = 1724.907.$$

a. Produce a scatterplot of the data.

b. Is the correlation significant? Use a significance level of 0.01.

c. Use equations (4) and (5) to find b_1 and b_0.

d. Write the equation of the least-squares regression line.

e. Predict y for x = 25. What does this prediction mean?

f. Predict y for x = 100. What does this prediction mean? Do you believe this prediction? Explain.

g. What percent of the variation in y is explained by x?

h. Find the residuals for all 10 data points. Verify that their sum is about 0. Are there any outliers? Explain. Is your conclusion apparent from the scatterplot? Explain.

i. Take the 10 residuals from **h.** above and do a stem-leaf plot. Is there reason to believe that the normality assumption is violated? Explain.

j. Compute the 95% confidence interval for the predicted value of y in part **e.** above.

k. Compute the 95% confidence interval for the predicted value of y in part **f.** above.

l. Why is the error bound in **k.** much larger than the error bound in **j.**?

7. Each of the following statements contains an inaccuracy. Explain in each case what is wrong.

a. There is a high correlation between the gender of American workers and their annual income.

b. We found a high correlation ($r = 1.25$) between faculty evaluation of faculty and student evaluation of faculty.

c. In baseball, the correlation between earned run average and winning percentage was found to be 0.95 games.

8. There is a strong positive correlation between years of education and annual income for statisticians employed in industry. In particular, statisticians with graduate degrees earn more than those with only a bachelor's degree. There is also a strong positive correlation between years of education and annual income for statisticians employed in academic institutions. However, when all these statisticians are lumped together, there is a *negative* correlation between annual income and years of education.

a. Explain what can cause such an apparent paradox.

b. On the same scatterplot, using different marks or color, sketch the situation for each group (industry and academia) so that there is a strong positive correlation for each group but a negative correlation overall.

9. A study of children in grades 1 – 6 shows a positive correlation between shoe size, x, and score on a reading comprehension test. What extraneous variable explains this correlation?

10. Suppose a set of bivariate data has correlation close to 0. That is, there is no significant linear relationship between x and y. Still, a least-squares regression line can be computed. Clearly, any predictions made using this line will be quite meaningless. What will be the values of b_1 and b_0 for this line? Explain.

11. For the situation of problem **6.**, test the set of hypotheses H_o: $\beta_1 = 0$ vs. H_a: $\beta_1 \neq 0$ at the 0.01 level of significance. Is your conclusion consistent with the result of problem **6b.**? Explain.

12. Fitting a model from data and using that model to make predictions are two different things. Consider the following situation. In the United States, around the end of World War II (circa 1945), there were about 2.2 people in each car on the highway. By 1955, this number had dropped to only 1.4 people in each car on the highway. Assume the relationship between time (from 1945) and number of people in cars to be linear.

    a. Let $t = 0$ in 1945 and $t = 10$ in 1955. Consider the two points $(0,2.2)$ and $(10,1.4)$. Write the equation of the line passing through these two points. Hint: if you don't recall how to do this, refer to problem **15.** in the Algebra Review in the Appendix.

    b. Find the coefficient of determination and explain what it means.

    c. Use the equation from **a.** to predict y in the year 2000 (i.e., let $t = 55$). Explain the meaning of this prediction. What is wrong?

13. Refer to the situation of problem **6.** In part **h.**, we asked you to identify any outliers. Hopefully you found that the point $(21, 0.6)$ is an outlier. Suppose this outlier is removed from the data and a new regression line is computed using the remaining 9 data points. Hint: the new regression line *need not* be computed to answer the questions below.

    a. How will the r for the remaining 9 data points compare to the original r? Explain.

    b. Same as **a.** but for the SSE. Explain.

    c. Suppose the new regression line is used to predict y for $x = 100$. Will you substantially change your answer to problem **6f.**? Explain.

Answers and Solutions to Selected Problems

Chapter 1

1. Deterministic

2. Random.
   a. X = closing price of DJIA at the end of a business day.
   b. X = 4700; 4805.5; 5050
   c. non-negative rational numbers
   d. continuous (i.e., a measured index of stocks)

3. Random
   a. X = number of people rejected until the team is chosen
   b. Let A = accepted; R = rejected. AAAAAA (0 people are rejected); RRAAAAARA (3 are rejected). AARRRRRRRRAAAA (9 are rejected).
   c. non-negative counting numbers
   d. discrete

10. Random
   a. Y = number of red marbles chosen
   b. RRRYY; RYYRY; YYYYY
   c. 0, 1, 2, 3
   d. discrete

14. Random
   a. W = no. of times a coin is flipped until 3 heads appear
   b. TTHHH (5 flips); HHH (3 flips); THTTTTHH (8 flips)
   c. Positive integers 3 or larger
   d. discrete

17. Random
   a. T = time, in hours, to fly from SF to NY
   b. T = 4.5, 5.1, 6.2
   c. any positive real number. However, realistically, there is a lower bound around 4 hours and, avoiding problems, there is an upper bound around 6 hours.
   d. continuous (i.e., we take the view that time is measured, not counted)

20. Deterministic

21. Department Chairpersons have incomes exceeding the rest of the teaching faculty

22. A subtle way of introducing bias is for all Department Chairpersons to fall in intervals of 5. It could also happen that every 5th faculty on the list has been there for over 20 years. In other words, the method leaves too many contingencies open, allowing for the introduction of biases.

23. A possible confounding effect is that when the 20 rats are split, the most aggressive ones are caught first. Instead, label the rats from 1 to 20, and select 10 at random. Those ten form one group and the rest the other group.

25. No. The reason being that not all sample of 500 engineers will have an equal chance of being chosen. For example, the probability of ending up with 500 female engineers is different from the probability of ending up with 500 male engineers.

28. Statistical

29. Statistical

33. Probabilistic

34. Neither (the no. of games is fixed by the schedule)

Chapter 2

1. b. $(10 + 16 + \ldots + 85 + 90)/13 \approx 43.62$. **c.** Since $n = 13$ is odd, median = middle observation = 38.

d. There is no mode

2. f.

stem	leaf
0	6 8
1	2 5 6 8
2	4 5
3	
4	0 6

3. Probably the median is most "typical". So, 17.

5. b. 50

6. a. $2 \cdot \$750{,}000 = \$1{,}500{,}000$

b. $(600{,}000 + x)/2 = 750{,}000 \Rightarrow x = \$900{,}000$

c. No. For a data set of two numbers, mean = median

d. They are the same.

7. Which average wage? It is impossible for every number in a data set to be higher than the average of the data. Perhaps the person meant for every American to exceed, at some time in the future, the average wage at the time the statement was made.

8. Median. That is, half of the cars go faster than you and the other half go slower.

9. Suppose one of the persons with zero income finds a job. Assume that person's income is near the bottom of the incomes for the rest of the group. This will cause the median income to go down. Here is an illustration. Median of data set: {10, 20, 30} is 20. Median of data set: {5, 10, 20, 30} is 15. The introduction of the data value 5 caused the median to drop. So, in economics terms, the median income of the group goes down when an income smaller than the median income is introduced. The paradox is apparent, but not clearly resolved. However, part of the solution is to include $0 as an income.

10. a. $50,000. **b.** Yes and Yes. The median is usually not affected by the introduction of a single extreme value.

11. a. pick five 1's and five 9's. The deviations from the mean for each number in the set is the largest it can be; thus, this produces largest variance.

12. b. 32 inches **d.** $39 - 9 = 30$ inches and $39 + 9 = 48$ inches

e. 42 inches (i.e., the top quartile) **g.** $\bar{x}$. Data came from a **sample**.

13. b. Applying the transformation $2x + 0$, we have: {2,4,4,6,10,16}

d. mean of transformed data set = 2•mean of original data set.

standard deviation of transformed data set = 2•standard deviation of original data set.

median of transformed data set = 2•median of original data set.

14. b. The mean is larger. Note the stemleaf is skewed right. This means there are extreme values in the right tail. Those values pull the mean towards them. The median happens early in the data. That is, most of the data are clustered between 20 and 40.

c. Larger than 10. Note the range of the data is 69. The mean of the data is about 45. In order to reach 91, the largest data value, it is not likely we will ever have to go beyond 4 standard deviations from the mean. Thus, expect a standard deviation exceeding 10 (in fact, s is about 17).

16. b. Second test has the lowest z–score (i.e., $z_2 = -0.375$)

17. a. $\bar{x}_1 = \bar{x}_1; s_1 < s_2$ **d.** $\bar{x}_1 = \bar{x}_1; s_1 > s_2$

18. a. mean > median implies data is skewed right.   **c.** 361 days

       g. 60 rats (i.e., 75% of 80).   **h.** Because of the one extreme observation of 600 days. Because of this, the interquartile range is a better representative of the overall spread.

19. Since 90% of all head sizes fall in the interval $23 - 3 = 20$ inches to $23 + 3 = 26$ inches, the smallest 5% is below 20 inches and the largest 5% is above 26 inches.

20. It seems that something went drastically wrong (i.e., a momentary power outage, a spilled bottle, etc...) to cause the one bottle with only 250 tablets. More than likely, there is nothing inherently wrong with the bottling process.

21. b. Set up and solve the simultaneous system: $110 = 5a + b$ and $130 = 7a + b$. The solution is $a = 10$ and $b = 60$.

23. a. 99.45   **e.** 14.28

       i. Choose about 7 intervals. Start at about 64 or 64.5.

24. b. means are =; $s_1 < s_2$.

Chapter 3

1. a. Sample space is: {(1,1), (1,2), (1,3), (1,4), (2,1), (2,2), (2,3), (2,4), (3,1), (3,2), (3,3), (3,4), (4,1), (4,2), (4,3), (4,4)}

b. outcomes for event A: (1,3), (2,3) (3,3), (4,3)
outcomes for event C: (1,2), (2,1), (2,2), (2,3), (3,2), (2,4), (4,2)

d. $P(A) = 4/16 = 1/4 = 0.25$; $P(C) = 7/16$; $P(A \text{ and } C) = 1/16$; $P(\text{not } B) = P(\bar{B}) = 1 - P(B) = 13/16$

e. Checking A, B: is $P(A \mid B) = P(A)$? Note that $P(A \mid B) = 1/3$. However, $P(A) = 1/4$. Thus, since $P(A \mid B) \neq P(A)$ the events A, B are **not** independent.

f. Checking A,B: is $P(A \text{ and } B) = 0$? Note that A,B have common events {i.e., (1,3)}; thus, $P(A \text{ and } B) \neq 0$. This means that A,B are **not** mutually exclusive.

2. a. Sample space is: {1,1,2,3,4,5,6}   **b.** $P(A) = 3/7$

e. $P(A \text{ and } B) = 0$ since A,B are mutually exclusive.

i. $P(B \mid C) = 2/3$. There are two ways to do this. First, you may think of a "reduced" sample space based on the fact that event C is given to have occurred. This produces a new sample space consisting of: {1,1,2}. Event B, within this sample space, consists of the outcome 1. There are two 1's; thus, the 2/3 probability. The other way to do this problem is to use the formula:
$P(B \mid C) = \dfrac{P(B \text{ and } C)}{P(C)}$. Note that $P(B \text{ and } C) = 2/7$ and $P(C) = 3/7$; thus $\dfrac{2/7}{3/7} = 2/3$.

3. a. $P(H \text{ or } W) = 0.8$. Independence means that $P(H \text{ and } W) = P(H) \cdot P(W)$. We know that $P(H) = 0.6$ and $P(H \text{ or } W) = P(H) + P(W) - P(H \text{ and } W)$; thus, $0.8 = 0.6 + P(W) - 0.6 \cdot P(W)$. Solving for $P(W)$ gives, $P(W) = 0.2/0.4 = 1/2$.

b. $P(H \text{ or } W) = P(H + P(W)$; thus, $0.8 = 0.6 + P(W) \Rightarrow P(W) = 0.2$.

d. $P(W \mid H) = 0.3$. Want to find $P(H \text{ and } W)$. Use the fact that $P(W \mid H) = \dfrac{P(H \text{ and } W)}{P(H)}$. This implies that $P(H \text{ and } W) = P(W \mid H) \cdot P(H)$. That is, $P(H \text{ and } W) = 0.3 \cdot 0.6 = 0.18$.

4. a. $P(M) = 100/1000 = 1/10 = 0.1$.
b. $P(F \text{ and } H) = P(F \cap H) = \dfrac{30}{1000}$.
c. $P(S \text{ or } H) = P(S \cup H) = P(S) + P(H) - P(S \text{ and } H) = \dfrac{300 + 200 - 60}{1000} = \dfrac{440}{1000}$

Answers and Solutions

d. $P(H \mid S) = 60/300;\ P(L \mid F) = 150/200$

e. $P(M \mid F) = 0.10$

i. Must form all crossed pairs and check each one for mutually exclusive. The crossed pairs are: F and M; F and H; F and L; S and M; S and H; S and L; J and M; J and H; J and L. It is pretty obvious from the table that none of these are mutually exclusive since $P(A \text{ and } B) \neq 0$ for all A, B.

j. Check all of the above crossed pairs for independence. Compute $P(A \mid B)$ and then $P(A)$. If they are the same, then the events are independent. For instance, the events H, S **are** independent since $P(H \mid S) = 60/300 = P(H) = 200/1000$.

5. b. $P(\text{Def. and C}) = P(\text{Def.} \mid C) \cdot P(C) = 0.05 \cdot 0.25 = 0.0125$.

d. $P(\text{Def.}) = P(\text{Def. and A}) + P(\text{Def. and B}) + P(\text{Def. and C}) = 0.009 + 0.0045 + 0.0125 = 0.026$.

e. $P(C \mid \text{Def.}) = P(C \text{ and Def.})/P(\text{Def.}) = 0.0125/0.026 = 0.481$.

6. a. Since $P(A \text{ and } B) = 0$ (i.e., they are mutually exclusive), then $P(A \mid B) = 0$. Since neither A nor B are empty, this means they are dependent.

7. b. For example, $P(d_2) = 2125/10000 = 0.2125$

c. For example, $P(+ + \mid d_1) = 2110/3215 = 0.6563$

d. For example, $P(d_3 \mid - +) = 73/1964 = 0.0372$

Note that as a "patient", you are interested in the "posterior" probabilities. The doctor knows the priors. Thus, once a diagnosis is made, posterior probabilities are computed in order to assess the chances of a successful prognosis and ensuing treatment.

8. b. Let A = biased coin is picked; B = fair coin is picked; H = a tail comes up
$P(H) = P(A) \cdot P(H \mid A) + P(B) \cdot P(H \mid B) = \dfrac{1}{2} \cdot \dfrac{1}{2} + \dfrac{1}{2} \cdot \dfrac{1}{2} = \dfrac{1}{4}$.

9. b. 1/3

Chapter 4

1. **a.** Range is: {1,2,3,4,5,6}   **b.** P(X = 6) = 1 − (0.4 + 0.5) = 0.1

   d. 0.6/0.7 = 6/7   **e.** μ = 3.7. It is the expected value of X.

2. **a.** 0.3   **d.** 0.15/0.3 = 1/2

3. **a.** k = 1/15   **c.** P(2 ≤ Y ≤ 4) = 9/15 = 0.6

4. **a.** Let X = profit (loss) for a single spin of the roulette. Then,

X	−$1	+$1
P(X = x)	20/38	18/38

   Thus, μ = −$1 · 20/38 + $1 · 18/38 = −0.053. This means that over many roulette games, the player is expected to lose about 5 cents for every dollar bet.

5. **a.** X = number of correctly answered questions   **b.** X = 0,1,2,...,10

   c. X ~ B(10, 0.20)   **d.** From Binomial Table, P(X ≥ 5) = 0.0328

7. **c.** X ~ B(15, 0.60)   **d.** μ = np = 15·0.60 = 9

   e. From Binomial Table, P(X = 9) = 0.2066

8. **c.** X ~ B(20, p) where p = probability of a defective fuse

   d. Let p = 0.1; thus, P(X ≤ 3) = 0.1216 + 0.2702 + 0.2852 + 0.1901 = 0.8671

11. **c.** X ~ B(4, 0.30)   **d.** P(X ≥ 1) = 0.7599

12. **a.** X ~ P(2)   **b.** The person is thinking in terms of weeks in 1 year.

13. **a.** X = number of at bat until the first base hit

    b. H; NH; NNH   **c.** P(X = 1) = 0.30

    d. μ = 1/p = 3.33.. If this experiment is performed many times, it takes an average of 3.333...at bat for the player to get the first base hit.

14. **a.** X = number of non-defective light bulbs   **b.** $X \sim H(990,10,20)$

     c. $P(X = 20)$

20. **a.** X = number of losses until the third win   **b.** $X \sim Pa(3, 0.40)$

     c. $P(X < 7)$

23. **a.** Let X = number of men hired. $X \sim B(20, 0.50)$. Note that we let $p = 0.5$ since the number of applicants is equally divided between men and women and all applicants are considered equally qualified. Note that $P(X \leq 7) = 0.2648$ and $\mu = 10$. Could build an argument on the probability of hiring 7 or fewer men being as low as 0.26 and the fact that the expected number of men that should have been hired is 10.

25. **a.** $X \sim H(400000, 100000, 10)$ **b.** $\{0,1,2, \dots , 10\}$

     d. $B(10, 0.80)$

Chapter 5

1. **a.** $4/7$

    b. $\dfrac{44.5 - 25}{60 - 25} = \dfrac{19.2}{35}$

    d. median is the 50th percentile. Thus, $0.5 = \dfrac{x - 25}{35} \Rightarrow x = 42.5$.

    e. 42.5

    g. $\sigma^2 = \dfrac{(b - a)^2}{12} = \dfrac{(60 - 25)^2}{12} = \dfrac{1225}{12}$

    h. 56.5

2. **a.** Note $\mu = 1/0.02 = 50$. CDF = $P(X < x) = 1 - e^{-x/\mu}$. Thus, $P(30 < X < 70) =$

    $$\left(1 - e^{-70/50}\right) - \left(1 - e^{-30/50}\right) = 0.7534 - 0.45112 = 0.30228.$$

    d. Note that median = 50th percentile. Thus,
    $$0.5 = 1 - e^{-x/50} \Rightarrow -0.5 = -e^{-x/50} \Rightarrow \ln 0.5 = -\frac{x}{50} \Rightarrow x = -50 \cdot \ln 0.5 = 80.472.$$

3. **b.** $P(X < 23) = \dfrac{(23 - 0)^2}{(50 - 0)^2} = 0.2116$

    f. $0.9 = \dfrac{(x - 0)^2}{(50 - 0)^2} \Rightarrow x^2 = 2250 \Rightarrow x = 47.4342$

5. Exponential. Most calls are of short duration with a few calls lasting longer (creating a long right tail).

6. Either exponential or uniform, depending on the supermarket, time of day, etc..

7. Exponential. Most students (or people, for that matter) don't carry much money in coins.

8. Triangular. Most people there are quite wealthy; thus, the distribution is skewed left.

9. Uniform.

10. Uniform

11. **a.** $X \sim U(25,95)$
    b. $2/7$
    c. 60
    e. $P(X > 75) = 2/7$
    f. $P(X > 70 \mid X > 60) = \dfrac{95 - 70}{95 - 60} = \dfrac{5}{7}$

12. **a.** $X \sim \text{Exp}(\text{decay} = 0.001)$

    d. $0.5 = 1 - e^{-x/1000} \Rightarrow \ln 0.5 = -\dfrac{x}{1000} \Rightarrow x = 693.15$

    f. 90% of all such bulbs would have died by the 2303 hour of operation. Another way of saying this is that only 10% of all such bulbs would last more than 2303 hours of use.

13. **a.** Uniform. That is, if X = serial numbers, then $X \sim U(1,b)$.

    b. From the data, the maximum serial number is 225. This is a candidate for b. We may also compute another candidate for b using the formula for the average of a uniform distribution. That is, $\mu \approx \bar{x} = \dfrac{662}{7} = \dfrac{1+b}{2} \Rightarrow b \approx 188$. The most likely of these two estimates is 225 since it is larger than 188. We may also estimate b by using the variance formulation for X. That is, $\sigma^2 \approx s^2 = \dfrac{(b-a)^2}{12}$. From data, $s = 91.929$; thus, $b \approx 319$.

Chapter 6

2. Want a z value such that the area to its right is 0.05. From table, z = 1.65.

3. (Area to the right of z = 2) = α = 1 – 0.9772 = 0.0228.

4. (Area to the right of z = –1.5) = α = 0.9332.

7. The area to the right of the required z is α = 0.01. The 99th percentile of the Z distribution is the value of z such that 0.99 of the area under the standard normal curve is to its left. Thus, z(α = 0.01) = z = 2.33.

9. 0.1815   12. b. 0   c. 0.2408   d. 5

        f. $z = \dfrac{x - 10}{5}$ where z = – 0.13 $\Rightarrow$ x = 9.35.

14. c. α = 0.5.   e. α = 0.   j. z(α = 0.04) = z = 1.75. α = 0.04

15. a. X ~ N(74, 6^2)   e. P(X > 80) = P(Z > $\dfrac{80 - 74}{6}$) = P(Z > 1) = 0.1587.

                       Thus, 15.87% of the scores are greater than the student who scored 80.

16. a. X = life of battery.   b. X ~ N(3.4, 0.64)

   c. P(3 < X < 4) = P(–0.5 < Z < 0.75) = 0.4649.

   f. $1.65 = \dfrac{x - 3.4}{0.8} \Rightarrow$ x = 4.72 years.   h. $-1.65 = \dfrac{x - 3.4}{0.8} \Rightarrow$ x = 2.08 years.

18. a. Let X = altitude at which parachute opens. X ~ N(200, 900). P(damage) = P(X < 110) = P(Z < –3) = 0.0013.

   b. Y = number of damaged cargo. Then, Y ~ B(5, 0.0013). Want P(Y ≥ 1). Note that P(Y ≥ 1) = 1 – P(Y = 0) = 1 – $(0.9987)^5$ ≈ 0.00648.

20. a. n = 500; np = 500•0.6 = 300; n•(1 – p) = 500•0.4 = 200. Thus, n ≥ 20 and both np and n(1 – p) exceed 5.

   b. For X ~ N(300, 120), P(279.5 < X < 330.5) = P(–1.87 < Z < 2.78) = 0.9666

   c. There is a 90% chance that 314 or fewer people out of the 500 wear seatbelts.

21. **b.** X = rate of return on stocks. $X \sim N(0.12, 0.17^2)$; thus, $P(X < 0) = P(Z < -0.71) = 0.2389$. So, the market is down in about 1 every 4 years.

c. 22.36% of the years.

22. Use the Normal approximation to the Binomial. If X = no. of base hits, then $X \sim N(16.24, 9.64656)$. $P(X < 20.5) = P(Z < 1.37) = 0.9147$.

25. **b.** Over 286.48 days.

26. **d.** Ask for the statistics on the maximum temperature for each summer day.

Chapter 7

1. **a.** The 9 samples of size 2 are: {1,1}; {1,3}; {1,5}; {3,1}; {3,3}; {3,5}; {5,1}; {5,3}; {5,5}.

   b. The nine means are: 1, 2, 3, 2, 3, 4, 3, 4, 5.

2. **a.** $N(100, 36)$ **b.** $N(100, 4)$ **c.** $N(1000, 360)$

   d. $P(X > 103) = P(Z > 0.5) = 0.3085$ $P(\overline{X} > 103) = P(Z > 1.5) = 0.0668$

   $P(\sum X < 1000) = P(Z < 0) = 0.5$ $P(\sum X < 960) = P(Z < -2.11) = 0.0174$

   40th % for $\sum X$: Find k so that $P(\sum X < k) = 0.4$. The z- value associated with a probability below it of 0.4 is -0.25. Thus, $-0.25 = \dfrac{k - 1000}{\sqrt{360}} \Rightarrow k = -0.25 \cdot \sqrt{360} + 1000 = 995.257$.

3. **a.** Note that $X \sim N(840,10000)$. $P(X > 820) = P(Z > -0.2) = 0.5793$

   b. Note that $\overline{X} \sim N(840,100)$. $P(\overline{X} > 820) = P(Z > -2) = 0.9772$

   c. The distribution of sample means has a much smaller variance; thus, 820 is a full 2 standard deviations to the left of 840.

4. **a.** 15% of 50,000 = 7,500.

   b. X = number of high school dropouts who receive the brochure. $X \sim B(50000, 0.15)$. Use the Normal approximation to the Binomial. Thus, $X \sim N[7500, n \cdot p \cdot (1 - p) = 6375]$. Correcting for continuity, $P(X > 7999.5) = P(Z > 6.26) = 0$.

6. **a.** $P(X \le 5) = 1 - e^{-5/4} = 0.7135$.

   c. $\overline{X} \sim N(4, 16/36)$. $P(\overline{X} \le 5) = P(Z < 1.5) = 0.9332$.

8. Note that $\sum X \sim N(300, 100)$. $P(\sum X > 320) = P(Z > 2) = 0.0228$

9. Let X = number of heads. Note X ~ B(1,0.5). For 10,000 flips, then X ~ N(5000, 2500).
$P(X \geq 5067) = P(Z > 1.33) = 0.0918$. The chances of Kerrich getting such result are about 9
in 100. This is not all that unusual. Could argue either way about the fairness of Kerrich's coin.

10. a. N(12,000, 1,000,000)   **b.** N(12,000, 40,000)   **c.** N(300,000, 25,000,000)

g. $1.28 = \dfrac{x - 12000}{1000} \Rightarrow x = 13280$. This means that 90% of all accounts have balances below \$13,280.

h. $1.28 = \dfrac{x - 12000}{200} \Rightarrow x = 12256$. This means that if we compute the average balance of groups of 25
randomly chosen accounts, there is a 90% chance that this average balance will fall below \$12,256.

i. $1.28 = \dfrac{x - 300000}{5000} \Rightarrow x = 306400$. This means that if we compute the sum of the balances of
groups of 25 randomly chosen accounts, there is a 90% chance that this sum will fall below \$306,400.

11. That eventually losing stocks will be "winners", given sufficient time.

12. It assumes that Brando is bisexual. In other words, the Law of Large Numbers can't possibly apply
unless there is a "chance" of something happening. Thus, assuming the probability of Brando being
bisexual is 0, then the passage is pure non-sense.

13. There are so many stocks, that the darts are likely to fall on some winners (as well as on losers). It doesn't
take that many winners to exceed the financial return of professionals.

Chapter 8

1. a. $\alpha = 0.05$; thus, $z(0.025) = 1.96$. $EB = 1.96 \cdot \dfrac{3}{1} = 5.88$. 95% C.I. is $(94.12, 105.88)$

b. $EB = 1.96 \cdot \dfrac{3}{6} = 0.98$. 95% C.I. is $(99.02, 100.98)$

2. $\alpha = 0.10$; thus $z(0.05) = 1.645$. $EB = 2 = 1.645 \cdot \dfrac{9}{\sqrt{n}} \Rightarrow n = \left(1.645 \cdot \dfrac{9}{2}\right)^2 = 55$.

4. $EB = 2.5 = z(\alpha/2) \cdot \dfrac{5}{5} \Rightarrow 2.5 = z(\alpha/2)$. So, $\alpha/2$ is the area to the right of $z = 2.5$. This area is 0.0062. Thus, $\alpha/2 = 0.0062$ or $\alpha = 0.0124$. Therefore, confidence $= 1 - \alpha = 98.78\%$.

5. a. $65/100 = 0.65$.   **b.** $EB = z(0.05) \cdot \sqrt{\dfrac{0.65 \cdot 0.35}{100}} = 1.645 \cdot 0.047697 = 0.0785$.
Thus, 90% C.I. is $(0.572, 0.729)$

d. $0.05 = z(\alpha/2) \cdot \sqrt{\dfrac{0.65 \cdot 0.35}{100}} \Rightarrow z(\alpha/2) = 1.05 \Rightarrow \alpha/2 = 0.1469$. Thus, $\alpha = 0.2938$ and confidence $= 1 - \alpha = 70.62\%$.

6. $n = 385$. Hint: use $p' = 0.5$ (worst case scenario).

7. c. $n = 206$

9. a. $EB = 1.96 \cdot \dfrac{40}{40} = 1.96$. Thus, C.I. is $(298.04, 301.96)$

b. $EB = 1.96 \cdot \dfrac{40}{20} = 3.92$. Thus, C.I. is $(296.08, 303.92)$

c. $EB = 1.96 \cdot \dfrac{40}{10} = 7.84$. Thus, C.I. is $(292.16, 307.84)$

d. Decreasing the sample size produces a larger error bound for fixed confidence and fixed σ.

10. a. In 95% of similarly taken polls, the percentage of voters who favor Carter would be between 49% and 53%.

b. Clearly a confidence interval of $(0.49, 0.53)$ does not guarantee being favored by the majority of voters; thus, the claim by the Gallup people that the election was "too close to call".

c. From the poll results, it is impossible to compute the probability that over half the voters favor Carter. The poll gives an estimate of the proportion of voters who favor Carter. However, as seen above, the confidence interval about this estimate includes values below 0.50.

11. **a.** The population should be all pharmacists in the West Coast of the United States. The major flaw in collecting the data is that of "convenience sampling". That is, the pharmacists who returned the survey were self selected. This causes biases, since mostly pharmacists with strong opinions would tend to respond.

d. The problem deals with the average response. By the CLT, averages are normally distributed, regardless of the distribution of the underlying population.

12. **a.** $EB = 1.96 \cdot \sqrt{\dfrac{0.315 \cdot 0.685}{500}} = 0.041$. The top end of the confidence interval would be the highest average he would achieve (with 95% probability): $0.315 + 0.041 = 0.356$.

b. $EB = 1.96 \cdot \sqrt{\dfrac{0.425 \cdot 0.575}{500}} = 0.043$. The lower end of the confidence interval would be: $0.425 - 0.043 = 0.382$.

c. It will be difficult for Bonds, perhaps unrealistic, to ever hit for a batting average much above 0.382 during the full course of a baseball season.

d. It is not likely that Bonds will be the person to challenge Ted Williams feat.

13. Note that s, not σ, is given. However, since the sample size is 50 (rather large), s should be an adequate estimate for σ.

c. n = 187.

15. **a.** $p' = 63/94 = 0.6702$ **b.** EB = 0.08. C.I. is (0.59, 0.75)   **e.** n = 384

Chapter 9

	Null	Alternative
1.	$\mu = 78$ or $\mu \geq 78$	$\mu < 78$ (less than...One tail on left)
2.	$p = 0.12$ or $p \geq 0.12$	$p < 0.12$ (declined...One tail on left)
3.	$\mu = 2$	$\mu \neq 2$ (either direction...Both tails)

5. Tends to favor the claim that, on average, motorists travel at a speed exceeding 60 mph.

6. Impossible to determine. The p-value can't be computed because n is not known; thus, it is not known how far from 0.40, 0.45 actually falls.

7. Yes. Since $0.35 < 0.40$, the data favors the null. The test is one tailed, on the right. In order to reject the null, the statistic must fall in the right tail of the distribution. This is clearly not the case.

8. **a.** H_o: $\mu = 18$ or $\mu \geq 18$ vs. H_a: $\mu < 18$.

Note $\overline{X} \sim N(18, 0.04)$. p-value $= P(\overline{X} < 17.5 \mid \mu = 18) = P(Z < -2.5) = 0.0062$.

b. With such a small p-value, there appears to be sufficient evidence against the null. The consumer group appears to be justified in claiming that the cereal boxes contain, on average, less than 18 ounces of cereal.

9. **a.** H_o: $p = 0.44$ vs. H_a: $p \neq 0.44$ (two-tailed...did not stay the same)

Note $P' \sim N(0.44, 0.000493)$. p-value $= P(P' < 0.42$ or $P' > 0.46 \mid p = 0.44) =$

$P(Z < -0.9$ or $Z > 0.9) = 0.3682$.

11. There are problems. If the 25 students in the class are not a random sample of all students, then the results will not be valid. For instance, if Professor Jenkins class is composed of underachievers, then he should be rewarded. If the opposite is true, then perhaps he should be reprimanded. If the 25 students are a truly random sample of the population of students taking Elementary Statistics, then the decision to take no action is warranted.

12. **a.** Parachute will not open

b. Parachute will open but Joe believes it will not; thus, he will not jump when he should.

c. Parachute will not open but Joe believes it will; thus, he jumps and probably dies or is badly injured.

d. (ii). A high α will make it fairly easy to reject the null and conclude that the parachute will not open.

14. **a.** $N(10,1)$ **c.** $\bar{x}_{\text{left critical}} = 7.42$; $\bar{x}_{\text{right critical}} = 12.58$

     d. test statistic $= z = \dfrac{12.3 - 10}{1} = 2.3$; p-value $= 2 \cdot P(\bar{X} > 12.3 \mid \mu = 10) = 2 \cdot P(Z > 2.3) = 0.0214$

     e. There is insufficient evidence to reject the null since p-value > pre-conceived α.

     f. EB $= z(0.005) \cdot 1 = 2.58$. Thus, 99% C.I. is: $(9.72, 14.88)$.

     g. Note: $\alpha = 0.01$ and $\bar{X} \sim N(12,1)$. Thus, $\beta = $ P(accepting null | null is not valid) $\Rightarrow$

         $\beta = P(7.42 < \bar{X} < 12.58 \mid \mu_a = 12) = P(-4.58 < Z < 0.58) = 0.719$.

17. $\beta = 0.078$. Since 14 is much farther from 10 than 12, it is not likely that with a sample of size 25 we will obtain a sample mean that will fall in the interval $(7.42, 12.58)$. That is, if the actual population mean is 14, it is very unlikely that the sample data would favor the null hypothesis; thus, the probability of favoring an invalid null is quite small.

18. $X \sim B(4, 0.7)$. Acceptance region is $X = 2,3,4$; thus, $\beta = P(X = 2,3,4 \mid p_a = 0.5) = 0.6875$.

21. It is not correct. Hypotheses testing has nothing to do with "truth". Statistically significant at the 0.01 significance level means that the probability of obtaining the sample data by pure luck is less than 0.01. In other words, the observed data more than likely did not happen by chance. This means that there is evidence against the null.

Chapter 10

1. **a.** $1 - 0.025 = 0.975$ **d.** $1 - 0.005 = 0.995$ **e.** $1 - 0.008 = 0.992$ (use the Normal)

    g. $0.995 - 0.900 = 0.095$

2. **a.** 1.75 **c.** -2.68 **f.** -2.58

3. **a.** 1.86 **c.** -1.83 **d.** $t_{20} = 2.09$

4. **b.** 0.025 and 0.01

5. **a.** $H_0: \mu = 22$ $H_a: \mu \neq 22$

    b. $\overline{X} \sim N\left(22, \dfrac{\sigma^2}{9}\right)$. Since σ is not known, t_8 is used.

    c. $t_{8, 0.025} = 2.31$; thus $2.31 = \dfrac{\overline{x}_{\text{right critical}} - 22}{3.1/3} \Rightarrow \overline{x}_{\text{right critical}} = 24.387$. Similarly, $\overline{x}_{\text{left critical}} = 19.613$.

    d. Since 20 is included in the interval $(19.613, 24.387)$ the data favors the null and the mean operating life of size D batteries does not appear to be different from 22 hours.

7. **b.** The distribution is quite symmetrical. No extreme values. No reason to believe that the results are not accurate.

8. $EB = t_{24, \, 0.025} \cdot \dfrac{s}{\sqrt{n}} = 2.06 \cdot 2 = 4.12 \Rightarrow$ 95% C.I. is $(67.88, 76.12)$

9. **a.** $H_a: \mu > 45$ (increase in output)

    d. $\overline{x}_{\text{right critical}} = 46.93$. Since $47 > 46.93$, it can be claimed that the adjustment was successful.

10. **a.** Favor the null. Note that $24 < 25$ (i.e., 25 is the critical value since "an average difference of 5 tomatoes per plant is considered to be significant").

    b. $\beta = P\left(\overline{X} < 25 \mid \mu_a = 26\right) = P\left(t_{24} < -0.5\right) > 0.10$. In fact, using a computer, $P\left(t_{24} < -0.5\right) = 0.311$.

    c. p-value = computed $\alpha = P\left(\overline{X} > 25 \mid \mu = 20\right) = P\left(t_{24} > 2.5\right) \approx 0.01$.

11. **a.** The data set represents the population; thus, the mean age is already μ.

b. Assume the data set of the ages is a *sample* from the population of all Presidents (including those in the future...)

13. 86.64% confident. Hint: $t_{35,\,\alpha/2} = 1.5$ and approximate with the Normal.

14. **a.** H_o: $\mu \geq 25$ H_a: $\mu < 25$ (single tail on left)

e. p-value $= P\left(t_{24} < -2.90\right) < 0.005$

15. **a.** H_o: $\mu = 65$ H_a: $\mu \neq 65$ (two-tailed)   **b.** $\overline{X} \sim N\left(65, \dfrac{25}{64}\right)$

d. Left critical value $= 63.775$. Right critical value $= 66.225$

e. p-value $= 2 \cdot P(Z < -8) = 0$.

16. **a.** H_o: $\mu = \$158{,}950$ H_a: $\mu > \$158{,}950$ (single tail on right)

e. p-value $= P\left(t_{15} > 2.60\right) = 0.01$.

18. **b.** $P'_M \sim N\left(0.5, \dfrac{0.5 \cdot 0.5}{535}\right)$

Chapter 11

1. two sample means   **2.** matched pairs   **4.** two proportions

6. two sample means

8. **a.** H_0: $\mu_d = 0$ Ha: $\mu_d > 0$ (increase, single tail on right)

Matched pairs. Use $t_{399} \approx Z$. p-value $P(Z > 30) = 0$. Thus, there is a significant difference and the data favors the alternative; thus, on average, the amounts charged have increased.

b. The amount charged may be skewed right, but the average of groups of customers is Normal (CLT). In fact, the sample size here is so large (i.e., 400), that the t is similar to the standard normal. (i.e., use Z).

c. One way of doing this is to offer the no annual fee feature but keep the interest rate fixed at whatever it was the previous year.

9. **a.** H_0: $\mu_{NE} - \mu_{SW} = 0$ H_a: $\mu_{NE} - \mu_{SW} \neq 0$ (two-tailed)

b. $t = \dfrac{14.5 - 16.7 - 0}{1.1902} = -1.85$

c. df = 22   **d.** p-value > 0.05; thus, favor the null. There appears to be no difference in mean life for roofs in the SW and NE.

10. **a.** H_0: $p_A - p_B = 0$ H_a: $p_A - p_B \neq 0$ (two-tailed)

b. $P'_A - P'_B \sim N\left(0, p_c(1 - p_c)\left(\dfrac{1}{100} + \dfrac{1}{100}\right)\right)$ where $p_c = \dfrac{70 + 78}{100 + 100} = 0.74$

c. test statistic = $z = \dfrac{-0.08}{\sqrt{0.74 \cdot 0.26 \cdot \dfrac{1}{50}}} = -1.29$. p-value $= 2 \cdot P(Z < -1.29) = 0.197$.

d. Data favors the null (i.e., fairly large p-value). No evidence to claim that voters opinion differs in the two districts.

13. H_a: $\mu_N - \mu_S > 0$ (single tail on right)

Use t_{20}. test statistic $= t = 2000/25.2587 = 79.18$. Thus, p-value $= 0$. Reject null. Data favors the alternative and the average selling price of homes north of Center Street is higher than those south of Center Street.

16. **a.** H_0: $\mu_A = \mu_B$ or $\mu_A \geq \mu_B$

b. $\overline{X}_A - \overline{X}_B \sim N\left(0, \dfrac{\sigma_A^2}{12} + \dfrac{\sigma_B^2}{15}\right)$. However, since the σ's are not known, we use t_{25}.

c. left critical value $= -3.66$.

f. since $(84.5 - 85.9) = -1.4 > -3.66$, the data favors the null

g. The 97.5% C.I. for $\mu_A - \mu_B$ is $(-5.82, 3.02)$. Hint: use $t_{25,0.0125} = 2.49$.

Chapter 12

1.   **a.** 37.57   **c.**   0.995   **d.**   0.005

2.   **a.** 30.58   **c.**   13.24   **d.**   32

3. H_a: $\sigma^2 > 0.8^2 = 0.64$ (single tail on right). Distribution is χ^2_{15}.

Test statistic $= \dfrac{15 \cdot 1.1^2}{0.64} = 28.35$. p-value $= P(\chi^2_{15} > 28.35)$. From the table, we note that the p-value is somewhere between 0.025 and 0.01. Thus, for pre-set $\alpha = 0.05$, the data favors the alternative that the life of the mufflers may have a variance in excess of 0.64.

4.   **a.** Reject H_0. Note that: $24 \cdot 0.0384/0.1225^2 = 61.41 > \chi^2_{24} = 36.42$.

5.   For **4b**: left tail critical value = 1.24; right tail critical value = 14.45. Thus, 95% C.I. is:

$$\frac{6 \cdot 0.0384}{14.45} < \sigma^2 < \frac{6 \cdot 0.0384}{1.24} \quad \text{or} \quad 0.016 < \sigma^2 < 0.186.$$

7.   **a.** H_0: All 5 sales people have equal sales records. This is the same as stating that the sales data follows a discrete uniform distribution.

b. Expected: 100   100   100   100   100

$\dfrac{(O - E)^2}{E}$:   1   9   9   1   0

c. $\chi^2_{4, 0.01} = 13.28 < \sum \dfrac{(O - E)^2}{E} = 20$. Reject H_0. Sales people don't have an equal sales record.

8.   **a.** 2 rows, 3 columns   **b.**   See table below

c. 0.143, 0.583, 0.017. Limit non-school related activities to somewhere between 5 and 20 hours per week. More than 20 hours per week seems to lead to failure. Not clear what having less than 5 hours per week of these activities is indicating.

d. H_0: hours per week not related to school is independent of success in school

e. Expected frequencies in *italics* and in parenthesis:

<u>Hours per week not related to school</u>

	< 5	5 to 20	> 20	**Totals**
C or better	12 *(14)*	70 *(65.1)*	2 *(4.9)*	**84**
D or F or W	8 *(6)*	23 *(27.9)*	5 *(2.1)*	**36**
Totals	**20**	**93**	**7**	**120**

f. $\chi^2_{2,\,0.05} = 5.99 < \sum \frac{(O - E)^2}{E} = 7.9$. Thus, reject H_0. Data favors the belief that success in school is not independent of hours per week not related to school.

g. Only one cell has a count below 5. This is well below 20% of the cells having counts of at least 5. No bearing on the reliability of the test procedure.

Chapter 13

1. **a.** 3.80   **c.** 0.99   **d.** 0.01   **2.** **a.** 2.45   **d.** 2.99

3. H_a: $\sigma_1^2 \neq \sigma_2^2$ (two-tailed). Note Group 1 (i.e, Lesion 1) has the largest variance; thus, it will be placed in the numerator of the F statistic.

    F statistic = $13.7/6.13 = 2.235$. From the 0.01 F table, $F_{15,15,0.01} = 3.52$. Since $2.235 < 3.52$, the evidence favors the null. Therefore, there is no difference in variability between the two groups at the 0.02 level of significance.

5. **a.** H_0: $\mu_1 = \mu_2 = \mu_3 = \mu_4$ H_a: not all of μ_1, μ_2, μ_3, μ_4 are equal.

    b. df for numerator = 3;   df for denominator = $24 - 4 = 20$.

    c. largest variance/smallest variance = $5.659/1.556 = 3.637 < 4$. Thus, the variances may be assumed to be the same.

    d. ANOVA F statistic = $6.237/3.325 = 1.99$.

    e. $F_{3,20,0.01} = 4.94$. Since $1.99 < 4.94$, the data favors the null. We conclude that there are no differences in mean typing speed among the four typists.

6. **b.** df for numerator = 4;   df for denominator = 50

    d. ANOVA F statistic = $16.374/5.597 = 2.93$

7. **a.** The stem-leaf shows that the optimal number of plants per acre is around 20,000. The yield begins to drop at the 24,000 and 28,000 plants per acre levels.

    b. $\overline{x}_{12,000} = 130.75$; $\overline{x}_{16,000} = 142.5$; $\overline{x}_{20,000} = 145.75$; $\overline{x}_{24,000} = 142.67$; $\overline{x}_{28,000} = 131.33$.

    c. The mean corn yield (bushels per acre) remains the same if different number of plants per acre are planted.

    f. The test has virtually no power since the sample sizes are too small. Even though there appears to be significant differences in the mean yields, the ANOVA F statistic will not detect them.

8. **b.** df for numerator = 3;   df for denominator = $38 - 3 = 35$.
        ANOVA F statistic = $10/4 = 2.5$.

Chapter 14

1. explanatory or control variable = number of calories

   response variable = sodium content

3. explanatory or control variable = number of pills taken

   response variable = time for headache to disappear

5. **a.** Yes. From the correlation table, $r = 0.85$ exceeds the critical values for all of the significance levels shown. Note $df = 20 - 2 = 18$.

   b. bushels per acre

   c. $0.25 \cdot 200 = 50$ bushels per acre. Note that this question only involves the slope. That is, the slope measures how yield increases as a function of fertilizer.

   d. $\hat{y} = 0.25 \cdot 200 + 2.5 = 52.5$

   e. 0.25   **f.** $r^2 = 0.85^2 = 0.7225$. 72.25% of the variation in yield is explained by the amount of fertilizer used.

   g. $s_{\hat{y}} = \sqrt{\dfrac{SSE}{n-2}} = \sqrt{\dfrac{1200}{18}} = 8.165$

6. **b.** Yes. $0.924 > 0.716$

   c. from equation (4): $b_1 = r\dfrac{s_y}{s_x} = 0.924 \cdot \dfrac{1.222}{13.844} = 0.082$

   from equation (5): $b_0 = \bar{y} - b_1 \cdot \bar{x} = 2.11 - 0.082 \cdot 26.1 = -0.0302$

   e. predicted annual savings for an annual income of $25,000 is about $2,020

   f. predicted annual savings for an annual income of $100,000 is about $8170. Probably not. The highest annual income included in the range of x is $50,000. We note that $100,000 is well out of the range of x values included in the study. As we have noted, extrapolation often yields inaccurate results.

7. **a.** the correlation can only be computed if the variables are quantitative. Note that gender is qualitative or categorical.

   b. r can never exceed 1.

   c. correlation is unitless.

8. **a.** Statisticians in industry are paid a lot more than those in academia, regardless of degree. Thus, there are statisticians with Bachelors and Masters getting paid a lot more than Ph.D's in academia.

9. As children grow older their reading gets better (i.e, more schooling – if nothing else...) The fact that their shoe size increases is a function of them getting taller, but has nothing to do with improving scores on a reading comprehension test.

10. b_1 will be about 0. $b_0 = \bar{y}$. This follows from the fact that $b_0 = \bar{y} - b_1 \cdot \bar{x}$, setting $b_1 = 0$.

12. **a.** $y = -0.08 \cdot t + 2.2$

   b. Since $r = 1$ (i.e., two points exactly determine a line), $r^2 = 100\%$. This means that the line explains 100% of the variation in y.

   c. For $t = 55$, $y = -2.20$. This is an absurd prediction since there can't be negative people riding in cars. What is wrong? Extrapolation. Clearly the relationship between number of people riding in cars on the highway and time is not linear.

13. **a.** It will be higher (i.e., less of a scatter)

   b. Smaller (i.e., less overall error)

   c. No. $x = 100$ is still beyond the range of values of x.

Answers and Solutions

Appendix

STANDARD NORMAL DISTRIBUTION
$P(Z \le z)$ for $Z \sim N(0,1)$

second decimal in z

z	0	1	2	3	4	5	6	7	8	9
-3.0⁻	0.0013	0.0013	0.0013	0.0012	0.0012	0.0011	0.0011	0.0011	0.0010	0.0010
-2.9	0.0019	0.0018	0.0017	0.0017	0.0016	0.0016	0.0015	0.0015	0.0014	0.0014
-2.8	0.0026	0.0025	0.0024	0.0023	0.0022	0.0022	0.0021	0.0021	0.0020	0.0019
-2.7	0.0035	0.0034	0.0033	0.0032	0.0031	0.0030	0.0029	0.0028	0.0027	0.0026
-2.6	0.0047	0.0045	0.0044	0.0043	0.0041	0.0040	0.0039	0.0038	0.0037	0.0036
-2.5	0.0062	0.0060	0.0059	0.0057	0.0055	0.0054	0.0052	0.0051	0.0049	0.0048
-2.4	0.0082	0.0080	0.0078	0.0075	0.0073	0.0071	0.0069	0.0068	0.0066	0.0064
-2.3	0.0107	0.0104	0.0102	0.0099	0.0096	0.0094	0.0091	0.0089	0.0087	0.0084
-2.2	0.0139	0.0136	0.0132	0.0129	0.0125	0.0122	0.0119	0.0116	0.0113	0.0110
-2.1	0.0179	0.0174	0.0170	0.0166	0.0162	0.0158	0.0154	0.0150	0.0146	0.0143
-2.0	0.0228	0.0222	0.0217	0.0212	0.0207	0.0202	0.0197	0.0192	0.0188	0.0183
-1.9	0.0287	0.0281	0.0274	0.0268	0.0262	0.0256	0.0250	0.0244	0.0239	0.0233
-1.8	0.0359	0.0351	0.0344	0.0336	0.0329	0.0322	0.0314	0.0307	0.0301	0.0294
-1.7	0.0446	0.0436	0.0427	0.0418	0.0409	0.0401	0.0392	0.0384	0.0375	0.0367
-1.6	0.0548	0.0537	0.0526	0.0516	0.0505	0.0495	0.0485	0.0475	0.0465	0.0455
-1.5	0.0668	0.0655	0.0643	0.0630	0.0618	0.0606	0.0594	0.0582	0.0571	0.0559
-1.4	0.0808	0.0793	0.0778	0.0764	0.0749	0.0735	0.0721	0.0708	0.0694	0.0681
-1.3	0.0968	0.0951	0.0934	0.0918	0.0901	0.0885	0.0869	0.0853	0.0838	0.0823
-1.2	0.1151	0.1131	0.1112	0.1093	0.1075	0.1056	0.1038	0.1020	0.1003	0.0985
-1.1	0.1357	0.1335	0.1314	0.1292	0.1271	0.1251	0.1230	0.1210	0.1190	0.1170
-1.0	0.1587	0.1562	0.1539	0.1515	0.1492	0.1469	0.1446	0.1423	0.1401	0.1379
-0.9	0.1841	0.1814	0.1788	0.1762	0.1736	0.1711	0.1685	0.1660	0.1635	0.1611
-0.8	0.2119	0.2090	0.2061	0.2033	0.2005	0.1977	0.1949	0.1922	0.1894	0.1867
-0.7	0.2420	0.2389	0.2358	0.2327	0.2296	0.2266	0.2236	0.2206	0.2177	0.2148
-0.6	0.2743	0.2709	0.2676	0.2643	0.2611	0.2578	0.2546	0.2514	0.2483	0.2451
-0.5	0.3085	0.3050	0.3015	0.2981	0.2946	0.2912	0.2877	0.2843	0.2810	0.2776
-0.4	0.3446	0.3409	0.3372	0.3336	0.3300	0.3264	0.3228	0.3192	0.3156	0.3121
-0.3	0.3821	0.3783	0.3745	0.3707	0.3669	0.3632	0.3594	0.3557	0.3520	0.3483
-0.2	0.4207	0.4168	0.4129	0.4090	0.4052	0.4013	0.3974	0.3936	0.3897	0.3859
-0.1	0.4602	0.4562	0.4522	0.4483	0.4443	0.4404	0.4364	0.4325	0.4286	0.4247
-0.0	0.5000	0.4960	0.4920	0.4880	0.4840	0.4801	0.4761	0.4721	0.4681	0.4641

Note: for $z \ge 4.0$ the areas are 1, accurate to four decimal places.

STANDARD NORMAL DISTRIBUTION (Continued)
$P(Z \leq z)$ for $Z \sim N(0,1)$

second decimal in z

z	0	1	2	3	4	5	6	7	8	9
0.0	0.5000	0.5040	0.5080	0.5120	0.5160	0.5199	0.5239	0.5279	0.5319	0.5359
0.1	0.5395	0.5438	0.5478	0.5517	0.5557	0.5596	0.5536	0.5675	0.5714	0.5753
0.2	0.5793	0.5832	0.5871	0.5910	0.5948	0.5987	0.6026	0.6064	0.6103	0.6141
0.3	0.6179	0.6217	0.6255	0.6293	0.6331	0.6368	0.6406	0.6443	0.6480	0.6517
0.4	0.6554	0.6591	0.6628	0.6664	0.6700	0.6736	0.6772	0.6808	0.6844	0.6879
0.5	0.6915	0.6950	0.6985	0.7019	0.7054	0.7088	0.7123	0.7157	0.7190	0.7224
0.6	0.7257	0.7291	0.7324	0.7357	0.7389	0.7422	0.7454	0.7486	0.7517	0.7549
0.7	0.7580	0.7611	0.7642	0.7673	0.7704	0.7734	0.7764	0.7794	0.7823	0.7852
0.8	0.7881	0.7910	0.7939	0.7967	0.7995	0.8023	0.8051	0.8078	0.8106	0.8133
0.9	0.8159	0.8186	0.8212	0.8238	0.8264	0.8289	0.8315	0.8340	0.8365	0.8384
1.0	0.8413	0.8438	0.8461	0.8485	0.8508	0.8531	0.8554	0.8577	0.8599	0.8621
1.1	0.8643	0.8665	0.8686	0.8708	0.8729	0.8749	0.8770	0.8790	0.8810	0.8830
1.2	0.8849	0.8869	0.8888	0.8907	0.8925	0.8944	0.8962	0.8980	0.8997	0.9015
1.3	0.9032	0.9049	0.9066	0.9082	0.9099	0.9115	0.9131	0.9147	0.9162	0.9177
1.4	0.9192	0.9207	0.9222	0.9236	0.9251	0.9265	0.9279	0.9292	0.9306	0.9319
1.5	0.9332	0.9345	0.9357	0.9370	0.9382	0.9394	0.9406	0.9418	0.9429	0.9441
1.6	0.9452	0.9463	0.9474	0.9484	0.9495	0.9505	0.9515	0.9525	0.9535	0.9545
1.7	0.9554	0.9564	0.9573	0.9582	0.9591	0.9599	0.9608	0.9616	0.9625	0.9633
1.8	0.9641	0.9649	0.9656	0.9664	0.9671	0.9678	0.9686	0.9693	0.9699	0.9706
1.9	0.9713	0.9719	0.9726	0.9732	0.9738	0.9744	0.9750	0.9756	0.9761	0.9767
2.0	0.9772	0.9778	0.9783	0.9788	0.9793	0.9798	0.9803	0.9808	0.9812	0.9817
2.1	0.9821	0.9826	0.9830	0.9834	0.9838	0.9842	0.9846	0.9850	0.9854	0.9857
2.2	0.9861	0.9864	0.9868	0.9871	0.9875	0.9878	0.9881	0.9884	0.9887	0.9890
2.3	0.9893	0.9896	0.9898	0.9901	0.9904	0.9906	0.9909	0.9911	0.9913	0.9916
2.4	0.9918	0.9920	0.9922	0.9925	0.9927	0.9929	0.9931	0.9932	0.9934	0.9936
2.5	0.9938	0.9940	0.9941	0.9943	0.9945	0.9946	0.9948	0.9949	0.9951	0.9952
2.6	0.9953	0.9955	0.9956	0.9957	0.9959	0.9960	0.9961	0.9962	0.9963	0.9964
2.7	0.9965	0.9966	0.9967	0.9968	0.9969	0.9970	0.9971	0.9972	0.9973	0.9974
2.8	0.9974	0.9975	0.9976	0.9977	0.9977	0.9978	0.9979	0.9979	0.9980	0.9981
2.9	0.9981	0.9982	0.9982	0.9983	0.9984	0.9984	0.9985	0.9985	0.9986	0.9986
3.0+	0.9987	0.9987	0.9987	0.9988	0.9988	0.9989	0.9989	0.9989	0.9990	0.9990

Note: for $z \geq 4.0$ the areas are 1, accurate to four decimal places.

Standard Normal Table

Critical Values of the STUDENT'S-t DISTRIBUTION
(Values of $t_{df,\alpha}$)

df \ α	0.10	0.05	0.025	0.01	0.005
1	3.08	6.31	12.71	31.82	63.66
2	1.89	2.92	4.30	6.96	9.92
3	1.64	2.35	3.18	4.54	5.84
4	1.53	2.13	2.78	3.75	4.60
5	1.48	2.02	2.57	3.36	4.03
6	1.44	1.94	2.45	3.14	3.71
7	1.42	1.89	2.36	3.00	3.50
8	1.40	1.86	2.31	2.90	3.36
9	1.38	1.83	2.26	2.82	3.25
10	1.37	1.81	2.23	2.76	3.17
11	1.36	1.80	2.20	2.72	3.11
12	1.36	1.78	2.18	2.68	3.05
13	1.35	1.77	2.16	2.65	3.01
14	1.35	1.76	2.14	2.62	2.98
15	1.34	1.75	2.13	2.60	2.95
16	1.34	1.75	2.12	2.58	2.92
17	1.33	1.74	2.11	2.57	2.90
18	1.33	1.73	2.10	2.55	2.88
19	1.33	1.73	2.09	2.54	2.86
20	1.33	1.72	2.09	2.53	2.85
21	1.32	1.72	2.08	2.52	2.83
22	1.32	1.72	2.07	2.51	2.82
23	1.32	1.71	2.07	2.50	2.81
24	1.32	1.71	2.06	2.49	2.80
25	1.32	1.71	2.06	2.49	2.79
26	1.31	1.71	2.06	2.48	2.78
27	1.31	1.70	2.05	2.47	2.77
28	1.31	1.70	2.05	2.47	2.76
29	1.31	1.70	2.05	2.46	2.76
30+	1.28	1.64	1.96	2.33	2.58

Note: The last row of the table gives values for z. For example, the table shows that z(0.10) = 1.28.

Student's-t Table

Critical Values of the CHI-SQUARE DISTRIBUTION
(Values of Chi-Square$_{df,\alpha}$)

α df	0.995	0.990	0.975	0.95	0.90	0.10	0.05	0.025	0.01	0.005
1	0.00	0.00	0.00	0.00	0.02	2.71	3.84	5.02	6.6.3	7.88
2	0.01	0.02	0.05	0.10	0.21	4.61	5.99	7.38	9.21	10.60
3	0.07	0.11	0.22	0.35	0.58	6.25	7.81	9.35	11.34	12.84
4	0.21	0.30	0.48	0.71	1.06	7.78	9.49	11.14	13.28	14.86
5	0.41	0.55	0.83	1.15	1.61	9.24	11.07	12.83	15.09	16.75
6	0.68	0.87	1.24	1.64	2.20	10.64	12.59	14.45	16.81	18.55
7	0.99	1.24	1.69	2.17	2.83	12.02	14.07	16.01	18.48	20.28
8	1.34	1.65	2.18	2.73	3.49	13.36	15.51	17.54	20.09	21.96
9	1.73	2.09	2.70	3.33	4.17	14.68	16.93	19.02	21.67	23.59
10	2.16	2.56	3.25	3.94	4.87	15.99	18.31	20.48	23.21	25.19
11	2.60	3.05	3.82	4.57	5.58	17.28	19.68	21.92	24.72	26.76
12	3.07	3.57	4.40	5.23	6.30	18.55	21.03	23.34	26.22	28.30
13	3.57	4.11	5.01	5.89	7.04	19.81	22.36	24.74	27.69	29.82
14	4.07	4.66	5.63	6.57	7.79	21.06	23.68	26.12	29.14	31.32
15	4.60	5.23	6.26	7.26	8.55	22.31	25.00	27.49	30.58	32.80
16	5.14	5.81	6.91	7.96	9.31	23.54	26.30	28.85	32.00	34.27
17	5.70	6.41	7.56	8.67	10.09	24.77	27.59	30.19	33.41	35.72
18	6.26	7.01	8.23	9.39	10.86	25.99	28.87	31.53	34.81	37.16
19	6.84	7.63	8.91	10.12	11.65	27.20	30.14	32.85	36.19	38.58
20	7.43	8.26	9.59	10.85	12.44	28.41	31.41	34.17	37.57	40.00
21	8.03	8.90	10.28	11.59	13.24	29.62	32.67	35.48	38.93	41.40
22	8.64	9.54	10.98	12.34	14.04	30.81	33.92	36.78	40.29	42.80
23	9.26	10.20	11.69	13.09	14.85	32.01	35.17	38.08	41.64	44.18
24	9.89	10.86	12.40	13.85	15.66	33.20	36.42	39.36	42.98	45.56
25	10.52	11.52	13.12	14.61	16.47	34.38	37.65	40.65	44.31	46.93
26	11.16	12.20	13.84	15.38	17.29	35.56	38.89	41.92	45.64	48.29
27	11.81	12.88	14.57	16.15	18.11	36.74	40.11	43.19	46.96	49.65
28	12.46	13.56	15.31	16.93	18.94	37.92	41.34	44.46	48.28	50.99
29	13.12	14.26	16.05	17.71	19.77	39.09	42.56	45.72	49.59	52.34
30	13.79	14.95	16.79	18.49	20.60	40.26	43.77	46.98	50.89	53.67
50	27.99	29.71	32.36	34.76	37.69	63.17	67.50	71.42	76.15	79.49
100	67.33	70.06	74.22	77.93	82.36	118.50	124.30	129.60	135.80	140.20
500	422.30	429.40	439.90	449.10	459.90	540.90	553.10	563.90	576.50	585.20

Critical Values for the F DISTRIBUTION
0.01 Significance Level (right tail probability)

df numerator

d f		2	3	4	5	6	7	8	9	10	11	12	15
d	2	99.00	99.17	99.25	99.30	99.33	99.36	99.37	99.39	99.40	99.41	99.42	99.43
d	3	30.82	29.46	28.71	28.24	27.91	27.67	27.49	27.35	27.23	27.13	27.05	26.87
e	4	18.00	16.69	15.98	15.52	15.21	14.98	14.80	14.66	14.55	14.45	14.37	14.20
n	5	13.27	12.06	11.39	10.97	10.67	10.46	10.29	10.16	10.05	9.94	9.89	9.72
o	6	10.92	9.78	9.15	8.75	8.47	8.26	8.10	7.98	7.87	7.79	7.72	7.56
m	7	9.55	8.45	7.85	7.46	7.19	6.99	6.84	6.72	6.62	6.54	6.47	6.31
i	8	8.65	7.59	7.01	6.63	6.37	6.18	6.03	5.91	5.81	5.73	5.67	5.52
n	9	8.02	6.99	6.42	6.06	5.80	5.61	5.47	5.35	5.26	5.18	5.11	4.96
a	10	7.56	6.55	5.99	5.64	5.39	5.20	5.06	4.94	4.85	4.77	4.71	4.56
t	11	7.21	6.22	5.67	5.32	5.07	4.89	4.74	4.63	4.54	4.46	4.40	4.25
o	12	6.93	5.95	5.41	5.06	4.82	4.64	4.50	4.39	4.30	4.22	4.16	4.01
r	15	6.36	5.42	4.89	4.56	4.32	4.14	4.00	3.89	3.80	3.73	3.67	3.52
	20	5.85	4.94	4.43	4.10	3.87	3.70	3.56	3.46	3.37	3.29	3.23	3.09
	25	5.57	4.68	4.18	3.85	3.63	3.46	3.32	3.22	3.13	3.06	2.99	2.85
	50	5.06	4.20	3.72	3.41	3.19	3.02	2.89	2.78	2.70	2.62	2.56	2.42

Critical Values for the F DISTRIBUTION
0.025 Significance Level (right tail probability)

df numerator

d f		2	3	4	5	6	7	8	9	10	11	12	15
d	2	39.00	39.17	39.25	39.30	39.33	39.36	39.37	39.39	39.40	39.41	39.42	39.43
d	3	16.04	15.44	15.10	14.89	14.74	14.62	14.54	14.47	14.42	14.37	14.34	14.25
e	4	10.65	9.98	9.60	9.36	9.20	9.07	8.98	8.90	8.84	8.79	8.75	8.66
n	5	8.43	7.76	7.39	7.15	6.98	6.85	6.76	6.68	6.62	6.57	6.52	6.43
o	6	7.26	6.60	6.23	5.99	5.82	5.70	5.60	5.52	5.46	5.41	5.37	5.27
m	7	6.54	5.89	5.52	5.29	5.12	4.99	4.90	4.82	4.76	4.71	4.67	4.57
i	8	6.06	5.42	5.05	4.82	4.65	4.53	4.43	4.36	4.30	4.24	4.20	4.10
n	9	5.71	5.08	4.72	4.48	4.32	4.20	4.10	4.03	3.96	3.91	3.87	3.77
a	10	5.46	4.83	4.47	4.24	4.07	3.95	3.85	3.78	3.72	3.66	3.62	3.52
t	11	5.26	4.63	4.28	4.04	3.88	3.76	3.66	3.59	3.53	3.47	3.43	3.33
o	12	5.10	4.47	4.12	3.89	3.73	3.61	3.51	3.44	3.37	3.32	3.28	3.18
r	15	4.77	4.15	3.80	3.58	3.41	3.29	3.20	3.12	3.06	3.05	2.96	2.86
	20	4.46	3.86	3.51	3.29	3.13	3.01	2.91	2.84	2.77	2.70	2.68	2.57
	25	4.29	3.69	3.35	3.13	2.97	2.85	2.75	2.68	2.61	2.56	2.51	2.41
	50	3.97	3.39	3.05	2.83	2.67	2.55	2.46	2.38	2.32	2.26	2.22	2.11

F Tables

Critical Values for the F DISTRIBUTION
0.05 Significance Level (right tail probability)

		2	3	4	5	6	7	8	9	10	11	12	15
						df numerator							
d f		2	3	4	5	6	7	8	9	10	11	12	15
	2	19.00	19.16	19.25	19.30	19.33	19.35	19.37	19.38	19.40	19.40	19.41	19.43
d	3	9.55	9.28	9.12	9.01	8.94	8.89	8.85	8.81	8.79	8.76	8.74	8.70
e	4	6.94	6.59	6.39	6.26	6.16	6.09	6.04	6.00	5.96	5.94	5.91	5.86
n	5	5.79	5.41	5.19	5.05	4.95	4.88	4.82	4.77	4.74	4.70	4.68	4.62
o	6	5.14	4.76	4.53	4.39	4.28	4.21	4.15	4.10	4.06	4.03	4.00	3.94
m	7	4.74	4.35	4.12	3.97	3.87	3.79	3.73	3.68	3.64	3.60	3.57	3.51
i	8	4.46	4.07	3.84	3.69	3.58	3.50	3.44	3.39	3.35	3.31	3.28	3.22
n	9	4.26	3.86	3.63	3.48	3.37	3.29	3.23	3.18	3.14	3.10	3.07	3.01
a	10	4.10	3.71	3.48	3.33	3.22	3.14	3.07	3.02	2.98	2.94	2.91	2.85
t	11	3.98	3.59	3.36	3.20	3.09	3.01	2.95	2.90	2.85	2.82	2.79	2.72
o	12	3.89	3.49	3.26	3.11	3.00	2.91	2.85	2.80	2.75	2.72	2.69	2.62
r	15	3.68	3.29	3.06	2.90	2.79	2.71	2.64	2.59	2.54	2.51	2.48	2.40
	20	3.49	3.10	2.87	2.71	2.60	2.51	2.45	2.39	2.35	2.31	2.28	2.20
	25	3.39	2.99	2.76	2.60	2.49	2.40	2.34	2.28	2.23	2.20	2.16	2.09
	50	3.18	2.79	2.56	2.40	2.29	2.20	2.13	2.07	2.03	1.99	1.95	1.87

Critical Values for the F DISTRIBUTION
0.10 Significance Level (right tail probability)

		2	3	4	5	6	7	8	9	10	11	12	15
						df numerator							
d f		2	3	4	5	6	7	8	9	10	11	12	15
	2	9.00	9.16	9.24	9.29	9.33	9.35	9.37	9.38	9.39	9.40	9.41	9.42
d	3	5.46	5.39	5.34	5.31	5.28	5.27	5.25	5.24	5.23	5.22	5.22	5.20
e	4	4.32	4.19	4.11	4.05	4.01	3.98	3.95	3.94	3.92	3.91	3.90	3.87
n	5	3.78	3.62	3.52	3.45	3.40	3.37	3.34	3.32	3.30	3.28	3.27	3.24
o	6	3.46	3.29	3.18	3.11	3.05	3.01	2.98	2.96	2.94	2.92	2.90	2.87
m	7	3.26	3.07	2.96	2.88	2.83	2.78	2.75	2.72	2.70	2.68	2.67	2.63
i	8	3.11	2.92	2.81	2.73	2.67	2.62	2.59	2.56	2.54	2.52	2.50	2.46
n	9	3.01	2.81	2.69	2.61	2.55	2.51	2.47	2.44	2.42	2.40	2.38	2.34
a	10	2.92	2.73	2.61	2.52	2.46	2.41	2.38	2.35	2.32	2.30	2.28	2.24
t	11	2.86	2.66	2.54	2.45	2.39	2.34	2.30	2.27	2.25	2.23	2.21	2.17
o	12	2.81	2.61	2.48	2.39	2.33	2.28	2.24	2.21	2.19	2.17	2.15	2.10
r	15	2.70	2.49	2.36	2.27	2.21	2.16	2.12	2.09	2.06	2.04	2.02	1.97
	20	2.59	2.38	2.25	2.16	2.09	2.04	2.00	1.96	1.94	1.91	1.89	1.84
	25	2.53	2.32	2.18	2.09	2.02	1.97	1.93	1.89	1.87	1.84	1.82	1.77
	50	2.41	2.20	2.06	1.97	1.90	1.84	1.80	1.76	1.73	1.70	1.68	1.63

Critical Values for r, the CORRELATION COEFFICIENT

Significance Level

d.f.	0.10	0.05	0.025	0.01	0.005
1	±0.951	±0.988	±0.997	±1.00	±1.00
2	0.800	0.900	0.950	0.980	0.990
3	0.687	0.805	0.878	0.934	0.959
4	0.608	0.729	0.812	0.882	0.917
5	0.551	0.670	0.754	0.832	0.874
6	0.507	0.621	0.707	0.788	0.835
7	0.472	0.581	0.666	0.750	0.798
8	0.443	0.549	0.633	0.716	0.765
9	0.419	0.521	0.602	0.685	0.735
10	0.398	0.497	0.576	0.658	0.708
11	0.380	0.477	0.553	0.634	0.684
12	0.365	0.457	0.533	0.612	0.661
13	0.351	0.441	0.514	0.592	0.641
14	0.338	0.426	0.496	0.574	0.623
15	0.327	0.412	0.482	0.557	0.606
16	0.317	0.401	0.468	0.542	0.590
17	0.308	0.389	0.456	0.529	0.575
18	0.299	0.378	0.444	0.515	0.562
19	0.291	0.369	0.432	0.503	0.549
20	0.284	0.359	0.423	0.492	0.794
21	0.277	0.351	0.413	0.482	0.525
22	0.271	0.344	0.404	0.472	0.515
23	0.265	0.336	0.396	0.462	0.506
24	0.260	0.330	0.388	0.453	0.496
25	0.255	0.324	0.381	0.446	0.487
26	0.250	0.318	0.375	0.437	0.479
27	0.245	0.311	0.367	0.429	0.470
28	0.241	0.306	0.361	0.423	0.462
29	0.237	0.301	0.356	0.416	0.456
30	0.228	0.287	0.337	0.391	0.426
40	0.199	0.251	0.296	0.346	0.378
50	0.178	0.226	0.267	0.313	0.343
60	0.163	0.207	0.245	0.288	0.316
70	0.151	0.192	0.228	0.268	0.295
80	0.142	0.180	0.214	0.252	0.277
90	0.134	0.170	0.202	0.239	0.262
100	0.127	0.162	0.192	0.227	0.250

Correlation Coefficient Table

BINOMIAL DISTRIBUTION
P(X = x) for X ~ B(n,p)

values of p

n	x	0.10	0.20	0.25	0.30	0.40	0.50	0.60	0.70	0.75	0.80	0.90
1	0	0.9000	0.8000	0.7500	0.7000	0.6000	0.5000	0.4000	0.3000	0.2500	0.2000	0.1000
	1	0.1000	0.2000	0.2500	0.3000	0.4000	0.5000	0.6000	0.7000	0.7500	0.8000	0.9000
2	0	0.8100	0.6400	0.5625	0.4900	0.3600	0.2500	0.1600	0.0900	0.0625	0.0400	0.0100
	1	0.1800	0.3200	0.3750	0.4200	0.4800	0.5000	0.4800	0.4200	0.3750	0.3200	0.1800
	2	0.0100	0.0400	0.0625	0.0900	0.1600	0.2500	0.3600	0.4900	0.5625	0.6400	0.8100
3	0	0.7290	0.5120	0.4219	0.3430	0.2160	0.1250	0.0640	0.0270	0.0156	0.0080	0.0010
	1	0.2430	0.3840	0.4219	0.4410	0.4320	0.3750	0.2880	0.1890	0.1406	0.0960	0.0270
	2	0.0270	0.0960	0.1406	0.1890	0.2880	0.3750	0.4320	0.4410	0.4219	0.3840	0.2430
	3	0.0010	0.0080	0.0156	0.0270	0.0640	0.1250	0.2160	0.3430	0.4219	0.5120	0.7290
4	0	0.6561	0.4096	0.3164	0.2401	0.1296	0.0625	0.0256	0.0081	0.0039	0.0016	0.0001
	1	0.2913	0.4096	0.4219	0.4116	0.3456	0.2500	0.1536	0.0756	0.0469	0.0256	0.0036
	2	0.0486	0.1536	0.2109	0.2646	0.3456	0.3750	0.3456	0.2646	0.2109	0.1536	0.0486
	3	0.0036	0.0256	0.0469	0.0756	0.1536	0.2500	0.3456	0.4116	0.4219	0.4096	0.2916
	4	0.0001	0.0016	0.0039	0.0081	0.0256	0.0625	0.1296	0.2401	0.3164	0.4096	0.6561
5	0	0.5905	0.3277	0.2373	0.1681	0.0778	0.0313	0.0102	0.0024	0.0010	0.0003	0.0000
	1	0.3281	0.4096	0.3955	0.3602	0.2592	0.1563	0.0768	0.0284	0.0146	0.0064	0.0005
	2	0.0729	0.2048	0.2637	0.3087	0.3456	0.3125	0.2304	0.1323	0.0879	0.0512	0.0081
	3	0.0081	0.0512	0.0879	0.1323	0.2304	0.3125	0.3456	0.3087	0.2637	0.2048	0.0729
	4	0.0004	0.0064	0.0146	0.0283	0.0768	0.1563	0.2592	0.3602	0.3955	0.4096	0.3281
	5	0.0000	0.0003	0.0010	0.0024	0.0102	0.0313	0.0778	0.1681	0.2373	0.3277	0.5905
6	0	0.5314	0.2621	0.1780	0.1176	0.0467	0.0156	0.0041	0.0007	0.0002	0.0001	0.0000
	1	0.3543	0.3932	0.3560	0.3025	0.1866	0.0938	0.0369	0.0102	0.0044	0.0015	0.0001
	2	0.0984	0.2458	0.2966	0.3241	0.3110	0.2344	0.1382	0.0595	0.0330	0.0154	0.0012
	3	0.0146	0.0819	0.1318	0.1852	0.2765	0.3125	0.2765	0.1852	0.1318	0.0819	0.0146
	4	0.0012	0.0154	0.0330	0.0595	0.1382	0.2344	0.3110	0.3241	0.2966	0.2458	0.0984
	5	0.0001	0.0015	0.0044	0.0102	0.0369	0.0938	0.1866	0.3025	0.3560	0.3932	0.3543
	6	0.0000	0.0001	0.0002	0.0007	0.0041	0.0156	0.0467	0.1176	0.1780	0.2621	0.5314
7	0	0.4783	0.2097	0.1335	0.0824	0.0280	0.0078	0.0016	0.0002	0.0001	0.0000	0.0000
	1	0.3720	0.3670	0.3115	0.2471	0.1306	0.0547	0.0172	0.0036	0.0013	0.0004	0.0000
	2	0.1240	0.2753	0.3115	0.3177	0.2613	0.1641	0.0774	0.0250	0.0115	0.0043	0.0002
	3	0.0230	0.1147	0.1730	0.2269	0.2903	0.2734	0.1935	0.0972	0.0577	0.0287	0.0026
	4	0.0026	0.0287	0.0577	0.0972	0.1935	0.2734	0.2903	0.2269	0.1730	0.1147	0.0230
	5	0.0002	0.0043	0.0115	0.0250	0.0774	0.1641	0.2613	0.3177	0.3115	0.2753	0.1240
	6	0.0000	0.0004	0.0013	0.0036	0.0172	0.0547	0.1306	0.2471	0.3115	0.3670	0.3720
	7	0.0000	0.0000	0.0001	0.0002	0.0016	0.0078	0.0280	0.0824	0.1335	0.2097	0.4783

BINOMIAL DISTRIBUTION (Continued)
P(X = x) for X ~ B(n,p)

values of p

n	x	0.10	0.20	0.25	0.30	0.40	0.50	0.60	0.70	0.75	0.80	0.90
8	0	0.4305	0.1678	0.1001	0.0576	0.0168	0.0039	0.0007	0.0001	0.0000	0.0000	0.0000
	1	0.3826	0.3355	0.2670	0.1977	0.0896	0.0312	0.0079	0.0012	0.0004	0.0001	0.0000
	2	0.1488	0.2936	0.3115	0.2965	0.2090	0.1094	0.0413	0.0100	0.0038	0.0011	0.0000
	3	0.0331	0.1468	0.2076	0.2541	0.2787	0.2188	0.1239	0.0467	0.0231	0.0092	0.0004
	4	0.0046	0.0459	0.0865	0.1361	0.2322	0.2734	0.2322	0.1361	0.0865	0.0459	0.0046
	5	0.0004	0.0092	0.0231	0.0467	0.1239	0.2188	0.2787	0.2541	0.2076	0.1468	0.0331
	6	0.0000	0.0011	0.0038	0.0100	0.0413	0.1094	0.2090	0.2965	0.3115	0.2936	0.1488
	7	0.0000	0.0001	0.0004	0.0012	0.0079	0.0312	0.0896	0.1977	0.2670	0.3355	0.3826
	8	0.0000	0.0000	0.0000	0.0001	0.0007	0.0039	0.0168	0.0576	0.1001	0.1678	0.4305
9	0	0.3874	0.1342	0.0751	0.0404	0.0101	0.0020	0.0003	0.0000	0.0000	0.0000	0.0000
	1	0.3874	0.3020	0.2253	0.1556	0.0605	0.0176	0.0035	0.0004	0.0001	0.0000	0.0000
	2	0.1722	0.3020	0.3003	0.2668	0.1612	0.0703	0.0212	0.0039	0.0012	0.0003	0.0000
	3	0.0446	0.1762	0.2336	0.2668	0.2508	0.1641	0.0743	0.0210	0.0087	0.0028	0.0001
	4	0.0074	0.0661	0.1168	0.1715	0.2508	0.2461	0.1672	0.0735	0.0389	0.0165	0.0008
	5	0.0008	0.0165	0.0389	0.0735	0.1672	0.2461	0.2508	0.1715	0.1168	0.0661	0.0074
	6	0.0001	0.0028	0.0087	0.0210	0.0743	0.1641	0.2508	0.2668	0.2336	0.1762	0.0446
	7	0.0000	0.0030	0.0012	0.0039	0.0212	0.0703	0.1612	0.2668	0.3003	0.3020	0.1722
	8	0.0000	0.0000	0.0001	0.0004	0.0035	0.0176	0.0605	0.1556	0.2253	0.3020	0.3874
	9	0.0000	0.0000	0.0000	0.0000	0.0003	0.0020	0.0101	0.0404	0.0751	0.1342	0.3874
10	0	0.3487	0.1074	0.0563	0.0282	0.0060	0.0010	0.0001	0.0000	0.0000	0.0000	0.0000
	1	0.3874	0.2684	0.1877	0.1211	0.0403	0.0098	0.0016	0.0001	0.0000	0.0000	0.0000
	2	0.1937	0.3020	0.2816	0.2335	0.1209	0.0439	0.0106	0.0014	0.0004	0.0001	0.0000
	3	0.0574	0.2013	0.2503	0.2668	0.2150	0.1172	0.0425	0.0090	0.0031	0.0008	0.0000
	4	0.0112	0.0881	0.1460	0.2001	0.2508	0.2051	0.1115	0.0368	0.0162	0.0055	0.0001
	5	0.0015	0.0264	0.0584	0.1029	0.2007	0.2461	0.2007	0.1029	0.0584	0.0264	0.0015
	6	0.0001	0.0055	0.0162	0.0368	0.1115	0.2051	0.2508	0.2001	0.1460	0.0881	0.0112
	7	0.0000	0.0008	0.0031	0.0090	0.0425	0.1172	0.2150	0.2668	0.2503	0.2013	0.0574
	8	0.0000	0.0001	0.0004	0.0014	0.0106	0.0439	0.1209	0.2335	0.2816	0.3020	0.1937
	9	0.0000	0.0000	0.0000	0.0001	0.0016	0.0098	0.0403	0.1211	0.1877	0.2684	0.3874
	10	0.0000	0.0000	0.0000	0.0000	0.0001	0.0010	0.0060	0.0282	0.0563	0.1074	0.3487

n	x	0.10	0.20	0.25	0.30	0.40	0.50	0.60	0.70	0.75	0.80	0.90
11	0	0.3138	0.0859	0.0422	0.0198	0.0036	0.0005	0.0000	0.0000	0.0000	0.0000	0.0000
	1	0.3835	0.2362	0.1549	0.0932	0.0266	0.0054	0.0007	0.0000	0.0000	0.0000	0.0000
	2	0.2131	0.2953	0.2581	0.1998	0.0887	0.0269	0.0052	0.0005	0.0001	0.0000	0.0000
	3	0.0710	0.2215	0.2581	0.2568	0.1774	0.0806	0.0234	0.0037	0.0011	0.0002	0.0000
	4	0.0158	0.1107	0.1721	0.2201	0.2365	0.1611	0.0701	0.0173	0.0064	0.0017	0.0000
	5	0.0025	0.0388	0.0803	0.1321	0.2207	0.2256	0.1471	0.0566	0.0268	0.0097	0.0003
	6	0.0003	0.0097	0.0268	0.0566	0.1471	0.2256	0.2207	0.1321	0.0803	0.0388	0.0025
	7	0.0000	0.0017	0.0064	0.0173	0.0701	0.1611	0.2365	0.2201	0.1721	0.1107	0.0158
	8	0.0000	0.0002	0.0011	0.0037	0.0234	0.0806	0.1774	0.2568	0.2581	0.2215	0.0710
	9	0.0000	0.0000	0.0001	0.0005	0.0052	0.0269	0.0887	0.1998	0.2581	0.2953	0.2131
	10	0.0000	0.0000	0.0000	0.0000	0.0007	0.0054	0.0266	0.0932	0.1549	0.2362	0.3835
	11	0.0000	0.0000	0.0000	0.0000	0.0000	0.0005	0.0036	0.0198	0.0422	0.0859	0.3138
12	0	0.2824	0.0687	0.0317	0.0138	0.0022	0.0002	0.0000	0.0000	0.0000	0.0000	0.0000
	1	0.3766	0.2062	0.1267	0.0712	0.0174	0.0029	0.0003	0.0000	0.0000	0.0000	0.0000
	2	0.2301	0.2835	0.2323	0.1678	0.0639	0.0161	0.0025	0.0002	0.0000	0.0000	0.0000
	3	0.0852	0.2362	0.2581	0.2397	0.1419	0.0537	0.0125	0.0015	0.0004	0.0001	0.0000
	4	0.0213	0.1329	0.1936	0.2311	0.2128	0.1208	0.0420	0.0078	0.0024	0.0005	0.0000
	5	0.0038	0.0532	0.1032	0.1585	0.2270	0.1934	0.1009	0.0291	0.0115	0.0033	0.0000
	6	0.0005	0.0155	0.0401	0.0792	0.1766	0.2256	0.1766	0.0792	0.0401	0.0155	0.0005
	7	0.0000	0.0033	0.0115	0.0291	0.1009	0.1934	0.2270	0.1585	0.1032	0.0532	0.0038
	8	0.0000	0.0005	0.0024	0.0078	0.0420	0.1208	0.2128	0.2311	0.1936	0.1329	0.0213
	9	0.0000	0.0001	0.0004	0.0015	0.0125	0.0537	0.1419	0.2397	0.2584	0.2361	0.0852
	10	0.0000	0.0000	0.0000	0.0002	0.0025	0.0161	0.0639	0.1678	0.2323	0.2835	0.2301
	11	0.0000	0.0000	0.0000	0.0000	0.0003	0.0029	0.0174	0.0712	0.1267	0.2062	0.3766
	12	0.0000	0.0000	0.0000	0.0000	0.0000	0.0002	0.0022	0.0138	0.0317	0.0687	0.2824
13	0	0.2542	0.0550	0.0238	0.0097	0.0013	0.0001	0.0000	0.0000	0.0000	0.0000	0.0000
	1	0.3672	0.1787	0.1029	0.0540	0.0113	0.0016	0.0001	0.0000	0.0000	0.0000	0.0000
	2	0.2448	0.2680	0.2059	0.1388	0.0453	0.0095	0.0012	0.0001	0.0000	0.0000	0.0000
	3	0.0997	0.2457	0.2517	0.2181	0.1107	0.0349	0.0065	0.0006	0.0001	0.0000	0.0000
	4	0.0277	0.1535	0.2097	0.2337	0.1845	0.0873	0.0243	0.0034	0.0009	0.0001	0.0000
	5	0.0055	0.0691	0.1258	0.1803	0.2214	0.1571	0.0656	0.0142	0.0047	0.0011	0.0000
	6	0.0008	0.0230	0.0559	0.1030	0.1968	0.2095	0.1312	0.0442	0.0186	0.0058	0.0001
	7	0.0000	0.0058	0.0186	0.0442	0.1312	0.2095	0.1968	0.1030	0.0559	0.0230	0.0008
	8	0.0000	0.0011	0.0047	0.0142	0.0656	0.1571	0.2214	0.1803	0.1258	0.0691	0.0055
	9	0.0000	0.0001	0.0009	0.0034	0.0243	0.0873	0.1845	0.2337	0.2097	0.1535	0.0277
	10	0.0000	0.0000	0.0001	0.0006	0.0065	0.0349	0.1107	0.2181	0.2517	0.2457	0.0997
	11	0.0000	0.0000	0.0000	0.0001	0.0012	0.0095	0.0453	0.1388	0.2059	0.2680	0.2448
	12	0.0000	0.0000	0.0000	0.0000	0.0001	0.0016	0.0113	0.0540	0.1029	0.1787	0.3672
	13	0.0000	0.0000	0.0000	0.0000	0.0000	0.0001	0.0013	0.0097	0.0238	0.0550	0.2542

values of p

n	x	0.10	0.20	0.25	0.30	0.40	0.50	0.60	0.70	0.75	0.80	0.90
14	0	0.2288	0.0440	0.0178	0.0068	0.0008	0.0001	0.0000	0.0000	0.0000	0.0000	0.0000
	1	0.3559	0.1539	0.0832	0.0407	0.0073	0.0009	0.0001	0.0000	0.0000	0.0000	0.0000
	2	0.2570	0.2501	0.1802	0.1134	0.0317	0.0056	0.0005	0.0000	0.0000	0.0000	0.0000
	3	0.1142	0.2501	0.2402	0.1943	0.0845	0.0220	0.0033	0.0002	0.0000	0.0000	0.0000
	4	0.0349	0.1720	0.2202	0.2290	0.1549	0.0611	0.0136	0.0014	0.0003	0.0000	0.0000
	5	0.0078	0.0860	0.1468	0.1963	0.2066	0.1222	0.0408	0.0066	0.0018	0.0003	0.0000
	6	0.0013	0.0322	0.0734	0.1262	0.2066	0.1833	0.0918	0.0232	0.0082	0.0020	0.0000
	7	0.0002	0.0092	0.0280	0.0618	0.1574	0.2095	0.1574	0.0618	0.0280	0.0092	0.0002
	8	0.0000	0.0020	0.0082	0.0232	0.0918	0.1833	0.2066	0.1262	0.0734	0.0322	0.0013
	9	0.0000	0.0003	0.0018	0.0066	0.0408	0.1222	0.2066	0.1963	0.1468	0.0860	0.0078
	10	0.0000	0.0000	0.0003	0.0014	0.0136	0.0611	0.1549	0.2290	0.2202	0.1720	0.0349
	11	0.0000	0.0000	0.0000	0.0002	0.0033	0.0220	0.0845	0.1943	0.2402	0.2501	0.1142
	12	0.0000	0.0000	0.0000	0.0000	0.0005	0.0056	0.0317	0.1134	0.1802	0.2501	0.2570
	13	0.0000	0.0000	0.0000	0.0000	0.0001	0.0009	0.0073	0.0407	0.0832	0.1539	0.3559
	14	0.0000	0.0000	0.0000	0.0000	0.0000	0.0001	0.0008	0.0068	0.0178	0.0440	0.2288
15	0	0.2059	0.0352	0.0134	0.0047	0.0005	0.0000	0.0000	0.0000	0.0000	0.0000	0.0000
	1	0.3432	0.1319	0.0668	0.0305	0.0047	0.0005	0.0000	0.0000	0.0000	0.0000	0.0000
	2	0.2669	0.2309	0.1559	0.0916	0.0219	0.0032	0.0003	0.0000	0.0000	0.0000	0.0000
	3	0.1285	0.2501	0.2252	0.1700	0.0634	0.0139	0.0016	0.0001	0.0000	0.0000	0.0000
	4	0.0428	0.1876	0.2252	0.2186	0.1268	0.0417	0.0074	0.0006	0.0001	0.0000	0.0000
	5	0.0105	0.1032	0.1651	0.2061	0.1859	0.0916	0.0245	0.0030	0.0007	0.0001	0.0000
	6	0.0019	0.0430	0.0917	0.1472	0.2066	0.1527	0.0612	0.0116	0.0034	0.0007	0.0000
	7	0.0003	0.0138	0.0393	0.0811	0.1771	0.1964	0.1181	0.0348	0.0131	0.0035	0.0000
	8	0.0000	0.0035	0.0131	0.0348	0.1181	0.1964	0.1771	0.0811	0.0393	0.0138	0.0003
	9	0.0000	0.0007	0.0034	0.0116	0.0612	0.1527	0.2066	0.1472	0.0917	0.0430	0.0019
	10	0.0000	0.0001	0.0007	0.0030	0.0245	0.0916	0.1859	0.2061	0.1651	0.1032	0.0105
	11	0.0000	0.0000	0.0001	0.0006	0.0074	0.0417	0.1268	0.2186	0.2252	0.1876	0.0428
	12	0.0000	0.0000	0.0000	0.0001	0.0016	0.0139	0.0634	0.1700	0.2252	0.2501	0.1285
	13	0.0000	0.0000	0.0000	0.0000	0.0003	0.0032	0.0219	0.0916	0.1559	0.2309	0.2669
	14	0.0000	0.0000	0.0000	0.0000	0.0000	0.0005	0.0047	0.0305	0.0668	0.1319	0.3432
	15	0.0000	0.0000	0.0000	0.0000	0.0000	0.0000	0.0005	0.0047	0.0134	0.0352	0.2059

BINOMIAL DISTRIBUTION (Continued)
$P(X = x)$ for $X \sim B(n,p)$

values of p

n	x	0.10	0.20	0.25	0.30	0.40	0.50	0.60	0.70	0.75	0.80	0.90
20	0	0.1216	0.0115	0.0032	0.0008	0.0000	0.0000	0.0000	0.0000	0.0000	0.0000	0.0000
	1	0.2702	0.0576	0.0211	0.0068	0.0005	0.0000	0.0000	0.0000	0.0000	0.0000	0.0000
	2	0.2852	0.1369	0.0669	0.0278	0.0031	0.0002	0.0000	0.0000	0.0000	0.0000	0.0000
	3	0.1901	0.2054	0.1339	0.0716	0.0123	0.0011	0.0000	0.0000	0.0000	0.0000	0.0000
	4	0.0898	0.2182	0.1897	0.1304	0.0350	0.0046	0.0003	0.0000	0.0000	0.0000	0.0000
	5	0.0319	0.1746	0.2023	0.1789	0.0746	0.0148	0.0013	0.0000	0.0000	0.0000	0.0000
	6	0.0089	0.1091	0.1686	0.1916	0.1244	0.0370	0.0049	0.0002	0.0000	0.0000	0.0000
	7	0.0020	0.0545	0.1124	0.1643	0.1659	0.0739	0.0146	0.0010	0.0002	0.0000	0.0000
	8	0.0004	0.0222	0.0609	0.1144	0.1797	0.1201	0.0355	0.0039	0.0008	0.0001	0.0000
	9	0.0001	0.0074	0.0271	0.0654	0.1597	0.1602	0.0710	0.0120	0.0030	0.0005	0.0000
	10	0.0000	0.0020	0.0099	0.0308	0.1171	0.1762	0.1171	0.0308	0.0099	0.0020	0.0000
	11	0.0000	0.0005	0.0030	0.0120	0.0710	0.1602	0.1597	0.0654	0.0271	0.0074	0.0001
	12	0.0000	0.0001	0.0008	0.0039	0.0355	0.1201	0.1797	0.1144	0.0609	0.0222	0.0040
	13	0.0000	0.0000	0.0002	0.0010	0.0146	0.0739	0.1659	0.1643	0.1125	0.0545	0.0020
	14	0.0000	0.0000	0.0000	0.0002	0.0049	0.0370	0.1244	0.1916	0.1686	0.1091	0.0089
	15	0.0000	0.0000	0.0000	0.0000	0.0013	0.0148	0.0746	0.1789	0.2023	0.1746	0.0319
	16	0.0000	0.0000	0.0000	0.0000	0.0003	0.0046	0.0350	0.1304	0.1897	0.2182	0.0898
	17	0.0000	0.0000	0.0000	0.0000	0.0000	0.0011	0.0123	0.0716	0.1339	0.2054	0.1901
	18	0.0000	0.0000	0.0000	0.0000	0.0000	0.0002	0.0031	0.0278	0.0669	0.1369	0.2852
	19	0.0000	0.0000	0.0000	0.0000	0.0000	0.0000	0.0005	0.0068	0.0211	0.0576	0.2702
	20	0.0000	0.0000	0.0000	0.0000	0.0000	0.0000	0.0000	0.0008	0.0032	0.0115	0.1216

Algebra Review

Where appropriate, you are expected to use a calculator in order to carry out the indicated operations.

1. Evaluate: $z = \dfrac{23 - 3}{2}$.

2. Evaluate: $z = \dfrac{23 - 3}{\sqrt{2}}$. Round to 3 decimal places.

3. Evaluate: $z = \dfrac{230 - \dfrac{100}{23.2}}{\sqrt{5}/_7}$. Round to 5 decimal places.

4. Solve for x: $1.76 = \dfrac{x - 8}{10}$.

5. Solve for x: $-3.04 = \dfrac{x - 23.5}{\sqrt{10}/_5}$. Round to 4 decimal places.

6. Find n: $2 = \dfrac{8}{\sqrt{n}}$.

7. Find n: $2.32 = \dfrac{5.32}{\sqrt{n}/_{5.1}}$. Round up so that n is a whole number.

8. $z = \dfrac{x - 8}{3}$. Solve for x in terms of z.

9. $x = 2z + 3$. Solve for z in terms of x.

10. $z = \dfrac{10}{\sqrt{n}/_3}$. Solve for n in terms of z.

11. Solve for x: $x^2 = 23.5$. Round to 3 decimal places.

12. Solve for x: $\ln 5 = x/8$. Round to 4 decimal places.

13. Solve for x: $2.56 = 1 + e^{-x/2}$. Round to 4 decimal places.

Algebra Review

14. a. Graph the line: $y = \dfrac{2}{3}x - 4$ **b.** Graph the line: $2x + 3y = 6$

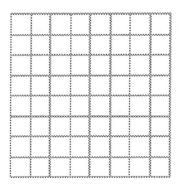

15. Find the equation of the given line.

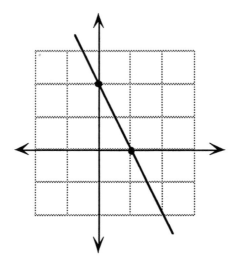

16. Given the equation $y = 3x - 4$.

    a. If $x = 3$, $y =$ **e.** If $y = 3$, $x =$

    b. If $x = 0$, $y =$ **f.** If $y = 0$, $x =$

    c. If $x = -2$, $y =$ **g.** If $y = -2$, $x =$

    d. If $x = \dfrac{5}{3}$, $y =$ **h.** If $y = \dfrac{5}{3}$, $x =$

17. Solve the simultaneous system for a and b: $10a + 4 = 2b$ and $3a - b = 6$.

Solutions to Problems in Algebra Review

1. $z = 10$

2. $z = 14.142$

3. $z = 706.52038$

4. $x = 1.76 \cdot 10 + 8 = 25.6$

5. $x = -3.04 \cdot \dfrac{\sqrt{10}}{5} + 23.5 = 21.5773$

6. $\sqrt{n} = \dfrac{8}{2} \Rightarrow n = 4^2 = 16$

7. $\sqrt{n} = \dfrac{5.32}{2.32/5.1} \Rightarrow n = \left(\dfrac{5.32}{2.32/5.1}\right)^2 \approx 137$

8. $x = 3z + 8$

9. $z = \dfrac{x - 3}{2}$

10. $n = \left(\dfrac{10}{z/3}\right)^2 = \dfrac{900}{z^2}$

11. $x = \pm\sqrt{23.5} = \pm 4.848$

12. $x = 8 \cdot \ln 5$. Use a calculator to get $\ln 5 \approx 1.60944$. Thus, $x = 12.8755$.

13. $2.56 - 1 = e^{-x/2} \Rightarrow 1.56 = e^{-x/2} \Rightarrow \ln 1.56 = \ln\left(e^{-x/2}\right) \Rightarrow 0.44469 = -\dfrac{x}{2}$. Thus, $x = -2 \cdot 0.44469 = -0.8894$.

14.

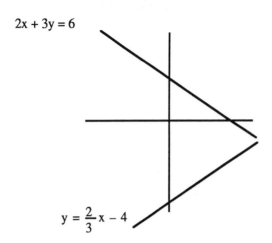

$2x + 3y = 6$

$y = \dfrac{2}{3}x - 4$

15. The coordinates of the two marked points are $(0,2)$ and $(1,0)$. The point-slope form of a line is:

$y - y_1 = \text{slope} \cdot (x - x_1)$ where (x_1, y_1) is any point on the line. Letting $(x_1, y_1) = (1,0)$ and

noting that $\text{slope} = \dfrac{\text{change in } y}{\text{change in } x} = \dfrac{2 - 0}{0 - 1} = -2$, we write: $y - 0 = -2(x - 1)$ or $y = -2x + 2$.

16. a. $y = 3(3) - 4 = 5$ **b.** $y = -4$ **c.** $y = 3(-2) - 4 = -10$

       d. $y = 3\left(\dfrac{5}{3}\right) - 4 = 5 - 4 = 1$ **e.** $3 = 3x - 4 \Rightarrow x = \dfrac{7}{3}$

       f. $x = 4/3$ **g.** $-2 = 3x - 4 \Rightarrow x = \dfrac{2}{3}$

       h. $\dfrac{5}{3} = 3x - 4 \Rightarrow x = \dfrac{\frac{5}{3} + 4}{3} = \dfrac{5 + 12}{9} = \dfrac{17}{9}$

17. $3a - b = 6 \Rightarrow b = 3a - 6$. Substituting for b in $10a + 4 = 2b$ yields $10a + 4 = 2(3a - 6)$.

Thus, $10a + 4 = 6a - 12 \Rightarrow 4a = -16$ or $a = -4$. Thus, $b = 3(-4) - 6 = -18$.

Details for Selected Distributions

Discrete Distributions

1. Binomial: $X \sim B(n,p)$. $P(X = x) = \binom{n}{x} p^x (1 - p)^{n - x}$ for $x = 0, 1, 2, ..., n$.

   Note that $\binom{n}{x} = \dfrac{n!}{x! \, (n - x)!}$ where $x! = x \, (x - 1) \, (x - 2) \, ... \, 1$.

   Mean $= \mu = np$. Variance $= np(1 - p)$.

2. Geometric: $X \sim G(p)$. $P(X = x) = (1 - p)^{x - 1} p$ for $x = 1, 2, ...$

   Mean $= \mu = \dfrac{1}{p}$. Variance $= \sigma^2 = \dfrac{1}{p}\left(\dfrac{1}{p} - 1\right)$.

3. Poisson: $X \sim P(\mu)$. $P(X = x) = \dfrac{e^{-\mu} \mu^x}{x!}$ for $x = 0,1,2, ..., n$.

   Note that $x! = x \, (x - 1) \, (x - 2) \, ... \, 1$ and $e =$ base of the natural logarithm $\approx 2.718282...$

   Mean $= \mu = np$. Variance $= \sigma^2 = \mu$.

4. Pascal: $X \sim Pa(r,p)$. $P(X = x) = \binom{x + r - 1}{x} (1 - p)^x p^r$ for $x = 0,1,2,...$

   Mean $= \mu = \dfrac{r(1 - p)}{p}$. Variance $= \sigma^2 = \dfrac{r(1 - p)}{p^2}$.

5. Hypergeometric: $X \sim H(n_1,n_2,n)$. $P(X = x) = \dfrac{\binom{n_1}{x}\binom{n_2}{n - x}}{\binom{n_1 + n_2}{n}}$ for $x = 0,1,2, ...,$ minimum $\{n_1, n\}$.

   Mean $= \mu = n\left(\dfrac{n_1}{n_1 + n_2}\right)$. Variance $= \sigma^2 = \dfrac{n n_1 n_2 (n_1 + n_2 - n)}{(n_1 + n_2)^2 (n_1 + n_2 - 1)}$.

Continuous Distributions

1. PDF for $X \sim N(\mu, \sigma^2)$ is $f(x) = \dfrac{1}{\sigma\sqrt{2\pi}}e^{-(x-\mu)^2/2\sigma^2}$ for $-\infty < x < \infty$.

2. If $W = \dfrac{\overline{x}-\mu}{\frac{s}{\sqrt{n}}}$ then $W \sim t_{n-1}$. The mean of $W = 0$ and the variance of $W = \dfrac{df}{df-2}$.

3. If $X \sim \chi^2_{df}$ then mean of $X = df$ and variance of $X = 2\cdot(df)$.

4. If $X \sim F_{v,w}$ then mean of $X = \dfrac{w}{w-2}$ and variance of $X = \dfrac{2w^2(v+w-2)}{v(w-2)^2(w-4)}$.

Index

A

accept,
> null hypothesis: see *favor*

addition (rule of probability): 38

alpha (α),
> area in right tail: 96
> probability of Type I error: 143
> pre-set significance: 139

alternative hypothesis: 133, 138

analysis of variance: 210

and (as a connective): 37

approximation,
> binomial and hypergeometric: 67
> binomial and Poisson: 57
> normal to binomial: 97
> student-t and normal: 156

area,
> as probability: 77, 79
> of a rectangular region: 82
> of a triangular region: 78

attribute,
> qualitative/categorical data: 2

average (or mean),
> difference of two independent: 171
> of a data set: 17
> in regression: 231
> of random variables,
>> binomial: 56
>> chi-square: 184
>> exponential: 84
>> F: 286
>> general (expected value): 50

>> geometric: 58
>> hypergeometric: 64
>> Pascal: 61
>> Poisson: 57
>> standard normal: 91
>> student-t: 286
>> sum of independent: 112
>> uniform: 83
> of regression prediction: 231

B

back-to-back,
> stem-leaf: 13

batting averages: 115

Bernoulli trial: 53

best fit: see *least squares*

beta (β),
> probability of Type II error: 144, 146

biased data: 7

bimodal: 19

binomial,
> distribution: 54
> normal approximation: 97
> table of probabilities: 276

bivariate data: 219

C

categorical data: 2

Central Limit Theorem: 107

discrete,
> data: 4
>
> random variables: 2, 48

distribution, see *density*

E

elements (in a contingency table): 198

empirical data: 34

equally likely: 35

error,
> bound (for CI): 121
>
> in regression: 227

estimation (point): 120

event(s),
> complementary: 39
>
> compound: 36, 37, 38
>
> definition: 35
>
> independent: 40
>
> mutually exclusive: 37

expected
> frequency: 34; (contingency tables): 190, 198;
> value (for a random variable): 50

explanatory variable: 219

extraneous variable: 230

extreme value: 18

exponential,
> distribution: 83

F

F,
> distribution: 206
>
> statistic: 205, 211
>
> for ANOVA: 211
>
> tables of probabilities: 273

factor (in a contingency table): 198

favor (in hypotheses testing): 134

fixed significance: 140

Fisher, R. A.: 151

frequency,
> cumulative: 59
>
> expected: 34
>
> relative: 14, 34

function,
> cumulative: 79
>
> probability density,
>> binomial: 54
>>
>> exponential: 83
>>
>> geometric: 58
>>
>> hypergeometric: 63
>>
>> normal: 91, 286
>>
>> Pascal: 60
>>
>> Poisson: 56
>>
>> triangular: 85
>>
>> uniform or rectangular: 82

G

gaming: 51, 52

geometric distribution: 58

Q

qualitative data: 4

quantitative data: 4

quartile: 20

R

random sample: 7

random variable,
  discrete: 2, 48
  continuous: 2, 76

range,
  of a data set: 19
  of a random variable: 2

rectangular (uniform) distribution: 82

regression (least squares),
  linear model: 226

rejection (critical) region: 141

relative frequency: 14, 34

residual (in regression): see *error*

S

sampling,
  distribution (of a statistic): 107
  simple random: 7
  proportional: 7

stratified: 7
systematic: 7, 10

scatterplot: 220

significance,
  fixed: 140
  practical: 150
  statistical: 150

skewness: 13, 15

slope of regression line: 227

standard deviation,
  of the population: 21
  of the sample: 21

standard error of the mean: 110

standard normal distribution,
  definition: 92
  table of probabilities: 269

standard score (also, *z-score*): 23

statistic: 4

stem-leaf plot: 12

stratified sampling: 7

strength (of linear relationship): 221

student's-t:
  distribution: 156, 286
  table of probabilities: 271

sum of squares,
  in regression: 227

systematic sampling: 7, 10

T

t-distribution: see *student's-t*

test-statistic: 139

test of hypothesis: see *hypothesis*

treatment groups (in ANOVA): 210

tree diagram: 36

two-sided test of hypothesis: 135

Type I and II errors: 144, 146

U

uniform (rectangular) distribution: 82

union (of events): 38

univariate data (single variable data): 12

V

variable,
   in regression: 219
   random: 1

variance,
   binomial distribution: 56
   chi-square distribution: 286

exponential distribution: 84
   F distribution: 286
   geometric distribution: 285
   hypergeometric distribution: 285
   in ANOVA: 211
   of discrete random variables: 50
   of the difference between means: 170
   of difference between proportions: 170
   of the regression slope: 234
   of single variable data: 21
   among sample means: 211
   among observations in sample: 211
   Pascal distribution: 285
   Poisson distribution: 285
   uniform (rectangular) distribution: 83

Venn diagram: 37

Z

z,
   score: 23
   standard normal distribution,
     definition: 92
     table of probabilities: 269

COMPUTER SOFTWARE

TUTORIAL, SIMULATION, GRAPHICS

Computer software is available as a supplement to **Statistics: A Model for Uncertainty**. Thoroughly tested at community colleges, universities, and high schools, this software is composed of a comprehensive tutorial package, emphasizing basic conceptual and computational elements of the major topics in an elementary statistics course, along with powerful simulation, graphics, and demonstration capabilities.

OUTSTANDING FEATURES:

✳ Random problems are generated for major topics with three levels of difficulty

✳ Students' scores are recorded and score pages can be printed

✳ The simulation component provides a convenient way to demonstrate some of the most difficult concepts of the course. (i.e., the Central Limit Theorem)

✳ Demonstration capabilities allow for the generation of data from 14 probability distributions and accompanying graphic demonstrations. (i.e., overlapping of theoretical and empirical results)

Not intended to be a "number cruncher", this software package involves your students in exploring and discovering the "why and how" of statistics at an elementary, yet highly conceptual, level. The authors have also written a set of laboratory assignments using the simulation and graphics component of the software, which are available from the Math Lab, upon adoption, with permission to reproduce them for classroom use only.

To order, contact: **The Math Lab, 10893 Leavesley Place, Cupertino, CA 95014**

Call (408) 257-7217
Fax (408) 252-2686

Quantity Ordered:	1-4	5-20	21+
Cost/Diskette:	$16	$14	$12

(Networking and site licenses are available.
Arrangements made on an individual basis.)